Species and Varieties

Their Origin by Mutation

Lectures Delivered at the University of California

by

Hugo DeVries

Professor of Botany in the University of Amsterdam

Edited by
Daniel Trembly MacDougal
Director Department of Botanical Research, Carnegie Institution of Washington

Third Edition,
Corrected and Revised

CHICAGO
The Open Court Publishing Company
1912

COPYRIGHT 1904
BY
THE OPEN COURT PUB. CO.
CHICAGO

THE ORIGIN OF SPECIES

The origin of species is a natural phenomenon.
LAMARCK.

The origin of species is an object of inquiry.
DARWIN.

The origin of species is an object of experimental investigation.
DE VRIES.

PREFACE BY THE AUTHOR

THE purpose of these lectures is to point out the means and methods by which the origin of species and varieties may become an object for experimental inquiry, in the interest of agricultural and horticultural practice as well as in that of general biologic science. Comparative studies have contributed all the evidence hitherto adduced for the support of the Darwinian theory of descent and given us some general ideas about the main lines of the pedigree of the vegetable kingdom, but the way in which one species originates from another has not been adequately explained. The current belief assumes that species are slowly changed into new types. In contradiction to this conception the theory of mutation assumes that new species and varieties are produced from existing forms by sudden leaps. The parent-type itself remains unchanged throughout this process, and may repeatedly give birth to new forms. These may arise simultaneously and in groups or separately at more or less widely distant periods.

The principal features of the theory of mutation have been dealt with at length in my book "Die Mutationstheorie" (Vol. I., 1901, Vol. II., 1903. Leipsic, Veit & Co.), in which I have endeavored to present as completely as possible the detailed evidence obtained from trustworthy historical records, and from my own experimental researches, upon which the theory is based.

The University of California invited me to deliver a series of lectures on this subject, at Berkeley, during the summer of 1904, and these lectures are offered in this form to a public now thoroughly interested in the progress of modern ideas on evolution. Some of my experiments and pedigree-cultures are described here in a manner similar to that used in the "Mutationstheorie," but partly abridged and partly elaborated, in order to give a clear conception of their extent and scope. New experiments and observations have been added, and a wider choice of the material afforded by the more recent current literature has been made in the interest of a clear representation of the leading ideas, leaving the exact and detailed proofs thereof to the students of the larger book.

Scientific demonstration is often long and encumbered with difficult points of minor importance. In these lectures I have tried to devote attention to the more important phases of the subject and have avoided the details of lesser interest to the general reader.

Considerable care has been bestowed upon the indication of the lacunae in our knowledge of the subject and the methods by which they may be filled. Many interesting observations bearing upon the little known parts of the subject may be made with limited facilities, either in the garden or upon the wild flora. Accuracy and perseverance, and a warm love for Nature's children are here the chief requirements in such investigations.

In his admirable treatise on Evolution and Adaptation (New York, Macmillan & Co., 1903), Thomas Hunt Morgan has dealt in a critical manner with many of the speculations upon problems subsidiary to the theory of descent, in so convincing and complete a manner, that I think myself justified in neglecting these questions here. His book gives an accurate survey of them all, and is easily understood by the general reader.

In concluding I have to offer my thanks to Dr. D. T. MacDougal and Miss A. M. Vail of the New York Botanical Garden for their painstaking work in the preparation of the manuscript for the press. Dr. MacDougal, by

Preface by the Author

his publications, has introduced my results to his American colleagues, and moreover by his cultures of the mutative species of the great evening-primrose has contributed additional proof of the validity of my views, which will go far to obviate the difficulties, which are still in the way of a more universal acceptation of the theory of mutation. My work claims to be in full accord with the principles laid down by Darwin, and to give a thorough and sharp analysis of some of the ideas of variability, inheritance, selection, and mutation, which were necessarily vague at his time. It is only just to state, that Darwin established so broad a basis for scientific research upon these subjects, that after half a century many problems of major interest remain to be taken up. The work now demanding our attention is manifestly that of the experimental observation and control of the origin of species. The principal object of these lectures is to secure a more general appreciation of this kind of work.

Hugo de Vries.

Amsterdam, October, 1904.

PREFACE BY THE EDITOR

Professor de Vries has rendered an additional service to all naturalists by the preparation of the lectures on mutation published in the present volume. A perusal of the lectures will show that the subject-matter of "Die Mutationstheorie" has been presented in a somewhat condensed form, and that the time which has elapsed since the original was prepared has given opportunity for the acquisition of additional facts, and a re-examination of some of the more important conclusions with the result that a notable gain has been made in the treatment of some complicated problems.

It is hoped that the appearance of this English version of the theory of mutation will do much to stimulate investigation of the various phases of the subject. This volume, however, is by no means intended to replace, as a work of reference, the larger book with its detailed recital of facts and its comprehensive records, but it may prove a substitute for the use of the general reader.

The revision of the lectures has been a task attended with no little pleasure, especially since it has given the editor the opportunity for an advance consideration of some of the more recent results, thus materially facilitating investigations which have been in progress at the New York Botanical Garden for some time. So far as the ground has been covered the researches in question corroborate the conclusions of de Vries in all important particulars. The preparation of the manuscript for the printer has consisted chiefly in the adaptation of oral discussions and demonstrations to a form suitable for permanent record, together with certain other alterations which have been duly submitted to the author. The original phraseology has been preserved as far as possible. The editor wishes to acknowledge material assistance in this work from Miss A. M. Vail, Librarian of the New York Botanical Garden.

D. T. MacDougal.

New York Botanical Garden, October, 1904.

PREFACE TO THE SECOND EDITION.

The constantly increasing interest in all phases of evolution has made necessary the preparation of a second edition of this book within a few months after the first appeared. The opportunity has been used to eliminate typographical errors, and to make alterations in the form of a few sentences for the sake of clearness and smoothness. The subject matter remains practically unchanged. An explanatory note has been added on page 575 in order to avoid confusion as to the identity of some of the plants which figure prominently in the experimental investigations in Amsterdam and New York.

The portrait which forms the frontispiece is a reproduction of a photograph taken by Professor F. E. Lloyd and Dr. W. A. Cannon during the visit of Professor de Vries at the Desert Botanical Laboratory of the Carnegie Institution, at Tucson, Arizona, in June, 1904.

D. T. MacDougal.

December 15, 1905.

CONTENTS

A. Introduction.

Lecture		Page
I.	Descent: theories of evolution and methods of investigation	1

The theory of descent and of natural selection. Evolution and adaptation. Elementary species and varieties. Methods of scientific pedigree-culture.

B. Elementary Species.

II.	Elementary species in nature . . .	32

Viola tricolor, Draba verna, Primula acaulis, and other examples. Euphorbia Ipecacuanha. Prunus maritima. Taraxacum and Hieracium.

III.	Elementary species of cultivated plants.	63

Beets, apples, pears, clover, flax and coconut.

IV.	Selection of elementary species . . .	92

Cereals. Le Couteur. Running out of varieties. Rimpau and Risler, Avena fatua. Meadows. Old Egyptian cereals. Selection by the Romans. Shirreff. Hays.

C. Retrograde Varieties.

V.	Characters of retrograde varieties . .	121

Seed varieties of pure, not hybrid origin. Differences from elementary species. Latent characters. Ray-florets of com-

Contents

Lecture		Page
	posites. Progressive red varieties. Apparent losses. Xanthium canadense. **Correlative variability.** Laciniate leaves and petals. Compound characters.	
VI.	Stability and real atavism . . . . Constancy of retrograde varieties. **Atavism in Ribes sanguineum albidum, in conifers, in Iris pallida.** Seedlings of Acacia. Reversion by buds.	154
VII.	Ordinary or false atavism . . . . Vicinism or variation under the influence of pollination by neighboring individuals. Vicinism in nurseries. Purifying new and old varieties. A case of running out of corn in Germany.	185
VIII.	Latent characters . . . . Leaves of seedlings, adventitious buds, systematic latency and retrogressive evolution. Degressive evolution. Latency of specific and varietal characters in wheat-ear carnation, in the green dahlias, in white campanulas and others. Systematic latency of flower colors.	216
IX.	Crossing of species and varieties . . Balanced and unbalanced, or species and variety crosses. Constant hybrids of Oenothera muricata and O. biennis. Aegilops, Medicago, brambles and other instances.	247
X.	Mendel's law of balanced crosses . . Pairs of antagonistic characters, one active and one latent. Papaver somnif-	276

LECTURE		PAGE
	erum Mephisto Danebrog. Mendel's laws. Unit-characters.	
	D. EVERSPORTING VARIETIES.	
XI.	Striped flowers	309
	Antirrhinum majus luteum rubro-striatum with pedigree. Striped flowers, fruits and radishes. Double stocks.	
XII.	"Five leaved" clover	340
	Origin of this variety. Periodicity of the anomaly. Pedigree-cultures. Ascidia.	
XIII.	Polycephalic poppies	369
	Permanency and high variability. Sensitive period of the anomaly. Dependency on external conditions.	
XIV.	Monstrosities	400
	Inheritance of monstrosities. Half races and middle races. Hereditary value of atavists. Twisted stems and fasciations. Middle races of tricotyls and syncotyls. Selection by the hereditary percentage among the offspring.	
XV.	Double adaptations	430
	Analogy between double adaptations and anomalous middle races. Polygonum amphibium. Alpine plants. Othonna crassifolia. Leaves in sunshine and shadow. Giants and dwarfs. Figs and ivy. Leaves of seedlings.	
	E. MUTATIONS.	
XVI.	Origin of the peloric toad-flax . . .	459
	Sudden and frequent origin in the wild state. Origin in the experiment-garden. Law of repeated mutations. Probable origin of other pelories.	

Lecture		Page
XVII.	The production of double flowers	488

Sudden appearance of double flowers in horticulture. Historical evidence. Experimental origin of Chrysanthemum segetum plenum. Dependency upon nourishment. Petalody of stamens.

XVIII.	New species of Oenothera	516

Mutations of Oenothera lamarckiana in the wild state near Hilversum. New varieties of O. laevifolia, O. brevistylis, and O. nanella. New elementary species, O. gigas, O. rubrinervis, albida, and oblonga. O. lata a pistillate form. Inconstancy of O. scintillans.

XIX.	Experimental pedigree-cultures	547

Pedigree of the mutative products of Oenothera lamarckiana in the Botanical Garden at Amsterdam. Laws of mutability. Sudden and repeated leaps from an unchanging main strain. Constancy of the new forms. Mutations in all directions.

XX.	Origin of wild species and varieties	576

Problems to solve. Capsella heegeri. Oenothera biennis cruciata. Epilobium hirsutum cruciatum. Hibiscus Moscheutos. Purple beech. Monophyllous strawberries. Chances of success with new mutations.

XXI.	Mutations in horticulture	604

Chelidonium majus lacinatum. Dwarf and spineless varieties. Laciniate leaves. Monophyllous and broom-like varieties.

Contents

LECTURE		PAGE
	Purple leaves. Celosia. Italian poplar. Cactus dahlia. Mutative origin of Dahlia fistulosa, and Geranium pratense in the experiment-garden.	
XXII.	Systematic atavism	630
	Reappearance of ancestral characters. Primula acaulis umbellata. Bracts of crucifers. Zea Mays cryptosperma. Equisetum, Dipsacus sylvestris torsus. Tomatoes.	
XXIII.	Taxonomic anomalies	658
	Specific characters occurring in other cases as casual anomalies. Papaver bracteatum monopetalum. Desmodium gyrans and monophyllous varieties. Peltate leaves and ascidia. Flowers on leaves. Leaves. Hordeum trifurcatum.	
XXIV.	Hypothesis of periodical mutations . .	686
	Discovering mutable strains. Periods of mutability and constancy. Periods of mutations. Genealogical trees. Limited life-time of the organic kingdom.	

F. FLUCTUATIONS.

XXV.	General laws of fluctuations	715
	Fluctuating variability. Quetelet's law. Individual and partial fluctuations. Linear variability. Influence of nutrition. Periodicity-curves.	
XXVI.	Asexual multiplication of extremes . .	742
	Selection between species and intra-specific selection. Excluding individual	

LECTURE		PAGE
	and embryonic variability. Sugar-canes. Flowering cannas. Double lilacs. Other instances. Burbank's method of selection.	
XXVII.	Inconstancy of improved races . . . Larger variability in the case of propagation by seed. Progression and regression after a single selection, and after repeated selections. Selection experiments with corn. Advantages and effect of repeated selection.	770
XXVIII.	Artificial and natural selection . . . Conclusions. Specific and intra-specific selection. Natural selection in the field. Acclimatization. Improvement-selection of sugar-beets by various methods. Rye. Hereditary percentage and centgener power as marks by which intra-specific selection may be guided.	798
	Index	827

A. INTRODUCTION

Lecture I

DESCENT: THEORIES OF EVOLUTION, AND METHODS OF INVESTIGATION

Newton convinced his contemporaries that natural laws rule the whole universe. Lyell showed, by his principle of slow and gradual evolution, that natural laws have reigned since the beginning of time. To Darwin we owe the almost universal acceptance of the theory of descent.

This doctrine is one of the most noted landmarks in the advance of science. It teaches the validity of natural laws of life in its broadest sense, and crowns the philosophy founded by Newton and Lyell.

Lamarck proposed the hypothesis of a common origin of all living beings and this ingenious and thoroughly philosophical conception was warmly welcomed by his partisans, but was not widely accepted owing to lack of supporting evidence. To Darwin was reserved the task of bringing the theory of common descent to its present high rank in scientific and social philosophy.

Two main features in his work have contributed to this early and unexpected victory. One of them is the almost unlimited amount of comparative evidence, the other is his demonstration of the possibility of a physiological explanation of the process of descent itself.

The universal belief in the independent creation of living organisms was revised by Linnaeus and was put upon a new foundation. Before him the genera were supposed to be created, the species and minor forms having arisen from them through the agency of external conditions. In his first book Linnaeus adhered to this belief, but later changed his mind and maintained the principle of the separate creation of species. The weight of his authority soon brought this conception to universal acceptance, and up to the present time the prevailing conception of a species has been chiefly based on the definition given by Linnaeus. His species comprised subspecies and varieties, which were in their turn, supposed to have evolved from species by the common method.

Darwin tried to show that the links which bind species to genera are of the same nature as those which determine the relationship of subspecies and varieties. If an origin by natural laws is conceded for the latter, it must, on this ground be granted for the first also. In this discussion he simply returned to the pre-Linnean attitude. But his material was such as to allow him to go one step further, and this step was an important and decisive one. He showed that the relation between the various genera of a family does not exhibit any features of a nature other than that between the species of a genus. What has been conceded for the one must needs be accepted for the other. The same holds good for the large groups. The conviction of the common origin of closely allied forms necessarily leads to the conception of a similar descent even in remote relationships.

The origin of subspecies and varieties as found in nature was not proved, but only generally recognized as evident. A broader knowledge has brought about the same state of opinion for greater groups of relationships. Systematic affinities find their one possible explanation by the aid of this principle; without it, all similarity is only apparent and accidental. Geographic and paleontologic facts, brought together by Darwin and others on a previously unequalled scale, point clearly in the same direction. The vast amount of evidence of all comparative sciences compels us to accept the idea. To deny it, is to give up all opportunity of conceiving Nature in her true form.

The general features of the theory of descent are now accepted as the basis of all biological science. Half a century of discussion and investigation has cleared up the minor points and brought out an abundance of facts; but they have not changed the principle. Descent with modification is now universally accepted as the chief law of nature in the organic world. In honor of him, who with unsurpassed genius, and by unlimited labor has made it the basis of modern thought, this law is called the "Darwinian theory of descent."

Darwin's second contribution to this attainment was his proof of the possibility of a physiological explanation of the process of descent itself. Of this possibility he fully convinced his contemporaries, but in indicating the particular means by which the change of species has been brought about, he has not succeeded in securing universal acceptation. Quite on the contrary, objections have been raised from the very outset, and with such force as to compel Darwin himself to change his views in his later writings. This however, was of no avail, and objections and criticisms have since steadily accumulated.

Physiologic facts concerning the origin of

species in nature were unknown in the time of Darwin. It was a happy idea to choose the experience of the breeders in the production of new varieties, as a basis on which to build an explanation of the processes of nature. In my opinion Darwin was quite right, and he has succeeded in giving the desired proof. But the basis was a frail one, and would not stand too close an examination. Of this Darwin was always well aware. He has been prudent to the utmost, leaving many points undecided, and among them especially the range of validity of his several arguments. Unfortunately this prudence has not been adopted by his followers. Without sufficient warrant they have laid stress on one phase of the problem, quite overlooking the others. Wallace has even gone so far in his zeal and ardent veneration for Darwin, as to describe as Darwinism some things, which in my opinion, had never been a part of Darwin's conceptions.

The experience of the breeders was quite inadequate to the use which Darwin made of it. It was neither scientific, nor critically accurate. Laws of variation were barely conjectured; the different types of variability were only imperfectly distinguished. The breeders' conception was fairly sufficient for practical purposes, but science needed a clear understanding of the factors in the general process of variation. Repeatedly Darwin tried to formulate these causes, but the evidence available did not meet his requirements.

Quetelet's law of variation had not yet been published. Mendel's claim of hereditary units for the explanation of certain laws of hybrids discovered by him, was not yet made. The clear distinction between spontaneous and sudden changes, as compared with the ever-present fluctuating variations, is only of late coming into recognition by agriculturists. Innumerable minor points which go to elucidate the breeders' experience, and with which we are now quite familiar, were unknown in Darwin's time. No wonder that he made mistakes, and laid stress on modes of descent, which have since been proved to be of minor importance or even of doubtful validity.

Notwithstanding all these apparently unsurmountable difficulties, Darwin discovered the great principle which rules the evolution of organisms. It is the principle of natural selection. It is the sifting out of all organisms of minor worth through the struggle for life. It is only a sieve, and not a force of nature, not a direct cause of improvement, as many of Darwin's adversaries, and unfortunately many of his followers also, have so often asserted. It is only a sieve, which decides what is to live, and what is to die. But evolutionary lines are of great length, and the evolution of a flower, or of an insectivorous plant is a way with many side-paths. It is the sieve that keeps evolution on the main line, killing all, or nearly all that try to go in other directions. By this means natural selection is the one directing cause of the broad lines of evolution.

Of course, with the single steps of evolution it has nothing to do. Only after the step has been taken, the sieve acts, eliminating the unfit. The problem, as to the manner in which the individual steps are brought about, is quite another side of the question.

On this point Darwin has recognized two possibilities. One means of change lies in the sudden and spontaneous production of new forms from the old stock. The other method is the gradual accumulation of those always present and ever fluctuating variations which are indicated by the common assertion that no two individuals of a given race are exactly alike. The first changes are what we now call "mutations," the second are designated as "individual variations," or as this term is often used in another sense, as "fluctuations." Darwin recognized both lines of evolution; Wallace disregarded the sudden changes and proposed fluctuations as the exclusive factor. Of late, however, this point of view has been abandoned by many investigators, especially in America.

The actual occurrence of mutations is now recognized, and the battle rages about the question, as to whether they are be regarded as the principal means of evolution, or, whether slow and gradual changes have not also played a large and important part.

The defenders of the theory of evolution by slow accumulation of slight fluctuations are divided into two camps. One group is called the Neo-Lamarckians; they assume a direct modifying agency of the environment, producing a corresponding and useful change in the organization. The other group call themselves Darwinians or selectionists, but to my mind with no other right beyond the arbitrary restriction of the Darwinian principles by Wallace. They assume fluctuating variations in all directions and leave the choice between them to the sieve of natural selection.

Of course we are far from a decision between these views, on the sole ground of the facts as known at present. Mutations under observation are as yet very rare; enough to indicate the possible and most probable ways, but no more. On the other hand the accumulation of fluctuations does not transgress relatively narrow limits as far as the present methods of selection go. But the question remains to be solved, whether our methods are truly the right ones, and whether by the use of new principles, new results might not cause the balance of opinion to favor the opposite side.

Of late, a thorough and detailed discussion of the opposing views has been given by Morgan in his valuable book on evolution and adaptation. He has subjected all the proposed theories to a severe criticism both on the ground of facts and on that of their innate possibility and logical value. He decides in favor of the mutation-theory. His arguments are incisive and complete and wholly adapted to the comprehension of all intelligent readers, so that his book relieves me entirely of the necessity of discussing these general questions, as it could not be done in a better or in a clearer way.

I intend to give a review of the facts obtained from plants which go to prove the assertion, that species and varieties have originated by mutation, and are, at present, not known to originate in any other way. This review consists of two parts. One is a critical survey of the facts of agricultural and horticultural breeding, as they have accumulated since the time of Darwin. This body of evidence is to be combined with some corresponding experiments concerning the real nature of species in the wild state. The other part rests on my own observations and experiments, made in the botanical garden of the University of Amsterdam.

For many years past I have tried to elucidate the hereditary conditions of species and varieties, and the occasional occurrence of mutations, that suddenly produce new forms.

The present discussion has a double purpose. On one side it will give the justification of the theory of mutations, as derived from the facts now at hand. On the other hand it will point out the deficiencies of available evidence, and indicate the ways by which the lacunae may gradually be filled. Experimental work on heredity does not require vast installments or a costly laboratory equipment. It demands chiefly assiduity and exactitude. Any one who has these two qualities, and who has a small garden at his disposal is requested to take part in this line of investigation.

In order to observe directly the birth of new forms it is necessary, in the first place, to be fully clear concerning the question as to what forms are to be expected to arise from others, and before proceeding to a demonstration of the origin of species, it is pertinent to raise the question as to what constitutes a species.

Species is a word, which always has had a

double meaning. One is the systematic species, which is the unit of our system. But these units are by no means indivisible. Long ago Linnaeus knew them to be compound in a great number of instances, and increasing knowledge has shown that the same rule prevails in other instances. Today the vast majority of the old systematic species are known to consist of minor units. These minor entities are called varieties in systematic works. However, there are many objections to this usage. First, the term variety is applied in horticulture and agriculture to things so widely divergent as to convey no clear idea at all. Secondly, the subdivisions of species are by no means all of the same nature, and the systematic varieties include units the real value of which is widely different in different cases. Some of these varieties are in reality as good as species, and have been "elevated," as it is called, by some writers, to this rank. This conception of the elementary species would be quite justifiable, and would at once get rid of all difficulties, were it not for one practical obstacle. The number of the species in all genera would be doubled and tripled, and as these numbers are already cumbersome in many cases, the distinction of the native species of any given country would lose most of its charm and interest.

In order to meet this difficulty we must recognize two sorts of species. The systematic species are the practical units of the systematists and florists, and all friends of wild nature should do their utmost to preserve them as Linnaeus has proposed them. These units however, are not really existing entities; they have as little claim to be regarded as such as genera and families. The real units are the elementary species; their limits often apparently overlap and can only in rare cases be determined on the sole ground of field-observations. Pedigree-culture is the method required and any form which remains constant and distinct from its allies in the garden is to be considered as an elementary species.

In the following lectures we shall consider this point at length, to show the compound nature of systematic species in wild and in cultivated plants. In both cases, the principle is becoming of great importance, and many papers published recently indicate its almost universal acceptation.

Among the systematic subdivisions of species, not all have the same claim to the title of elementary species. In the first place the cases in which the differences may occur between parts of the same individual are to be excluded. Dividing an alpine plant into two halves and planting one in a garden, varietal differences at once arise and are often designated in systematic works under different varietal names. Secondly all individual differences which are of a fluctuating nature are to be combined into a group. But with these we shall deal later.

Apart from these minor points the subdivisions of the systematic species exhibit two widely different features. I will now try to make this clear in a few words, but will return in another lecture to a fuller discussion of this most interesting contrast.

Linnaeus himself knew that in some cases all subdivisions of a species are of equal rank, together constituting the group called species. No one of them outranks the others; it is not a species with varieties, but a group consisting only of varieties. A closer inquiry into the cases treated in this manner by the great master of systematic science, shows that here his varieties were exactly what we now call elementary species.

In other cases the varieties are of a derivative nature. The species constitutes a type that is pure in a race which ordinarily is still growing somewhere, though in some cases it may have died out. From this type the varieties are derived, and the way of this derivation is usually quite manifest to the botanist. It is ordinarily by the disappearance of some superficial character that a variety is distinguished from its species, as by the lack of color in the flowers, of hairs on stems and foliage, of the spines and thorns, &c. Such varieties are, strictly speaking, not to be treated in the same way as elementary species, though they often are. We shall designate them by the term of " retrograde varieties," which clearly indicates the nature of their relationship to the species from which they are assumed to have sprung. In order to lay more stress on the contrast between elementary species and retrograde varieties, it should be stated at once, that the first are considered to have originated from their parent-form in a progressive way. They have succeeded in attaining something quite new for themselves, while retrograde varieties have only thrown off some peculiarity, previously acquired by their ancestors.

The whole vegetable kingdom exhibits a constant struggle between progression and retrogression. Of course, the great lines of the general pedigree are due to progression, many single steps in this direction leading together to the great superiority of the flowering plants over their cryptogamous ancestors. But progression is nearly always accompanied by retrogression in the principal lines of evolution, as well as in the collateral branches of the genealogical tree. Sometimes it prevails, and the monocotyledons are obviously a reduced branch of the primitive dicotyledons. In orchids and aroids, in grasses and sedges, reduction plays a most important part, leaving its traces on the flowers as well as on the embryo of the seed. Many instances could be given to prove that progression and retrogression are the two main principles of evolution at large. Hence the conclusion that our analysis must dissect the complicated phenomena of evolution so far as to show the separate functions of these two contrasting principles. Hundreds of steps were needed to evolve the family of the orchids, but the experimenter must take the single steps for the object of his inquiry. He finds that some are progressive and others retrogressive and so his investigation falls under two heads, the origin of progressive characters, and the subsequent loss of the same. Progressive steps are the marks of elementary species, while retrograde varieties are distinguished by apparent losses. They have equal claim to our interest and our study.

As already stated I propose to deal first with the elementary species and afterwards with the retrograde varieties. I shall try to depict them to you in the first place as they are seen in nature and in culture, leaving the question of their origin to a subsequent experimental treatment.

The question of the experimental origin of new species and varieties has to be taken up from two widely separated starting points. This may be inferred from what we have already seen concerning the two opposing theories, derived and isolated from Darwin's original broad conception. One of them considers mutations as the origin of new forms, while the other assumes fluctuations to be the source of all evolution.

As mentioned above, my own experience has led me to accept the first view. Therefore I shall have to show that mutations do yield new and constant forms, while fluctuations are not adequate to do so. Retrograde varieties and elementary species may both be seen to be produced by sudden mutations. Varieties have often been observed to appear at once and quite unexpectedly in horticulture and agriculture, and a survey of these historical facts will be the subject of one of my lectures. In some instances I have succeeded in repeating these observations in my garden under the strict conditions of a scientific experiment, and these instances teach us the real nature of the process of mutation in all its visible features. New elementary species are far more rare, but I have discovered in the great evening-primrose, or *Oenothera lamarckiana* a strain which is producing them yearly in the wild state as well as in my garden. These observations and pedigree-experiments will be dealt with at due length in subsequent lectures.

Having proved the existence and importance of mutations, it remains to inquire how far the improvements may go which are due only to fluctuating variability. As the term indicates, this variability is fluctuating to and fro, oscillating around an average type. It never fails nor does it, under ordinary circumstances, depart far from the fixed average.

But the deviation may be enlarged by a choice of extremes. In sowing their seed, the average of the strain is seen to be changed, and in repeating the experiment the change may be considerable. It is not clear, whether theoretically by such an accumulation, deviations might be reached which could not be attained at once in a single sowing. This question is hardly susceptible of an experimental answer, as it would require such an enormous amount of seed from a few mother plants as can scarcely ever be produced.

The whole character of the fluctuations shows them to be of an opposite nature, contrasting manifestly with specific and varietal characters. By this method they may be proved to be inadequate ever to make a single step along the great lines of evolution, in regard to progressive as well as to retrograde development.

First of all fluctuations are linear, amplifying or lessening the existing qualities, but not really changing their nature. They are not observed to produce anything quite new, and evolution of course, is not restricted to the increase of the already existing peculiarities, but depends chiefly on the continuous addition of new characters to the stock. Fluctuations always oscillate around an average, and if removed from this for some time, they show a tendency to return to it. This tendency, called retrogression, has never been observed to fail, as it should, in order to free the new strain from the links with the average, while new species and new varieties are seen to be quite free from their ancestors and not linked to them by intermediates.

The last few lectures will be devoted to questions concerning the great problem of the analogy between natural and artificial selection. As already stated, Darwin made this analogy the foundation stone of his theory of descent, and he met with the severest objections and criticisms precisely on this point. But I hope to show that he was quite right, and that the cause of the divergence of opinions is due simply to the very incomplete state of knowledge concerning both processes. If both are critically analyzed they may be seen to comprise the same factors and further discussion may be limited to the appreciation of the part, which each of them has played in nature and among cultivated plants.

Both natural and artificial selection are partly specific, and partly intra-specific or individual. Nature of course, and intelligent men first chose the best elementary species from among the swarms. In cultivation this is the process of variety-testing. In nature it is the survival of the fittest species, or, as Morgan designates it, the survival of species in the struggle for existence. The species are not changed by this struggle, they are only weighed against each other, the weak being thrown aside.

Within the chosen elementary species there is also a struggle. It is obvious, that the fluctuating variability adapts some to the given circumstances, while it lessens the chances of others. A choice results, and this choice is what is often exclusively called selection, either natural or artificial. In cultivation it produces the improved and the local races; in nature little is known about improvement in this way, but local adaptations with slight changes of the average character in separate localities, seem to be of quite normal occurrence.

A new method of individual selection has been used in recent years in America, especially by W. M. Hays. It consists in judging the hereditary worth of a plant by the average condition of its offspring, instead of by its own visible characters. If this determination of the " centgener power," as Hays calls it, should prove to be the true principle of selection, then indeed the analogy between natural and artificial selection would lose a large part of its importance. We will reserve this question for the last lecture, as it pertains more to the future, than to our present stock of knowledge.

Something should be said here concerning hybrids and hybridism. This problem has of late reached such large proportions that it cannot be dealt with adequately in a short survey of the phenomena of heredity in general. It requires a separate treatment. For this reason I shall limit myself to a single phase of the problem, which seems to be indispensable for a true and at the same time easy distinction between elementary species and retrograde varieties. According to accepted terminology, some crosses are to be considered as unsymmetrical, while others are symmetrical. The first are one-sided, some peculiarity being found in one of the parents and lacking in the other. The second are balanced, as all the characters are present in both parents, but are found in a different condition. Active in one of them, they are concealed or inactive in the other. Hence pairs of contrasting units result, while in unbalanced crosses no pairing of the particular character under consideration is possible. This leads to the principal difference between species and varieties, and to an experimental method of deciding between them in difficult and doubtful cases.

Having thus indicated the general outlines of the subjects I shall deal with, something now may be said as to methods of investigation.

There are two points in which scientific investigation differs from ordinary pedigree-culture in practice. First the isolation of the individuals and the study of individual inheritance, instead of averages. Next comes the task of keeping records. Every individual must be entered, its ancestry must be known as completely as possible, and all its relations must be noted in such a form, that the most complete reference is always possible. Mutations may come unexpectedly, and when once arisen, their parents and grand-parents should be known. Records must be available which will allow of a most complete knowledge of the whole ancestral line. This, and approximately this only, is the essential difference between experimental and accidental observation.

Mutations are occurring from time to time in the wild state as well as in horticulture and agriculture. A selection of the most interesting instances will be given later. But in all such cases the experimental proof is wanting. The observations as a rule, only began when the mutation had made its appearance. A more or less vague remembrance about the previous state of the plants in question might be available, though even this is generally absent. But on doubtful points, concerning possible crosses or possible introduction of foreign strains, mere recollection is insufficient. The fact of the mutation may be very probable, but the full proof is, of course, wanting. Such is the case with the mutative origin of *Xanthium commune Wootoni* from New Mexico and of *Oenothera biennis cruciata* from Holland. The same doubt exists as to the origin of the *Capsella heegeri* of Solms-Laubach, and of the oldest recorded mutation, that of *Chelidonium laciniatum* in Heidelberg about 1600.

First, we have doubts about the fact itself. These, however, gradually lose their importance in the increasing accumulation of evidence. Secondly, the impossibility of a closer inquiry into the real nature of the change. For experimental purposes a single mutation does not suffice; it must be studied repeatedly, and be produced more or less arbitrarily, according to the nature of the problems to be solved. And in order to do this, it is evidently not enough to have in hand the mutated individual, but it is indispensable to have also the mutable parents, or the mutable strain from which it sprang.

All conditions previous to the mutation are to be considered as of far higher importance than all those subsequent to it.

Now mutations come unexpectedly, and if the ancestry of an accidental mutation is to be known, it is of course necessary to keep accounts of all the strains cultivated. It is evident that the required knowledge concerning the ancestry of a supposed mutation, must necessarily nearly all be acquired from the plants in the experimental garden.

Obviously this rule is as simple in theory, as it is difficult to carry out in practice. First of all comes the book-keeping. The parents, grandparents and previous ancestors must be known individually. Accounts of them must be kept under two headings. A full description of their individual character and peculiarities must always be available on the one hand, and on the other, all facts concerning their hereditary qualities. These are to be deduced from the composition of the progeny, and in order to obtain complete evidence on this point, two successive generations are often required. The investigation must ascertain the average condition of this offspring and the occurrence of any deviating specimens, and for both purposes it is necessary to cultivate them in relatively large numbers. It is obvious that, properly speaking, the whole family of a mutated individual, including all its nearer and more remote relatives, should be known and recorded.

Hence pedigree-book-keeping must become the general rule. Subordinate to this are two further points, which should likewise be stated here. One pertains to the pure or hybrid nature of the original strain, and the other to the life-conditions and all other external influences. It is manifest that a complete understanding of a mutation depends upon full information upon these points.

All experiments must have a beginning. The starting-point may be a single individual, or a small group of plants, or a lot of seeds. In many cases the whole previous history is obscure, but sometimes a little historical evidence is at hand. Often it is evident that the initial material belongs to a pure species, but with respect to the question of elementary species it is not rarely open to doubt. Large numbers of hybrid plants and hybrid races are in existence, concerning the origin of which it is impossible to decide. It is impossible in many instances to ascertain whether they are of hybrid or of pure origin. Often there is only one way of determining the matter; it is to guess at the probable parents in case of a cross and to repeat the cross. This is a point which always requires great care in the interpretation of unusual facts.

Three cases are to be distinguished as to heredity. Many plants are so constituted as to be fertilized with their own pollen. In this case the visits of insects have simply to be excluded, which may be done by covering plants with iron gauze or with bags of prepared paper. Sometimes they fertilize themselves without any aid, as for instance, the common evening-primrose; in other cases the pollen has to be placed on the stigma artificially, as with Lamarck's evening-primrose and its derivatives. Other plants need cross-fertilization in order to produce a normal yield of seeds. Here two individuals have always to be combined, and the pedigree becomes a more complicated one. Such is the case with the toad-flax, which is nearly sterile with its own pollen. But even in these cases the visits of insects bringing pollen from other plants, must be carefully excluded. A special lecture will be devoted to this very interesting source of impurity and of uncertainty in ordinary cultures.

Of course, crosses may lie in the proposed line of work, and this is the third point to be alluded to. They must be surrounded with the same careful isolation and protection against bees, as any other fertilizations. And not only the seed-parent, but also the pollen must be kept pure from all possible foreign admixtures.

A pure and accurately recorded ancestry is thus to be considered as the most important condition of success in experimental plant-breeding. Next to this comes the gathering of the seeds of each individual separately. Fifty or sixty, and often more, bags of seeds are by no means uncommon for a single experiment, and in ordinary years the harvest of my garden is preserved in over a thousand separate lots.

Complying with these conditions, the origin of species may be seen as easily as any other phenomenon. It is only necessary to have a plant in a mutable condition. Not all species are in such a state at present, and therefore I have begun by ascertaining which were stable and which were not. These attempts, of course, had to be made in the experimental garden, and large quantities of seed had to be procured and sown. Cultivated plants of course, had only a small chance to exhibit new qualities, as they have been so strictly controlled during so many years. Moreover their purity of origin is in many cases doubtful. Among wild plants only those could be expected to reward the investigator which were of easy cultivation. For this reason I have limited myself to the trial of wild plants of Holland, and have had the good fortune to find among them at least one species in a state of mutability. It was not really a native plant, but one that had been introduced from America and belongs to an American genus. I refer to the great evening-primrose or the evening-primrose of Lamarck. A strain of this beautiful species is growing in an abandoned field in the vicinity of Hilversum, at a short distance from Amsterdam. Here it has escaped from a park and multiplied. In doing so it has produced and is still producing quite a number of new types, some of which may be considered as retrograde varieties, while others evidently are of the nature of progressive elementary species.

This interesting plant has afforded me the means of observing directly how new species originate, and of studying the laws of these changes. My researches have followed a double line of inquiry. On one side, I have limited myself to direct field observations, and to tests of seed, collected from the wild plants in their native locality. Obviously the mutations are decided within the seed, and the culture of young plants from them had no other aim than that of ascertaining what had occurred in the field. And then the many chances of destruction that threaten young plants in a wild state, could be avoided in the garden, where enviromental factors can be controlled.

My second line of inquiry was an experimental repetition of the phenomena which were only partly discerned at the native locality. It was not my aim to intrude into the process, nor to try to bring out new features. My only object was to submit to the precepts just given concerning pure treatment, individual seed-gathering, exclusion of crosses and accurate recording of all the facts. The result has been a pedigree which now permits of stating the relation between all the descendants of my original introduced plant. This pedigree at once exhibits the laws followed by the mutating species. The main fact is, that it does not change itself gradually, but remains unaffected during all succeeding generations. It only throws off new forms, which are sharply contrasted with the parent, and which are from the very beginning as perfect and as constant, as narrowly defined and as pure of type as might be expected of any species.

These new species are not produced once or in single individuals, but yearly and in large numbers. The whole phenomenon conveys the idea of a close group of mutations, all belonging to one single condition of mutability. Of course this mutable state must have had a beginning, as it must sometime come to an end. It is to be considered as a period within the life-time of the species and probably it is only a small part of it.

The detailed description of this experiment, however, I must delay to a subsequent lecture, but I may be allowed to state, that the discovery of this period of mutability is of a definite theoretical importance. One of the greatest objections to the Darwinian theory of descent arose from the length of time it would require, if all evolution was to be explained on the theory of slow and nearly invisible changes. This difficulty is at once met and fully surmounted by the hypothesis of periodical but sudden and quite noticeable steps. This assumption requires only a limited number of mutative periods, which might well occur within the time allowed by physicists and geologists for the existence of animal and vegetable life on the earth.

Summing up the main points of these introductory remarks, I propose to deal with the subjects mentioned above at some length, devoting to each of them, if possible at least an entire lecture. The decisive facts and discussions upon which the conclusions are based will be given in every case. Likewise I hope to point out the weak places and the lacunae in our present knowledge, and to show the way in which each of you may try to contribute his part towards the advancement of science in this subject. Lastly I shall try to prove that sudden mutation is the normal way in which nature produces new species and new varieties. These mutations are more readily accessible to observation and experiment than the slow and gradual changes surmised by Wallace and his followers, which are entirely beyond our present and future experience.

The theory of mutations is a starting-point for direct investigation, while the general belief in slow changes has held back science from such investigations during half a century.

Coming now to the subdivisions and headings under which my material is to be presented, I propose describing first the real nature of the elementary species and retrograde varieties, both in normal form and in hybridizations. A discussion of other types of varieties, including monstrosities will complete the general plan. The second subdivision will deal with the origin of species and varieties as taught by experiment and observation, treating separately the sudden variations which to my mind do produce new forms, and subsequently the fluctuations which I hold to be not adequate to this purpose.

B. ELEMENTARY SPECIES

Lecture II

ELEMENTARY SPECIES IN NATURE

What are species? Species are considered as the true units of nature by the vast majority of biologists. They have gained this high rank in our estimation principally through the influence of Linnaeus. They have supplanted the genera which were the accepted units before Linnaeus. They are now to be replaced in their turn, by smaller types, for reasons which do not rest upon comparative studies but upon direct experimental evidence.

Biological studies and practical interests alike make new demands upon systematic botany. Species are not only the subject-material of herbaria and collections, but they are living entities, and their life-history and life-conditions command a gradually increasing interest. One phase of the question is to determine the easiest manner to deal with the collected forms of a country, and another feature is the problem as to what groups are real units and will remain constant and unchanged through all the years of our observations.

Before Linnaeus, the genera were the real units of the system. De Candolle pointed out that the old common names of plants, such as roses and clover, poplars and oaks, nearly all refer to genera. The type of the clovers is rich in color, and the shape of the flower-heads and the single flowers escape ordinary observation; but notwithstanding this, clovers are easily recognized, even if new types come to hand. White and red clovers and many other species are distinguished simply by adjectives, the generic name remaining the same for all.

Tournefort, who lived in the second half of the 17th century (1656-1708), is generally considered as the author of genera in systematic botany. He adopted, what was at that time the general conception and applied it throughout the vegetable kingdom. He grouped the new and the rare and the previously overlooked forms in the same manner in which the more conspicuous plants were already arranged by universal consent. Species were distinguished by minor marks and often indicated by short descriptions, but they were considered of secondary importance.

Based on the idea of a direct creation of all

living beings, the genera were then accepted as the created forms. They were therefore regarded as the real existing types, and it was generally surmised that species and varieties owed their origin to subsequent changes under the influence of external conditions. Even Linnaeus agreed with this view in his first treatises and in his "Philosophical Botany" he still kept to the idea that all genera had been created at once with the beginning of life.

Afterwards Linnaeus changed his opinion on this important point, and adopted species as the units of the system. He declared them to be the created forms, and by this decree, at once reduced the genera to the rank of artificial groups. Linnaeus was well aware that this conception was wholly arbitrary, and that even the species are not real indivisible entities. But he simply forbade the study of lesser subdivisions. At his time he was quite justified in doing so, because the first task of the systematic botanists was the clearing up of the chaos of forms and the bringing of them into connection with their real allies.

Linnaeus himself designated the subdivisions of the species as varieties, but in doing so he followed two clearly distinct principles. In some cases his species were real plants, and the varieties seemed to be derived from them by some simple changes. They were subordinated to the parent-species. In other cases his species were groups of lesser forms of equal value, and it was not possible to discern which was the primary and which were the derivatives.

These two methods of subdivision seem in the main, and notwithstanding their relatively imperfect application in many single examples, to correspond with two really distinct cases. The derivative varieties are distinguished from the parent-species by some single, but striking mark, and often this attribute manifests itself as the loss of some apparent quality. The loss of spines and of hairs and the loss of blue and red flower-colors are the most notorious, but in rarer cases many single peculiarities may disappear, thereby constituting a variety. This relation of varieties to the parent-species is gradually increasing in importance in the estimation of botanists, sharply contrasting with those cases, in which such dependency is not to be met with.

If among the subdivisions of a species, no single one can be pointed out as playing a primary part, and the others can not be traced back to it, the relation between these lesser units is of course of another character. They are to be considered of equal importance. They are distinguished from each other by more than one character, often by slight differences in nearly all their organs and qualities. Such forms have come to be designated as "elementary species." They are only varieties in a broad and vague systematic significance of the word, not in the sense accorded to this term in horticultural usage, nor in a sharper and more scientific conception.

Genera and species are, at the present time, for a large part artificial, or stated more correctly, conventional groups. Every systematist is free to delimit them in a wider or in a narrower sense, according to his judgment. The greater authorities have as a rule preferred larger genera, others of late have elevated innumerable subgenera to the rank of genera. This would work no real harm, if unfortunately, the names of the plants had not to be changed each time, according to current ideas concerning genera. Quite the same inconstancy is observed with species. In the Handbook of the British Flora, Bentham and Hooker describe the forms of brambles under 5 species, while Babington in his Manual of British Botany makes 45 species out of the same material. So also in other cases. For instance, the willows which have 13 species in one and 31 species in the other of these manuals, and the hawkweeds for which the figures are 7 and 32 respectively. Other authors have made still greater numbers of species in the same groups.

It is very difficult to estimate systematic differences on the ground of comparative studies alone. All sorts of variability occur, and no individual or small group of specimens can really be considered as a reliable representative of the supposed type. Many original diagnoses of new species have been founded on divergent specimens and of course, the type can afterwards neither be derived from this individual, nor from the diagnosis given.

This chaotic state of things has brought some botanists to the conviction that even in systematic studies only direct experimental evidence can be relied upon. This conception has induced them to test the constancy of species and varieties, and to admit as real units only such groups of individuals as prove to be uniform and constant throughout succeeding generations. The late Alexis Jordan, of Lyons in France, made extensive cultures in this direction. In doing so, he discovered that systematic species, as a rule, comprise some lesser forms, which often cannot easily be distinguished when grown in different regions, or by comparing dried material. This fact was, of course, most distasteful to the systematists of his time and even for a long period afterwards they attempted to discredit it. Milde and many others have opposed these new ideas with some temporary success. Only of late has the school of Jordan received due recognition, after Thuret, de Bary, Rosen and others tested its practices and openly pronounced for them. Of late Wittrock of Sweden has joined them, making extensive experimental studies concerning the real units of some of the larger species of his country.

From the evidence given by these eminent authorities, we may conclude that systematic species, as they are accepted nowadays, are as a rule compound groups. Sometimes they consist of two or three, or a few elementary types, but in other cases they comprise twenty, or fifty, or even hundreds of constant and well differentiated forms.

The inner constitution of these groups is however, not at all the same in all cases. This will be seen by the description of some of the more interesting of them. The European heartsease, from which our garden-pansies have been chiefly derived, will serve as an example. The garden-pansies are a hybrid race, won by crossing the *Viola tricolor* with the large flowered and bright yellow *V. lutea*. They combine, as everyone knows, in their wide range of varieties, the attributes of the latter with the peculiarities of the former species.

Besides the *lutea,* there are some other species, nearly allied to *tricolor,* as for instance, *cornuta, calcarata,* and *altaica,* which are combined with it under the head of *Melanium* as a subgenus, and which together constitute a systematic unity of undoubted value, but ranging between the common conceptions of genus and species. These forms are so nearly allied to the heartsease that they have of late been made use of in crosses, in order to widen the range of variability of garden-pansies.

Viola tricolor is a common European weed. It is widely dispersed and very abundant, growing in many localities in large numbers. It is an annual and ripens its seeds freely, and if opportunity is afforded, it multiplies rapidly.

Viola tricolor has three subspecies, which have been elevated to the rank of species by some authors, and which may here be called, for brevity's sake, by their binary names. One is the typical *V. tricolor,* with broad flowers, variously colored and veined with yellow, purple and white. It occurs in waste places on sandy soil. The second is called *V. arvensis* or the field-pansy; it has small inconspicuous flowers, with pale yellowish petals which are shorter than the sepals. It pollinates itself without the aid of insects, and is widely dispersed in cultivated fields. The third form, *V. alpestris*, grows in the Alps, but is of lesser importance for our present discussion.

Anywhere throughout the central part of Europe *V. tricolor* and *V. arvensis* may be seen, each occupying its own locality. They may be considered as ranging among the most common native plants of the particular regions they inhabit. They vary in the color of the flowers, branching of the stems, in the foliage and other parts, but not to such an extent as to constitute distinct strains. They have been brought into cultivation by Jordan, Wittrock and others, but throughout Europe each of them constitutes a single type.

These types must be very old and constant, fluctuating always within the same distinct and narrow limits. No slow, gradual changes can have taken place. In different countries their various habitats are as old as the historical records, and probably many centuries older. They are quite independent of one another, the distance being in numerous cases far too great for the exchange of pollen or of seeds. If slow and gradual changes were the rule, the types could not have remained so uniform throughout the whole range of these two species. They would necessarily have split up into thousands and thousands of minor races, which would show their peculiar characteristics if tested by cultures in adjacent beds. This however, is not what happens. As a matter of fact *V. tricolor* and *V. arvensis* are widely distributed but wholly constant types.

Besides these, there occur distinct types in numerous localities. Some of them evidently have had time and opportunity to spread more or less widely and now occupy larger regions or even whole countries. Others are narrowly limited, being restricted to a single locality. Wittrock collected seeds or plants from as many localities as possible in different parts of Sweden and neighboring states and sowed them in his garden near Stockholm. He secured seeds from his plants, and grew from them a second, and in many cases a third generation in order to estimate the amount of variability. As a rule the forms introduced into his garden proved constant, notwithstanding the new and abnormal conditions under which they were propagated.

First of all we may mention three perennial forms called by him *Viola tricolor ammotropha*, *V. tricolor coniophila* and *V. stenochila*. The typical *V. tricolor* is an annual plant, sowing itself in summer and germinating soon afterwards. The young plants thrive throughout the latter part of the summer and during the fall, reaching an advanced stage of development of the branched stems before winter. Early in the spring the flowers begin to open, but after the ripening of the seeds the whole plant dies.

The three perennial species just mentioned develop in the same manner in the first year. During their flowering period, however, and afterwards, they produce new shoots from the lower parts of the stem. They prefer dry and sandy soils, often becoming covered with the sand that is blown on them by the winds. They are prepared for such seemingly adverse circumstances by the accumulation of food in the older stems and by the capacity of the new shoots to thrive on this food till they have become long enough to reach the light. *V. tricolor ammotropha* is native near Ystad in Sweden, and the other two forms on Gotland. All three have narrowly limited habitats.

The typical tricolored heartsease has remained annual in all its other subspecies. It may be divided into two types in the first place: *V. tricolor genuina* and *V. tricolor versicolor*. Both of them have a wide distribution and seem to be the prototypes from which the rarer forms must have been derived. Among these latter Wittrock describes seven local types, which proved to be constant in his pedigree-cultures. Some of them have produced other forms, related to them in the way of varieties. They all have nearly the same general habit and do not exhibit any marked differences in their growth, in the structure and branching of the stems, or in the character of their foliage. Differentiating points are to be found mainly in the colors and patterns of the flowers. The veins, which radiate from the centre of the corolla are branched in some and undivided in others; in one elementary species they are wholly lacking. The purple color may be absent, leaving the flowers of a pale or a deep yellow. Or the purple may be reddish or bluish. Of the petals all five may have the purple hue on their tips, or this attribute may be limited to the two upper ones. Contrasting with this wide variability is the stability of the yellow spot in the centre, which is always present and becomes inconspicuous only, when the whole petals are of the same hue. It is a general conception that colors and color-markings are liable to great variability and do not constitute reliable standards. But the cultures of Wittrock have proved the contrary, at least in the case of the violets. No pattern, however quaint, appears changeable, if one elementary species only is considered. Hundreds of plants from seeds from one locality may be grown, and all will exhibit exactly the same markings. Most of these forms are of very local occurrence. The most beautiful of all, the *ornatissima,* is found only in Jemtland, the *aurobadia* only in Sodermanland, the *anopetala* in other localities in the same country, the *roseola* near Stockholm, and the yellow *lutescens* in Finmarken.

The researches of Wittrock included only a small number of elementary species, but every one who has observed the violets in the central parts of Europe must be convinced that many dozens of constant forms of the typical *Viola tricolor* might easily be found and isolated.

We now come to the field pansy, the *Viola arvensis,* a very common weed in the grain-fields of central Europe. I have already mentioned its small corolla, surpassed by the lobes of the calyx and its capacity of self-fertilization. It has still other curious differentiating characters; the pollen grains, which are square in *V. tricolor,* are five-sided in *V. arvensis.* Some transgressive fluctuating variability may occur in both cases through the admixture of pollen-grains. Even three-angled pollen-grains are seen sometimes. Other marks are observed in the form of the anthers and the spur.

There seem to be very many local subspecies

of the field-pansy. Jordan has described some from the vicinity of Lyons, and Wittrock others from the northern parts of Europe. They diverge from their common prototype in nearly all attributes, the flowers not showing the essential differentiating characters as in the *V. tricolor*. Some have their flower-stalks erect, and in others the flowers are held nearly at right angles to the stem. *V. pallescens* is a small, almost unbranched species with small pale flowers. *V. segetalis* is a stouter species with two dark blue spots on the tips of the upper petals. *V. agrestis* is a tall and branched, hairy form. *V. nemausensis* attains a height of only 10 cm., has rounded leaves and long flower-stalks. Even the seeds afford characters which may be made use of in isolating the various species.

The above-mentioned elementary forms belong to the flora of southern France, and Wittrock has isolated and cultivated a number of others from the fields of Sweden. A species from Stockholm is called *Viola patens; V. arvensis curtisepala* occurs in Gotland, and *V. arvensis striolata* is a distinct form, which has appeared in his cultures without its true origin being ascertained.

The alpine violets comprise a more widespread type with some local elementary species derived exactly in the same way as the tricolored field-pansies.

Summarizing the general result of this description we see that the original species *Viola tricolor* may be split up into larger and lesser groups of separate forms. These last prove to be constant in pedigree-cultures, and therefore are to be considered as really existent units. They are very numerous, comprising many dozens in each of the two larger subdivisions.

All systematic grouping of these forms, and their combination into subspecies and species rests on the comparative study of their characters. The result of such studies must necessarily depend on principles which underlie them. According to the choice of these principles, the construction of the groups will be found to be different. Wittrock trusts in the first place to morphologic characters, and considers the development as passing from the more simple to the more complex types. On the other hand the geographic distribution may be considered as an indication of the direction of evolution, the wide-spread forms being regarded as the common parents of the minor local species.

However, such considerations are only of secondary importance. It must be borne in mind that an ordinary systematic species may include many dozens of elementary forms, each of which remains constant and unchanged in successive generations, even if cultivated in the same garden and under similar external conditions.

Leaving the violets, we may take the vernal whitlow-grass or *Draba verna* for a second illustration. This little annual cruciferous plant is common in the fields of many parts of the United States, though originally introduced from Europe. It has small basal rosettes which develop during summer and winter, and produce numerous leafless flowering stems early in the spring. It is a native of central Europe and western Asia, and may be considered as one of the most common plants, occurring anywhere in immense numbers on sandy soils. Jordan was the first to point out that it is not the same throughout its entire range. Although a hasty survey does not reveal differences, they show themselves on closer inspection. De Bary, Thuret, Rosen and many others confirmed this result, and repeated the pedigree-cultures of Jordan. Every type is constant and remains unchanged in successive generations. The anthers open in the flower-buds and pollinate the stigmas before the expansion of the flowers, thus assuring self-fertilization. Moreover, these inconspicuous little flowers are only sparingly visited by insects. Dozens of subspecies may be cultivated in the same garden without any real danger of their intercrossing. They remain as pure as under perfect isolation.

It is very interesting to observe the aspect of such types, when growing near each other. Hundreds of rosettes exhibit one type, and are undoubtedly similar. The alternative group is distinguishable at first sight, though the differentiating marks are often so slight as to be traceable with difficulty. Two elementary species occur in Holland, one with narrow leaves in the western provinces and one with broader foliage in the northern parts. I have cultivated them side by side, and was as much struck with the uniformity within each group, as with the contrast between the two sets.

Nearly all organs show differences. The most marked are those of the leaves, which may be small or large, linear or elliptic or oblong and even rhomboidal in shape, more or less hairy with simple or with stellate branched hairs, and finally of a pure green or of a glaucous color. The petals are as a rule obcordate, but this type may be combined with others having more or less broad emarginations at the summit, and with differences in breadth which vary from almost linear types to others which touch along their margins. The pods are short and broad, or long and narrow, or varying in sundry other ways. All in all there are constant differences which are so great that it has been possible to distinguish and to describe large numbers of types.

Many of them have been tested as to their constancy from seed. Jordan made numerous cultures, some of which lasted ten or twelve years; Thuret has verified the assertion concerning their constancy by cultures extending over seven years in some instances; Villars and de Bary made numerous trials of shorter duration. All agree as to the main points. The local races are uniform and come true from seed; the variability of the species is not of a fluctuating, but of a polymorphous nature. A given elementary species keeps within its limits and cannot vary beyond them, but the whole group gives the impression of variability by its wide range of distinct, but nearly allied forms.

The geographic distribution of these elementary species of the whitlow-grass is quite distinct from that of the violets. Here predominant species are limited to restricted localities. Most of them occupy one or more departments of France, and in Holland two of them are spread over several provinces. An important number are native in the centre of Europe, and from the vicinity of Lyons, Jordan succeeded in establishing about fifty elementary species in his garden. In this region they are crowded together and not rarely two or even more quite distinct forms are observed to grow side by side on the same spot. Farther away from this center they are more widely dispersed, each holding its own in its habitat. In all, Jordan has distinguished about two hundred species of *Draba verna* from Europe and western Asia. Subsequent authors have added new types to the already existing number from time to time.

The constancy of these elementary species is directly proven by the experiments quoted above, and moreover it may be deduced from the uniformity of each type within its own domain. These are so large that most of the localities are practically isolated from one another, and must have been so for centuries. If the types were slowly changing such localities would often, though of course not always, exhibit slighter differences, and on the geographic limits of neighboring species intermediates would be found. Such however, are not on record. Hence the elementary species must be regarded as old and constant types.

The question naturally arises how these groups of nearly allied forms may originally have been produced. Granting a common origin for all of them, the changes may have been simultaneous or successive. According to the geographic distribution, the place of common origin must probably be sought in the southern part of central Europe, perhaps even in the vicinity of Lyons. Here we may assume that the old *Draba verna* has produced a host or a swarm of new types. Thence they must have spread over Europe, but whether in doing so they have remained constant, or whether some or many of them have repeatedly undergone specific mutations, is of course unknown.

The main fact is, that such a small species as *Draba verna* is not at all a uniform type, but comprises over two hundred well distinguished and constant forms.

It is readily granted that violets and whitlow-grasses are extreme instances of systematic variability. Such great numbers of elementary species are not often included in single species of the system. But the numbers are of secondary importance, and the fact that systematic species consist, as a rule, of more than one independent and constant subspecies, retains its almost universal validity.

In some cases the systematic species are manifest groups, sharply differentiated from one another. In other instances the groups of elementary forms as they are shown by direct observation, have been adjudged by many authors to be too large to constitute species. Hence the polymorphous genera, concerning the systematic subdivisions of which hardly two authors agree. Brambles and roses are widely known instances, but oaks, elms, apples, and pears, *Mentha, Prunus, Vitis, Lactuca, Cucumis, Cucurbita* and numerous others are in the same condition.

In some instances the existence of elementary species is so obvious, that they have been described by taxonomists as systematic varieties or even as good species. The primroses afford a widely known example. Linnaeus called them *Primula veris,* and recognized three types as pertaining to this species, but Jacquin and others have elevated these subspecies to the full rank of species. They now bear the names of *Primula elatior* with larger, *P. officinalis* with smaller flowers, and *P. acaulis*. In the last named the common flower-stalk is lacking and the flowers of the umbel seem to be borne in the axils of the basal leaves.

In other genera such nearly allied species are more or less universally recognized. *Galium Mollugo* has been divided into *G. elatum* with a long and weak stem, and *G. erectum* with shorter and erect stems; *Cochlearia danica, anglica* and *officinalis* are so nearly allied as to be hardly distinguishable. *Sagina apetala* and *pat-*

ula, Spergula media and *salina* and many other pairs of allied species have differentiating characters of the same value as those of the elementary species of *Draba verna*. *Filago, Plantago, Carex, Ficaria* and a long series of other genera afford proofs of the same close relation between smaller and larger groups of species. The European frost-weeds or *Helianthemum* include a group of species which are so closely allied, that ordinary botanical descriptions are not adequate to give any idea of their differentiating features. It is almost impossible to determine them by means of the common analytical keys. They have to be gathered from their various native localities and cultivated side by side in the garden to bring out their differences. Among the species of France, according to Jordan, *Helianthemum polifolium, H. apenninum, H. pilosum* and *H. pulverulentum* are of this character.

A species of cinquefoil, *Potentilla Tormentilla*, which is distinguished by its quaternate flowers, occurs in Holland in two distinct types, which have proved constant in my cultural experiments. One of them has broad petals, meeting together at the edges, and constituting a rounded saucer without breaks. The other has narrow petals, which are strikingly separated from one another and show the sepals between them.

In the same manner bluebells vary in the size and shape of the corolla, which may be wide or narrow, bell-shaped or conical, with the tips turned downwards, sidewards or backwards.

As a rule all of the more striking elementary types have been described by local botanists under distinct specific names, while they are thrown together into the larger systematic species by other authors, who study the distribution of plants over larger portions of the world. Everything depends on the point of view taken. Large floras require large species. But the study of local floras yields the best results if the many forms of the region are distinguished and described as completely as possible. And the easiest way is to give to each of them a specific name. If two or more elementary species are united in the same district, they are often treated in this way, but if each region had its own type of some given species, commonly the part is taken for the whole, and the sundry forms are described under the same name, without further distinctions.

Of course these questions are all of a practical and conventional nature, but involve the different methods in which different authors deal with the same general fact. The fact is that systematic species are compound groups, exactly like the genera and that their real units can only be recognized by comparative experimental studies.

Though the evidence already given might be esteemed to be sufficient for our purpose, I should like to introduce a few more examples; two of them pertain to American plants.

The Ipecac spurge or *Euphorbia Ipecacuanha* occurs from Connecticut to Florida, mainly near the coast, preferring dry and sandy soil. It is often found by the roadsides. According to Britton and Brown's "Illustrated Flora" it is glabrous or pubescent, with several or many stems, ascending or nearly erect; with green or red leaves, which are wonderfully variable in outline, from linear to orbicular, mostly opposite, the upper sometimes whorled, the lower often alternate. The glands of the involucres are elliptic or oblong, and even the seeds vary in shape.

Such a wide range of variability evidently points to the existence of some minor types. Dr. John Harshberger has made a study of those which occur in the vicinity of Whitings in New Jersey. His types agree with the description given above. Others were gathered by him at Brown's Mills in the pinelands, New Jersey, where they grew in almost pure sand in the bright sunlight. He observed still other differentiating characters. The amount of seed produced and the time of flowering were variable to a remarkable degree.

Dr. Harshberger had the kindness to send me some dried specimens of the most interesting of these types. They show that the peculiarities are individual, and that each specimen has its own characters. It is very probable that a comparative experimental study will prove the existence of a large number of elementary species, differing in many points; they will probably also show differences in the amount of the active chemical substances, especially of emetine, which is usually recorded as present in about 1%, but which will undoubtedly be found in larger quantities in some, and in smaller quantities in other elementary species. In this way the close and careful distinction of the really existing units might perhaps prove of practical importance.

Macfarlane has studied the beach-plum or *Prunus maritima,* which is abundant along the coast regions of the Eastern States from Virginia to New Brunswick. It often covers areas from two to two hundred acres in extent, sometimes to the exclusion of other plants. It is most prolific on soft drifting sand near the sea or along the shore, where it may at times be washed with ocean-spray. The fruit usually become ripe about the middle of August, and show extreme variations in size, shape, color, taste, consistency and maturation period, indicating the existence of separate races or elementary species, with widely differing qualities. The earlier varieties begin to ripen from August 10 to 20, and a continuous supply can be had till September 10, while a few good varieties continue to ripen till September 20. But even late in October some other types are still found maturing their fruits.

Exact studies were made of fruit and stone variations, and their characteristics as to color, weight, size, shape and consistency were fully described. Similar variations have been observed, as is well known, in the cultivated plums. Fine blue-black fruits were seen on some shrubs and purplish or yellow fruits on others. Some exhibit a firmer texture and others a more watery pulp. Even the stones show differences which are suggestive of distinct races.

Recently Mr. Luther Burbank of Santa Rosa, California, has made use of the beach-plum to produce useful new varieties. He observed that it is a very hardy species, and never fails to bear, growing under the most trying conditions of dry and sandy, or of rocky and even of heavy soil. The fruits of the wild shrubs are utterly worthless for anything but preserving.

But by means of crossing with other species and especially with the Japanese plums, the hardy qualities of the beach-plum have been united with the size, flavor and other valuable qualities of the fruit, and a group of new plums have been produced with bright colors, ovoid and globular forms which are never flattened and have no suture. The experiments were not finished, when I visited Mr. Burbank in July, 1904, and still more startling improvements were said to have been secured.

I may perhaps be allowed to avail myself of this opportunity to point out a practical side of the study of elementary species. This always appears whenever wild plants are subjected to cultivation, either in order to reproduce them as pure strains, or to cross them with other already cultivated species. The latter practice is as a rule made use of whenever a wild species is found to be in possession of some quality which is considered as desirable for the cultivated forms. In the case of the beach-plum it is the hardiness and the great abundance of fruits of the wild species which might profitably be combined with the recognized qualities of the ordinary plums. Now it is manifest, that in order to make crosses, distinct individual plants are to be chosen, and that the variability of the wild species may be of very great importance. Among the range of elementary species those should be used which not only possess the desired advantages in the highest degree, but which promise the best results in other respects or their earliest attainment. The fuller our knowledge of the elementary species constituting the systematic groups, the easier and the more reliable will be the choice for the breeder. Many Californian wild flowers with bright colors seem to consist of large numbers of constant elementary forms, as for instance, the lilies, godetias, eschscholtias and others. They have been brought into cultivation many times, but the minutest distinction of their elementary forms is required to attain the highest success.

In concluding, I will point out a very interesting difficulty, which in some cases impedes the clear understanding of elementary species. It is the lack of self-fertilization. It occurs in widely distant families, but has a special interest for us in two genera, which are generally known as very polymorphous groups.

One of them is the hawkweed or *Hieracium,* and the other is the dandelion or *Taraxacum officinale.* Hawkweeds are known as a genus in which the delimitation of the species is almost impossible. Thousands of forms may be cultivated side by side in botanical gardens, exhibiting slight but undoubted differentiating features, and reproduce themselves truly by seed. Descriptions were formerly difficult and so complicated that the ablest writers on this genus, Fries and Nägeli are said not to have been able to recognize the separate species by the descriptions given by each other. Are these types to be considered as elementary species, or only as individual differences? The decision of course, would depend upon their behavior in cultures. Such tests have been made by various experimenters. In the dandelion the bracts of the involucre give the best characters. The inner ones may be linear or linear-lanceolate, with or without appendages below the tip; the outer ones may be similar and only shorter, or noticeably larger, erect, spreading or even reflexed, and the color of the involucre may be a pure green or glaucous; the leaves may be nearly entire or pinnatifid, or sinuate-dentate, or very deeply runcinate-pinnatifid, or even pinnately divided, the whole plant being more or less glabrous.

Raunkiaer, who has studied experimentally a dozen types from Denmark, found them constant, but observed that some of them have no pollen at all, while in others the pollen, though present, is impotent. It does not germinate on the stigma, cannot produce the ordinary tube, and hence has no fertilizing power. But the young ovaries do not need such fertilization. They are sufficient unto themselves. One may cut off all the flowers of a head before the opening of the anthers, and leave the ovaries untouched, and the head will ripen its seeds quite as well. The same thing occurs in the hawkweeds. Here, therefore, we have no fertilization and the extensive widening of the variability, which generally accompanies this process is, of course, wanting. Only partial or vegetative variability is present. Unfertilized eggs when developing into embryos are equivalent to buds, separated from the parent-plant and planted for themselves. They repeat both the specific and the individual characters of the parent. In the case of the hawkweed and the dandelion there is at present no means of distinguishing between these two contrasting causes of variability. But like the garden-varieties which are always propagated in the vegetative way, their constancy and uniformity are only apparent and afford no real indication of hereditary qualities.

In addition to these and other exceptional cases, seed-cultures are henceforth to be considered as the sole means of recognizing the really existing systematic units of nature. All other groups, including systematic species and genera, are equally artificial or conventional.

In other words we may state " that current misconceptions as to the extreme range of fluctuating variability of many native species have generally arisen from a failure to recognize the composite nature of the forms in question," as has been demonstrated by MacDougal in the case of the common evening-primrose, *Oenothera biennis*. " It is evident that to study the behavior of the characters of plants we must have them in their simplest combinations; to investigate the origin and movements of species we must deal with them singly and uncomplicated."

Lecture III

ELEMENTARY SPECIES OF CULTIVATED PLANTS

Recalling the results of the last lecture, we see that the species of the systematists are not in reality units, though in the ordinary course of floristic studies they may, as a rule, seem to be so. In some cases representatives of the same species from different countries or regions, when compared with one another do not exactly agree. Many species of ferns afford instances of this rule, and Lindley and other great systematists have frequently been puzzled by the wide range of differences between the individuals of a single species.

In other cases the differing forms are observed to grow near each other, sometimes in neighboring provinces, sometimes in the same locality, growing and flowering in mixtures of two or three or even more elementary types. The violets exhibit widespread ancient types, from which the local species may be taken to have arisen. The common ancestors of the whitlow-grasses are probably not to be found among existing forms, but numerous types are crowded together in the southern part of central Europe and more thinly scattered elsewhere, even as far as western Asia. There can be little doubt that their common origin is to be sought in the center of their geographic distribution.

Numerous other cases exhibit smaller numbers of elementary units within a systematic species; in fact purely uniform species seem to be relatively rare. But with small numbers there are of course no indications to be expected concerning their common origin or the starting point of their distribution.

It is manifest that these experiences with wild species must find a parallel among cultivated plants. Of course cultivated plants were originally wild and must have come under the general law. Hence we may conclude that when first observed and taken up by man, they must already have consisted of sundry elementary subspecies. And we may confidently assert that some must have been rich and others poor in such types.

Granting this state of things as the only probable one, we can easily imagine what must have been the consequences. If a wild species had been taken into cultivation only once, the cultivated form would have been a single elementary type. But it is not very likely that such partiality would occur often. The conception that different tribes at different times and in distant countries would have used the wild plants of their native regions seems far more natural than that all should have obtained plants for cultivation from the same source or locality. If this theory may be relied upon, the origin of many of the more widely cultivated agricultural plants must have been multiple, and the number of the original elementary species of the cultivated types must have been so much the larger, the more widely distributed and variable the plants under consideration were before the first period of cultivation.

Further it would seem only natural to explain the wide variability of many of our larger agricultural and horticultural stocks by such an incipient multiformity of the species themselves. Through commercial intercourse the various types might have become mixed so as to make it quite impossible to point out the native localities for each of them.

Unfortunately historical evidence on this point is almost wholly lacking. The differences in question could not have been appreciated at that remote period, and interest the common observer but little even today. The history of most of the cultivated plants is very obscure, and even the most skillful historians, by sifting the evidence afforded by the older writers, and that obtained by comparative linguistic investigations have been able to do little more than frame the most general outline of the cultural history of the most common and most widely used plants.

Some authors assume that cultivation itself might have been the principal cause of variability, but it is not proved, nor even probable, that cultivated plants are intrinsically more variable than their wild prototypes. Appearances in this case are very deceptive. Of course widely distributed plants are as a rule richer in subspecies than forms with limited distribution, and the former must have had a better chance to be taken into cultivation than the latter. In many cases, especially with the more recent cultivated species, man has deliberately chosen variable forms, because of their greater promise. Thirdly, wide variability is the most efficient means of acclimatization, and only species with many elementary units would have offered the adequate material for introduction into new countries.

From this discussion it would seem that it is more reasonable to assert that variability is one of the causes of the success of cultivation, than to assume that cultivation is a cause of variability at large. And this assumption would be equally sufficient to explain the existing conditions among cultivated plants.

Of course I do not pretend to say that cultivated plants should be expected to be less variable than in the wild state, or that swarms of elementary species might not be produced during cultivation quite as well as before. However the chance of such an event, as is easily seen, cannot be very great, and we shall have to be content with a few examples of which the coconut is a notable one.

Leaving this general discussion of the subject, we may take up the example of the beets. The sugar-beet is only one type from among a horde of others, and though the origin of all the single types is not historically known, the plant is frequently found in the wild state even at the present time, and the native types may be compared with the corresponding cultivated varieties.

The cultivation of beets for sugar is not of very ancient date. The Romans knew the beets and used them as vegetables, both the roots and the leaves. They distinguished a variety with white and one with red flesh, but whether they cultivated them, or only collected them from where they grew spontaneously, appears to be unknown.

Beets are even now found in large quantities along the shores of Italy. They prefer the vicinity of the sea, as do so many other members of the beet-family, and are not limited to Italy, but are found growing elsewhere on the littoral of the Mediterranean, in the Canary Islands and through Persia and Babylonia to India. In most of their native localities they occur in great abundance.

The color of the foliage and the size of the roots are extremely variable. Some have red leafstalks and veins, others a uniform red or green foliage, some have red or white or yellow roots, or exhibit alternating rings of a red and of a white tinge on cut surfaces. It seems only natural to consider the white and the red, and even the variegated types as distinct varieties, which in nature do not transgress their limits nor change into one another. In a subsequent lecture I will show that this at least is the rule with the corresponding color-varieties in other genera.

The fleshiness or pulpiness of the roots is still more variable. Some are as thick as the arm and edible, others are not thicker than a finger and of a woody composition, and the structure of this woody variety is very interesting. The sugar-beet consists, as is generally known, of concentric layers of sugar-tissue and of vascular strands; the larger the first and the smaller the latter, the greater is, as a rule, the average amount of sugar of the race. Through the kindness of the late Mr. Rimpau, a well-known German breeder of sugar-beet varieties, I obtained specimens from seed of a native wild locality near Bukharest. The plants produced quite woody roots, showing almost no sugar-tissue at all. Woody layers of strongly developed fibrovascular strands were seen to be separated one from another only by very thin layers of parenchymatous cells. Even the number of layers is variable; it was observed to be five in my plants; but in larger roots double this number and even more may easily be met with.

Some authors have distinguished specific types among these wild forms. While the cultivated beets are collected under the head of *Beta vulgaris,* separate types with more or less woody roots have been described as *Beta maritima* and *Beta patula.* These show differences in the habit of the stems and the foliage. Some have a strong tendency to become annual, others to become biennial. The first of course do not store a large quantity of food in their roots, and remain thin, even at the time of flowering. The biennial types occur in all sizes of roots. In the annuals the stems may vary from erect to ascending, and the name *patula* indicates stems which are densely branching from the base with widely spreading branches throughout. Mr. Em. von Proskowetz of Kwassitz, Austria, kindly sent me seeds of this *Beta patula,* the variability of which was so great in my cultures as to range from nearly typical sugar-beets to the thin woody type of Bukharest.

Broad and narrow leaves are considered to be differentiating marks between *Beta vulgaris* and *Beta patula,* but even here a wide range of forms seem to occur.

Rimpau, Proskowetz, Schindler and others have made cultures of beets from wild localities in order to discover a hypothetical common ancestor of all the present cultivated types. These researches point to the *B. patula* as the probable ancestor, but of course they were not made to decide the question as to whether the origination of the several now existing types had taken place before or during culture. From a general point of view the variability of the wild species is parallel to that of the cultivated forms to such a degree as to suggest the multiple origin of the former. But a close investigation of this highly important problem has still to be made.

The varieties of the cultivated beets are commonly included in four subspecies. The two smallest are the salad-beets and the ornamental forms, the first being used as food, and ordinarily cultivated in red varieties, the second being used as ornamental plants during the fall, when they fill the beds left empty by summer flowers, with a bright foliage that is exceedingly rich in form and color. Of the remaining subspecies, one comprises the numerous sorts cultivated as forage-crops and the other the true sugar-beets. Both of them vary widely as to the shape and the size of the roots, the quality of the tissue, the foliage and other characteristics.

Some of these forms, no doubt, have originated during culture. Most of them have been improved by selection, and no beet found in the wild state ever rivals any cultivated variety. But the improvement chiefly affects the size, the amount of sugar and nutrient substances and some other qualities which recur in most of the varieties. The varietal attributes themselves however, are more or less of a specific nature, and have no relation to the real industrial value of the race. The short-rooted and the horn-shaped varieties might best be cited as examples.

The assertion that the sundry varieties of forage-beets are not the result of artificial selection, is supported in a large measure by the historic fact that the most of them are far older than the method of conscious selection of plants itself. This method is due to Louis Vilmorin and dates from the middle of the last century. But in the sixteenth century most of our present varieties of beets were already in cultivation. Caspar Bauhin gives a list of the beets of his time and it is not difficult to recognize in it a large series of subspecies and varieties and even of special forms, which are still cultivated. A more complete list was published towards the close of the same century by Olivier de Serres in his world-renowned "Theatre d'Agriculture" (Paris, 1600).

The red forage-beets which are now cultivated on so large a scale, had been introduced from Italy into France only a short time before.

From this historic evidence, the period during which the beets were cultivated from the time of the Romans or perhaps much later, up to the time of Bauhin and De Serres, would seem far too short for the production by the unguided selection of man of all the now existing types. On the other hand, the parallelism between the characters of some wild and some cultivated varieties goes to make it very probable that other varieties have been found in the same way, some in this country and others in that, and have been taken into cultivation separately. Afterwards of course all must have been improved in the direction required by the needs of man.

Quite the same conclusion is afforded by apples. The facts are to some extent of another character, and the rule of the derivation of the present cultivated varieties from original wild forms can be illustrated in this case in a more direct way. Of course we must limit ourselves to the varieties of pure ancestry and leave aside all those which are of hybrid or presumably hybrid origin.

Before considering their present state of culture, something must be said about the earlier history and the wild state of the apples.

The apple-tree is a common shrub in woods throughout all parts of Europe, with the only exception of the extreme north. Its distribution extends to Anatolia, the Caucasus and Ghilan in Persia. It is found in nearly all forests of any extent and often in relatively large numbers of individuals. It exhibits varietal characters, which have led to the recognition of several spontaneous forms, especially in France and in Germany.

The differentiating qualities relate to the shape and indumentum of the leaves. Nothing is known botanically as to differences between the fruits of these varieties, but as a matter of fact the wild apples of different countries are not at all the same.

Alphonse De Candolle, who made a profound study of the probable origin of most of our cultivated plants, comes to the conclusion that the apple-tree must have had this wide distribution in prehistoric times, and that its cultivation began in ancient times everywhere.

This very important conclusion by so high an authority throws considerable light on the relation between cultivated and wild varieties at large. If the historic facts go to prove a multiple origin for the cultivation of some of the more important useful plants, the probability that different varieties or elementary species have been the starting points for different lines of culture, evidently becomes stronger.

Unfortunately, this historic evidence is scanty. The most interesting facts are those concerning the use of apples by the Romans and by their contemporaries of the Swiss and middle European lake-dwellings. Oswald Heer has collected large numbers of the relics of this prehistoric period. Apples were found in large quantities, ordinarily cut into halves and with the signs of having been dried. Heer distinguished two varieties, one with large and one with small fruits. The first about 3 and the other about 1.5-2 cm. in diameter. Both are therefore very small compared with our present ordinary varieties, but of the same general size as the wild forms of the present day. Like these, they must have been of a more woody and less fleshy tissue. They would scarcely have been tasteful to us, but in ancient times no better varieties were known and therefore no comparison was possible.

There is no evidence concerning the question, as to whether during the periods mentioned apples were cultivated or only collected in the wild state. The very large numbers which are found, have induced some writers to believe in their culture, but then there is no reason why they should not have been collected in quantity from wild shrubs. The main fact is that the apple was not a uniform species in prehistoric times but showed even then at least some amount of variability.

At the present day the wild apples are very rich in elementary species. Those of Versailles are not the same as those of Belgium, and still others are growing in England and in Germany. The botanical differences derived from the blossoms and the leaves are slight, but the flavor, size and shape of the fruits diverge widely. Two opinions have been advanced to explain this high degree of variability, but neither of them conveys a real explanation; their aim is chiefly to support different views as to the causes of variability, and the origin of elementary species at large.

One opinion, advocated by De Candolle, Darwin and others, claims that the varieties owe their origin to the direct influence of cultivation, and that the corresponding forms found in the wild state, are not at all original, but have escaped from cultivation and apparently become wild. Of course this possibility cannot be denied, at least in any single instance, but it seems too sweeping an assertion to make for the whole range of observed forms.

The alternative theory is that of van Mons, the Belgian originator of commercial varieties of apples, who has published his experiments in a large work called "Arbres fruitiers ou Pomonomie belge." Most of the more remarkable apples of the first half of the last century were produced by van Mons, but his greatest merit is not the direct production of a number of good varieties, but the foundation of the method, by which new varieties may be obtained and improved.

According to van Mons, the production of a new variety consists chiefly of two parts. The first is the discovery of a subspecies with new desirable qualities. The second is the transformation of the original small and woody apple into a large, fleshy and palatable variety. Subspecies, or what we now call elementary species were not produced by man; nature alone creates new forms, as van Mons has it. He examined with great care the wild apples of his country, and especially those of the Ardennes, and found among them a number of species with different flavors. For the flavor is the one great point, which must be found ready in nature and which may be improved, but can never be created by artificial selection. The numerous differences in flavor are quite original; all of them may be found in the wild state and most of them even in so limited a region as the Ardennes Mountains. Of course van Mons preferred not to start from the wild types themselves, when the same flavor could be met with in some cultivated variety. His general method was, to search for a new flavor and to try to bring the bearer of it up to the desired standard of size and edibility.

The latter improvement, though it always makes the impression of an achievement, is only the last stone to be added to the building up of the commercial value of the variety. Without it, the best flavored apple remains a crab; with it, it becomes a conquest. According to the method of van Mons it may be reached within two or three generations, and a man's life is wholly sufficient to produce in this way many new types of the very best sorts, as van Mons himself has done. It is done in the usual way, sowing on a large scale and selecting the best, which are in their turn brought to an early maturation of their fruit by grafting, because thereby the life from seed to seed may be reduced to a few years.

Form, taste, color, flavor and other valuable marks of new varieties are the products of nature, says van Mons, only texture, fleshiness and size are added by man. And this is done in each new variety by the same method and according to the same laws. The richness of the cultivated apples of the present day was already present in the large range of original wild elementary species, though unobserved and requiring improvement.

An interesting proof of this principle is afforded by the experience of Mr. Peter M. Gideon, as related by Bailey. Gideon sowed large quantities of apple-seeds, and one seed produced a new and valuable variety called by him the " Wealthy " apple. He first planted a bushel of apple-seeds, and then every year, for nine years, planted enough seeds to produce a thousand trees. At the end of ten years all seedlings had perished except one hardy seedling crab. This experiment was made in Minnesota, and failed wholly. Then he bought a small lot of seeds of apples and crab-apples in Maine and from these the "Wealthy" came. There were only about fifty seeds in the lot of crab-apple seed which produced the "Wealthy," but before this variety was obtained, more than a bushel of seed had been sown. Chance afforded a species with an unknown taste; but the growing of many thousands of seedlings of known varieties was not the best means to get something really new.

Pears are more difficult to improve than apples. They often require six or more generations to be brought from the wild woody state to the ordinary edible condition. But the varieties each seem to have a separate origin, as with apples, and the wide range of form and of taste must have been present in the wild state, long before cultivation. Only recently has the improvement of cherries, plums, currants and gooseberries been undertaken with success by Mr. Burbank, and the difference between the wild and cultivated forms has hitherto been very small. All indications point to the existence, before the era of cultivation, of larger or smaller numbers of elementary species.

The same holds good with many of the larger forage crops and other plants of great industrial value. Clover exhibits many varieties, which have been cultivated indiscriminately, and often in motley mixtures. The flower-heads may be red or white, large or small, cylindric or rounded, the leaves are broader or narrower, with or without white spots of a curious pattern. They may be more or less hairy and so forth. Even the seeds exhibit differences in size, shape or color, and of late Martinet has shown, that by the simple means of picking out seeds of the same pattern, pure strains of clover may be obtained, which are of varying cultural value. In this way the best subspecies or varieties may be sought out for separate cultivation. Even the white spots on the leaflets have proved to be constant characters corresponding with noticeable differences in yield.

Flax is another instance. It was already cultivated, or at least made use of during the period of the lake-dwellers, but at that time it was a species referred to as *Linum angustifolium,* and not the *Linum usitatissimum,* which is our present day flax. There are now many subspecies, elementary species, and varieties under cultivation. The oldest of them is known as the " springing flax," in opposition to the ordinary " threshing flax." It has capsules which open of themselves, in order to disseminate the seeds, while the ordinary heads of the flax remain closed until the seeds are liberated by threshing. It seems probable that the first form or *Linum crepitans* might thrive in the wild state as well as any other plant, while in the common species those qualities are lacking which are required for a normal dissemination of the seeds. White or blue flowers, high or dwarf stems, more or less branching at the base and sundry other qualities distinguish the varieties, aside from the special industrial difference of the fibres. Even the life-history varies from annual and biennial, to perennial.

It would take us too long to consider other instances. It is well known that corn, though considered as a single botanical species, is represented by different subspecies and varieties in nearly every region in which it is grown. Of course its history is unknown and it is impossible to decide whether all the tall and dwarf forms, or starchy and sweet varieties, dented or rounded kernels, and hundreds of others are older than culture or have come into existence during historic times, or as some assume, through the agency of man. But our main point now is not the origin, but only the existence of constant and sharply differentiated forms within botanical species. Nearly every cultivated plant affords instances of such diversity. Some include a few types only, while others show a large number of forms clearly separated to a greater or lesser degree.

In some few instances it is obvious that this variability is of later date than culture. The most conspicuous case is that of the coconut. This valuable palm is found on nearly all tropical coasts, in America, as well as in Asia, but in Africa and Australia there are many hundreds of miles of shore line, where it is not found. Its importance is not at all the same everywhere. On the shores and islands of the Indian Ocean and the Malay Archipelago, man is chiefly dependent upon it, but in America it is only of subordinate usefulness.

In connection with these facts, it abounds in subspecies and varieties in the East Indian regions, but on the continent of America little attention has as yet been given to its diverging qualities. In the Malayan region it affords nearly all that is required by the inhabitants. The value of its fruit as food, and the delicious beverage which it yields, are well known. The fibrous rind is not less useful; it is manufactured into a kind of cordage, mats and floor-cloths. An excellent oil is obtained from the kernel by compression. The hard covering of the stem is converted into drums and used in the construction of huts; the lower part is so hard as to take on a beautiful polish when it resembles agate. Finally the unexpanded terminal bud is a delicate article of food. Many other uses could be mentioned, but these may suffice to indicate how closely the life of the inhabitants is bound up with the culture of this palm, and how sharply, in consequence, its qualities must have been watched by early man. Any divergence from the ordinary type must have been noted; those which were injurious must have been rejected, but the useful ones must have been appreciated and propagated. In a word any degree of variability afforded by nature must have been noticed and cultivated.

More than fifty different sorts of the coconut are described from the Indian shores and islands, with distinct local and botanical names. Miquel, who was one of the best systematists of tropical plants, of the last century, described a large number of them, and since, more have been added. Nearly all useful qualities vary in a higher or lesser degree in the different varieties. The fibrous strands of the rind of the nut are developed in some forms to such a length and strength as to yield the industrial product known as the coir-fibre. Only three of them are mentioned by Miquel that have this quality, the *Cocos nucifera rutila, cupuliformis* and *stupposa*. Among them the *rutila* yields the best and most supple fibres, while those of the *stupposa* are stiff and almost unbending.

The varieties also differ greatly in size, color, shape and quality, and the trees have also peculiar characteristics. One variety exhibits leaves which are nearly entire, the divisions being only imperfectly separated, as often occurs in the very first leaves of the seedlings of other varieties. The flavor of the flesh, oil and milk likewise yield many good varietal marks.

In short, the coconut-palm comes under the general rule, that botanical species are built up of a number of sharply distinguishable types, which prove their constancy and relative independence by their wide distribution in culture. In systematic works all these forms are called varieties, and a closer investigation of their real systematic value has not yet been made. But the question as to the origin of the varieties and of the coconut itself has engrossed the attention of many botanists, among whom are De Candolle in the middle of the last century, and Cook at its close.

Both questions are closely connected. De Candolle claimed an Asiatic origin for the whole species, while Cook's studies go to prove that its original habitat is to be sought in the northern countries of South America. Numerous varieties are growing in Asia and have as yet not been observed to occur in America, where the coconut is only of subordinate importance, being one of many useful plants, and not the only one relied upon by the natives for their subsistence. If therefore, De Candolle's opinion is the right one, the question as to whether the varieties are older or younger than the cultivated forms of the species, must always remain obscure. But if the proofs of an American origin should be forthcoming, the possibility, and even the probability that the varieties are of later date than the begining of their culture, and have originated while in this condition must at once be granted. An important point in the controversy is the manner in which the coconuts were disseminated from shore to shore, from island to island. De Candolle, Darwin and most of the European writers claim that the dispersal was by natural agencies, such as ocean-currents. They point out that the fibrous rind or husk would keep the fruits afloat, and uninjured, for many days or even many weeks, while being carried from one country to another in a manner that would explain their geographic distribution. But the probability of the nuts being thrown upon the strand, and far enough from the shore to find suitable conditions for their germination, is a very small one. To insure healthy and vigorous seedlings the nuts must be fully ripe, after which planting cannot be safely delayed for more than a few weeks. If kept too moist the nuts rot. If once on the shore, and allowed to lie in the sun, they become overheated and are thereby destroyed; if thrown in the shade of other shrubs and trees, the seedlings do not find the required conditions for a vigorous growth.

Some authors have taken the fibrous rind to be especially adapted to transport by sea, but if this were so, this would argue that water is the normal or at least the very frequent medium of dissemination, which of course it is not. We may claim with quite as much right that the thick husk is necessary to enable the heavy fruit to drop from tall trees with safety. But even for this purpose the protection is not sufficient, as the nuts often suffer from falling to such a degree as to be badly injured as to their germinating qualities. It is well known that nuts, which are destined for propagation, are as a rule not allowed to fall off, but are taken from the trees with great care.

Summing up his arguments, Cook concludes that there is little in the way of known facts to support the poetic theory of the coconut-palm dropping its fruits into the sea to float away to barren islands and prepare them for human habitation. Shipwrecks might furnish a successful method of launching viable coconuts, and such have no doubt sometimes contributed to their distribution. But this assumption implies a dissemination of the nuts by man, and if this principal fact is granted, it is far more natural to believe in a conscious intelligent dissemination.

The coconut is a cultivated tree. It may be met with in some spots distant from human dwellings, but whenever such cases have been subjected to a closer scrutiny, it appears that evidently, or at least probably, huts had formerly existed in their neighborhood, but having been destroyed by some accident, had left the palm trees uninjured. Even in South America, where it may be found in forests at great distances from the sea-shore, it is not at all certain that true native localities occur, and it seems to be quite lost in its natural condition.

Granting the cultivated state of the palms as the only really important one, and considering the impossibility or at least great improbability of its dissemination by natural means, the distribution by man himself, according to his wants, assumes the rank of an hypothesis fully adequate to the explanation of all the facts concerning the life-history of the tree.

We now have to inquire into the main question, whether it is probable that the coconut is of American or of Asiatic origin, leaving aside the historic evidence which goes to prove that nothing is known about the period in which its dissemination from one hemisphere to another took place, we will now consider only the botanic and geographic evidence, brought forward by Cook. He states that the whole family of coconut-palms, consisting of about 20 genera and 200 species, are all strictly American with the exception of the rather aberrant African oil-palm, which has, however, an American relative referred to the same genus. The coconut is the sole representative of this group which is connected with Asia and the Malayan region, but there is no manifest reason why other members of the same group could not have established themselves there, and maintained an existence under conditions, which are not at all unfavorable to them. The only obvious reason is the assumption already made, that the distribution was brought about by man, and thus only affected the species, chosen by him for cultivation. That the coconut cannot have been imported from Asia into America seems to be the most obvious conclusion from the arguments given. It should be briefly noted, that it was known and widely distributed in tropical America at the time of the discovery of that continent by Columbus, according to accounts of Oviedo and other contemporary Spanish writers.

Concluding we may state that according to the whole evidence as it has been discussed by De Candolle and especially by Cook, the coconut-palm is of American origin and has been distributed as a cultivated tree by man through the whole of its wide range. This must have happened in a prehistoric era, thus affording time enough for the subsequent development of the fifty and more known varieties. But the possibility that at least some of them have originated before culture and have been deliberately chosen by man for distribution, of course remains unsettled.

Coconuts are not very well adapted for natural dispersal on land, and this would rather induce us to suppose an origin within the period of cultivation for the whole group. There are a large number of cultivated varieties of different species which by some peculiarity do not seem adapted for the conditions of life in the wild state. These last have often been used to prove the origin of varietal forms during culture. One of the oldest instances is the variety or rather subspecies of the opium-poppy, which lacks the ability to burst open its capsules. The seeds, which are thrown out by the wind, in the common forms, through the apertures underneath the stigma, remain enclosed. This is manifestly a very useful adaption for a cultivated plant, as by this means no seeds are lost. It would be quite a disadvantage for a wild species, and is therefore claimed to have been connected from the beginning with the cultivated form.

The large kernels of corn and grain, of beans and peas, and even of the lupines were considered by Darwin and others to be unable to cope with natural conditions of life. Many valuable fruits are quite sterile, or produce extremely few seeds. This is notoriously the case with some of the best pears and grapes, with the pine-apples, bananas, bread-fruits, pomegranate and some members of the orange tribe. It is open to discussion as to what may be the immediate cause of this sterility, but it is quite evident, that all such sterile varieties must have originated in a cultivated condition. Otherwise they would surely have been lost.

In horticulture and agriculture the fact that new varieties arise from time to time is beyond all doubt, and it is not this question with which we are now concerned. Our arguments were only intended to prove that cultivated species, as a rule, are derived from wild species, which obey the laws discussed in a previous lecture. The botanic units are compound entities, and the real systematic units in elementary species play the same part as in ordinary wild species. The inference that the origin of the cultivated plants is multiple, in most cases, and that more than one, often many separate elementary forms of the same species must originally have been taken into cultivation, throws much light upon many highly important problems of cultivation and selection. This aspect of the question will therefore be the subject of the next lecture.

Lecture IV

SELECTION OF ELEMENTARY SPECIES

The improvement of cultivated plants must obviously begin with already existing forms. This is true of old cultivated sorts as well as for recent introductions. In either case the starting-point is as important as the improvement, or rather the results depend in a far higher degree on the adequate choice of the initial material than on the methodical and careful treatment of the chosen varieties. This however, has not always been appreciated as it deserves, nor is its importance at present universally recognized. The method of selecting plants for the improvement of the race was discovered by Louis Vilmorin about the middle of the last century. Before his time selection was applied to domestic animals, but Vilmorin was the first to apply this principle to plants. As is well known, he used this method to increase the amount of sugar in beets and thus to raise their value as forage-crops, with such success, that his plants have since been used for the production of sugar. He must have made some choice among the numerous available sorts of beets, or chance must have placed in his hands one of the most appropriate forms. On this point however, no evidence is at hand.

Since the work of Vilmorin the selection-principle has increased enormously in importance, for practical purposes as well as for the theoretical aspect of the subject. It is now being applied on a large scale to nearly all ornamental plants. It is the one great principle now in universal practice as well as one of preeminent scientific value. Of course, the main arguments of the evolution theory rest upon morphologic, systematic, geographic and paleontologic evidence. But the question as to how we can coördinate the relation between existing species and their supposed ancestors is of course one of a physiologic nature. Direct observation or experiments were not available for Darwin and so he found himself constrained to make use of the experience of breeders. This he did on a broad scale, and with such success that it was precisely this side of his arguments that played the major part in convincing his contemporaries.

The work of the breeders previous to Darwin's time had not been very critically performed. Recent analyses of the evidence obtained from them show that numerous types of variability were usually thrown together. What type in each case afforded the material, which the breeder in reality made use of, has only been inquired into in the last few decades. Among those who have opened the way for thorough and more scientific treatment are to be mentioned Rimpau and Von Rümker of Germany and W. M. Hays of America.

Von Rümker is to be considered as the first writer, who sharply distinguished between two phases of methodical breeding-selection. One side he calls the production of new forms, the other the improvement of the breed. He dealt with both methods extensively. New forms are considered as spontaneous variations occurring or originating without human aid. They have only to be selected and isolated, and their progeny at once yields a constant and pure race. This race retains its character as long as it is protected against the admixture of other minor varieties, either by cross-pollination, or by accidental seeds.

Improvement, on the other hand, is the work of man. New varieties of course can only be isolated if chance offers them; the improvement is not incumbent on chance. It does not create really anything new, but develops characters, which were already existing. It brings the race above its average, and must guard constantly against the regression towards this average which usually takes place.

Hays has repeatedly insisted upon the principle of the choice of the most favorable varieties as the foundation for all experiments in improving races. He asserts that half the battle is won by choosing the variety which is to serve as a foundation stock, while the other half depends upon the selection of parent-plants within the chosen variety. Thus the choice of the variety is the first principle to be applied in every single case; the so-called artificial selection takes only a secondary place. Calling all minor units within the botanic species by the common name of varieties, without regard to the distinction between elementary species and retrograde varieties, the principle is designated by the term of "variety-testing." This testing of varieties is now, as is universally known, one of the most important lines of work of the agricultural experiment stations. Every state and every region, in some instances even the larger farms, require a separate variety of corn, or wheat, or other crops. They must be segregated from among the hundreds of generally cultivated forms, within each single botanic species. Once found, the type may be ameliorated according to the local conditions and needs, and this is a question of improvement.

The fact that our cultivated plants are commonly mixtures of different sorts, has not always been known. The first to recognize it seems to have been the Spanish professor of botany, Mariano Lagasca, who published a number of Spanish papers dealing with useful plants and botanical subjects between 1810 and 1830, among them a catalogue of plants cultivated in the Madrid Botanical Garden. Once when he was on a visit to Colonel Le Couteur on his farm in Jersey, one of the Channel Islands off the coast of France, in discussing the value of the fields of wheat, he pointed out to his host, that they were not really pure and uniform, as was thought at that time, and suggested the idea that some of the constituents might form a larger part in the harvest than others. In a single field he succeeded in distinguishing no less than 23 varieties, all growing together. Colonel Le Couteur took the hint, and saved the seeds of a single plant of each supposed variety separately. These he cultivated and multiplied till he got large lots of each and could compare their value. From among them he then chose the variety producing the greatest amount of the finest, whitest and most nutritious flour. This he eventually placed in the market under the name of "Talavera de Bellevue." It is a tall, white variety, with long and slender white heads, almost without awns, and with fine white pointed kernels. It was introduced into commerce about 1830, and is still one of the most generally cultivated French wheats. It was highly prized in the magnificent collection of drawings and descriptions of wheats, published by Vilmorin under the title "Les meilleurs blés" and is said to have quite a number of valuable qualities, branching freely and producing an abundance of good grain and straw. It is however, sensitive to cold winters in some degree and thereby limited in its distribution. Hallett, the celebrated English wheat-breeder, tried in vain to improve the peculiar qualities of this valuable production of Le Couteur's.

Le Couteur worked during many years along this line, long before the time when Vilmorin conceived the idea of improvement by race-selections, and he used only the simple principle of distinguishing and isolating the members of his different fields. Later he published his results in a work on the varieties, peculiarities and classification of wheat (1843), which though now very rare, has been the basis and origin of the principle of variety-testing.

The discovery of Lagasca and Le Couteur was

of course not applicable to the wheat of Jersey alone. The common cultivated sorts of wheat and other grains were mixtures then as they are even now. Improved varieties are, or at least should be, in most cases pure and uniform, but ordinary sorts, as a rule, are mixtures. Wheat, barley and oats are self-fertile and do not mix in the field through cross-pollination. Every member of the assemblage propagates itself, and is only checked by its own greater or less adaptation to the given conditions of life. Rimpau has dealt at large with the phenomenon as it occurs in the northern and middle parts of Germany. Even Rivett's "Bearded wheat," which was introduced from England as a fine improved variety, and has become widely distributed throughout Germany, cannot keep itself pure. It is found mingled almost anywhere with the old local varieties, which it was destined to supplant. Any lot of seed exhibits such impurities, as I have had the opportunity of observing myself in sowings in the experimental-garden. But the impurities are only mixtures, and all the plants of Rivett's "Bearded wheat," which of course constitute the large majority, are of pure blood. This may be confirmed when the seeds are collected and sown separately in cultures that can be carefully guarded.

In order to get a closer insight into the causes of this confused condition of ordinary races, Rimpau made some observations on Rivett's wheat. He found that it suffers from frost during winter more than the local German varieties, and that from various causes, alien seeds may accidentally, and not rarely, become mixed with it. The threshing-machines are not always as clean as they should be and may be the cause of an accidental mixture. The manure comes from stables, where straw and the dust from many varieties are thrown together, and consequently living kernels may become mixed with the dung. Such stray grains will easily germinate in the fields, where they find more congenial conditions than does the improved variety. If winter arrives and kills quantities of this latter, the accidental local races will find ample space to develop. Once started, they will be able to multiply so rapidly, that in one or two following generations they will constitute a very considerable portion of the whole harvest. In this way the awnless German wheat often prevails over the introduced English variety, if the latter is not kept pure by continuous selection.

The Swiss wheat-breeder Risler made an experiment which goes to prove the certainty of the explanation given by Rimpau. He observed on his farm at Salèves near the lake of Geneva that after a lapse of time the " Galland-wheat " deteriorated and assumed, as was generally believed, the characters of the local sorts. In order to ascertain the real cause of this apparent change, he sowed in alternate rows in a field, the " Galland " and one of the local varieties. The " Galland " is a race with obvious characters and was easily distinguished from the other at the time when the heads were ripe. They are bearded when flowering, but afterwards throw off the awns. The kernels are very large and yield an extraordinarily good, white flour.

During the first summer all the heads of the " Galland " rows had the deciduous awns but the following year these were only seen on half of the plants, the remainder having smooth heads, and the third year the " Galland " had nearly disappeared, being supplanted by the competing local race. The cause of this rapid change was found to be twofold. First the " Galland," as an improved variety, suffers from the winter in a far higher degree than the native Swiss sorts, and secondly it ripens its kernels one or two weeks later. At the time of harvest it may not have become fully ripe, while the varieties mixed with it had reached maturity.

The wild oat, *Avena fatua,* is very common in

Europe from whence it has been introduced in the United States. In summers which are unfavorable to the development of the cultivated oats it may be observed to multiply with an almost incredible rapidity. It does not contribute to the harvest, and is quite useless. If no selection were made, or if selection were discontinued, it would readily supplant the cultivated varieties.

From these several observations and experiments it may be seen, that it is not at all easy to keep the common varieties of cereals pure and that even the best are subject to the encroachment of impurities. Hence it is only natural that races of cereals, when cultivated without the utmost care, or even when selected without an exact knowledge of their single constituents, are always observed to be more or less in a mixed condition. Here, as everywhere with cultivated and wild plants, the systematic species consist of a number of minor types, which pertain to different countries and climates, and are growing together in the same climate and under the same external conditions. They do not mingle, nor are their differentiating characters destroyed by intercrossing. They each remain pure, and may be isolated whenever and wherever the desirability for such a proceeding should arise. The purity of the races is a condition implanted in them by man, and nature always strives against this arbitrary and one-sided improvement. Numerous slight differences in characters and numerous external influences benefit the minor types and bring them into competition with the better ones. Sometimes they tend to supplant the latter wholly, but ordinarily sooner or later a state of equilibrium is reached, in which henceforth the different sorts may live together. Some are favored by warm and others by cool summers, some are injured by hard winters, while others thrive then and are therefore relatively at an advantage. The mixed condition is the rule, purity is the exception.

Different sorts of cereals are not always easily distinguishable by the layman and therefore I will draw your attention to conditions in meadows, where a corresponding phenomenon can be observed in a much simpler way.

Only artificial pasture-grounds are seen to consist of a single species of grass or clover. The natural condition in meadows is the occurrence of clumps of grasses and some clovers, mixed up with perhaps twenty or more species of other genera and families. The numerical proportion of these constituents is of great interest, and has been studied at Rothamstead in England and on a number of other farms. It is always changing. No two successive years show exactly the same proportions. At one time one species prevails, at another time one or two or more other species. The weather during the spring and summer benefits some and hurts others, the winter may be too cold for some, but again harmless for others, the rainfall may partly drown some species, while others remain uninjured. Some weeds may be seen flowering profusely during some years, while in other summers they are scarcely to be found in the same meadow. The whole population is in a fluctuating state, some thriving and others deteriorating. It is a continuous response to the ever changing conditions of the weather. Rarely a species is wholly annihilated, though it may apparently be so for years; but either from seeds or from rootstocks, or even from neighboring lands, it may sooner or later regain its foothold in the general struggle for life.

This phenomenon is a very curious and interesting one. The struggle for life, which plays so considerable a part in the modern theories of evolution, may be seen directly at work. It does not alter the species themselves, as is commonly supposed, but it is always changing their numerical proportion. Any lasting change in the external conditions will of course alter the average oscillation and the influence of such alterations will manifest itself in most cases simply in new numerical proportions. Only extremes have extreme effects, and the chance for the weaker sorts to be completely overthrown is therefore very small.

Any one, who has the opportunity of observing a waste field during a series of years, should make notes concerning the numerical proportions of its inhabitants. Exact figures are not at all required; approximate estimates will ordinarily prove to be sufficient, if only the standard remains the same during the succeeding years.

The entire mass of historic evidence goes to prove that the same conditions have always prevailed, from the very beginning of cultivation up to the present time. The origin of the cultivation of cereals is to be sought in central Asia. The recent researches of Solms-Laubach show it to be highly probable that the historic origin of the wheat cultivated in China, is the same as that of the wheat of Egypt and Europe. Remains of cereals are found in the graves of Egyptian mummies, in the mounds of waste material of the lake-dwellings of Central Europe, and figures of cereals are to be seen on old Roman coins. In the sepulchre of King Ra-n-Woser of the Fifth Dynasty of Egypt, who lived about 2000 years B. C., two tombs have recently been opened by the German Oriental Society. In them were found quantities of the tares of the *Triticum dicoccum*, one of the more primitive forms of wheat. In other temples and pyramids and among the stones of the walls of Dashur and El Kab studied by Unger, different species and varieties of cereals were discovered in large quantities, that showed their identity with the present prevailing cultivated races of Egypt.

The inhabitants of the lake-dwellings in Switzerland possessed some varieties of cereals, which have entirely disappeared. They are distinguished by Heer under special names. The small barley and the small wheat of the lake-dwellers are among them. All in all there were ten well distinguished varieties of cereals, the *Panicum* and the *Setaria* or millet being of the number. Oats were evidently introduced only toward the very last of the lake-dwelling period, and rye is of far later introduction into western Europe. Similar results are attained by the examination of the cereals figured by the Romans of the same period.

All these are archaeologic facts, and give but slight indications concerning the methods of cultivation or the real condition of the cultivated races of that time. Virgil has left us some knowledge of the requirements of methodical culture of cereals of his time. In his poem Georgics (I. 197) the following lines are found:

Vidi lecta diu, et multo spectata labore
Degenerare tamen, ni vis humana quotannis
Maxima quaeque manu legeret.
(The chosen seed, through years and labor improved,
Was seen to run back, unless yearly
Man selected by hand the largest and fullest of ears.)

Elsewhere Virgil and also some lines of Columella and Varro go to prove in the same way that selection was applied by the Romans to their cereals, and that it was absolutely necessary to keep their races pure. There is little doubt, but that it was the same principle as that which has led, after many centuries, to the complete isolation and improvement of the very best races of the mixed varieties. It further proves that the mixed conditions of the cereals was known to man at that time, although distinct ideas of specific marks and differences were of course still wholly lacking. It is proof also that cultivated cereals from the earliest times must have been built up of numerous elementary forms. Moreover it is very probable, that in the lapse of centuries a goodly number of such types must have disappeared. Among the vanished forms are the special barley and wheat of the lake-dwellings, the remains of which have been accidentally preserved, but most of the forms must have disappeared without leaving any trace.

This inference is supported by the researches of Solms-Laubach, who found that in Abyssinia numerous primitive types of cereals are still in culture. They are not adequate to compete with our present varieties, and would no doubt also have disappeared, had they not been preserved by such quite accidental and almost primitive isolation.

Closing this somewhat long digression into history we will now resume our discussion concerning the origin of the method of selecting cereals for isolation and segregate-cultivation. Some decades after Le Couteur, this method was taken up by the celebrated breeder Patrick Sheriff of Haddington in Scotland. His belief, which was general at that time, was " That cultivation has not been found to change well defined kinds, and that improvement can be best attained by selecting new and superior varieties, which nature occasionally produces, as if inviting the husbandman to stretch forth his hand and cultivate them."

Before going into the details of Sheriff's work it is as well to say something concerning the use of the word "selection." This word was used by Sheriff as seen in the quotation given, and it was obviously designed to convey the same idea as the word "lecta" in the quotation from Virgil. It was a choice of the best plants from among known mixed fields, but the chosen individuals were considered to be representatives of pure and constant races, which could only be isolated, but not ameliorated. Selection therefore, in the primitive sense of the word, is the choice of elementary species and varieties, with no other purpose than that of keeping them as pure as possible from the admixture of minor sorts. The Romans attained this end only imperfectly, simply because the laws governing the struggle for life and the competition of numerous sorts in the fields were unsuspected by them.

Le Couteur and Sheriff succeeded in the solution of the problem, because they had discovered the importance of isolation. The combination of a careful choice with subsequent isolation was all they knew about it, and it was one of the great achievements to which modern agriculture owes its success.

The other great principle was that of Vilmorin. It was the improvement within the race, or the "amelioration of the race" as it was termed by him. It was introduced into

Selection of Elementary Species 109

England by F. F. Hallett of Brighton in Sussex, who at once called it " pedigree-culture," and produced his first new variety under the very name of " Pedigree-wheat." This principle, which yields improved strains, that are not constant but dependent on the continued and careful choice of the best plants in each succeeding generation, is now generally called " selection." But it should always be remembered that according to the historic evolution of the idea, the word has the double significance of the distinction and isolation of constant races from mixtures, and that of the choice of the best representatives of a race during all the years of its existence. Even sugar-beets, the oldest " selected " agricultural plants are far from having freed themselves from the necessity of continuous improvement. Without this they would not remain constant, but would retrograde with great rapidity.

The double meaning of the word selection still prevailed when Darwin published his " Origin of Species." This was in the year 1859, and at that time Shirreff was the highest authority and the most successful breeder of cereals. Vilmorin's method had been applied only to beets, and Hallett had commenced his pedigree-cultures only a few years before and his first publication of the " Pedigree-wheat " appeared some years later at the International Exhibition of London in 1862. Hence, whenever Darwin speaks of selection, Shirreff's use of the word may as well be meant as that of Vilmorin.

However, before going deeper into such theoretical questions, we will first consider the facts, as given by Shirreff himself.

During the best part of his life, in fact during the largest part of the first half of the nineteenth century, Shirreff worked according to a very simple principle. When quite young he had noticed that sometimes single plants having better qualities than the average were seen in the fields. He saved the grains, or sometimes the whole heads of such plants separately, and tried to multiply them in such manner as to avoid intermixtures.

His first result was the "Mungoswell's wheat." In the spring of 1819 he observed quite accidentally in a field of the farm of that name, a single plant which attracted his attention by a deeper green and by being more heavily headed out. Without going into further details, he at once chose this specimen as the starting point of a new race. He destroyed the surrounding plants so as to give it more space, applied manure to its roots, and tended it with special care. It yielded 63 heads and nearly

2500 grains. All of these were sown the following fall, and likewise in the succeeding years the whole harvest was sown in separate lots. After two years of rapid multiplication it proved to be a good new variety and was brought into commerce. It has become one of the prominent varieties of wheat in East Lothian, that county of Scotland of which Haddington is the principal borough.

The grains of " Mungoswell's wheat " are whiter than those of the allied " Hunter's wheat," more rounded but otherwise of the same size and weight. The straw is taller and stronger, and each plant produces more culms and more heads.

Shirreff assumed, that the original plant of this variety was a sport from the race in which he had found it, and that it was the only instance of this sport. He gives no details about this most interesting side of the question, omitting even to tell the name of the parent-variety. He only asserts that it was seen to be better, and afterwards proved so by the appreciation of other breeders and its success in trade. He observed it to be quite constant from the beginning, no subsequent selection being needed. This important feature was simply assumed by him to be true as a matter of course.

Some years afterwards, in the summer of 1824, he observed a large specimen of oats in one of the fields of the same farm. Being at that time occupied in making a standard collection of oats for a closer comparison of the varieties, he saved the seeds of that plant and sowed them in a row in his experiment-field. It yielded the largest culms of the whole collection and bore long and heavy kernels with a red streak on the concave side and it excelled all other sorts by the fine qualities of its very white meal. In the unequal length of its stalks it has however a drawback, as the field appears thinner and more meager than it is in reality. "Hopetown oats," as it is called, has found its way into culture extensively in Scotland and has even been introduced with success into England, Denmark and the United States. It has been one of the best Scottish oats for more than half a century.

The next eight years no single plant judged worthy of selection on his own farm attracted Shirreff's attention. But in the fall of 1832 he saw a beautiful plant of wheat on a neighboring farm and he secured a head of it with about 100 grains. From this he produced the "Hopetown wheat." After careful separation from the kernels this original ear was preserved, and was afterwards exhibited at the Stirling Agricultural Museum. The "Hopetown wheat" has proved to be a constant variety, excelling the ordinary "Hunter's wheat" by larger grains and longer heads; it yields likewise a straw of superior quality and has become quite popular in large districts of England and Scotland, where it is known by the name of "White Hunter's" from its origin and the brilliant whiteness of its heads.

In the same way Shirreff's oats were discovered in a single plant in a field where it was isolated in order to be brought into commerce after multiplication. It has won the surname of "Make-him-rich." Nothing is on record about the details of its origin.

Four valuable new varieties of wheat and oats were obtained in this way in less than forty years. Then Shirreff changed his ideas and his method of working. Striking specimens appeared to be too rare, and the expectation of a profitable result too small. Therefore he began work on a larger scale. He sought and selected during the summer of 1857 seventy heads of wheat, each from a single plant showing some marked and presumably favorable peculiarity. These were not gathered on one field, but were brought together from all the fields to which he had access in his vicinity. The grains of each of these selected heads were sown separately, and the lots compared during their whole life-period and chiefly at harvest time. Three of the lots were judged of high excellence, and they alone were propagated, and proving to be constant new varieties from the outset were given to the trade under the names of " Shirreff's bearded white," " Shirreff's bearded red," and " Pringle's wheat." They have found wide acceptance, and the first two of them are still considered by Vilmorin as belonging to the best wheats of France.

This second method of Shirreff evidently is quite analogous to the principle of Lagasca and Le Couteur. The previous assumption that new varieties with striking features were being produced by nature from time to time, was abandoned, and a systematic inquiry into the worth of all the divergent constituents of the fields was begun. Every single ear at once proved to belong to a constant and pure race, but most of these were only of average value. Some few however, excelled to a degree, which made them worth multiplying, and to be introduced into trade as separate varieties.

Once started, this new method of comparison, selection and isolated multiplication was of course capable of many improvements. The culture in the experiment-field was improved, so as to insure a fuller and more rapid growth.

The ripe heads had to be measured and counted and compared with respect to their size and the number of their kernels. Qualities of grain and of meal had to be considered, and the influence of climate and soil could not be overlooked.

Concerning the real origin of his new types Shirreff seems never to have been very inquisitive. He remarks that only the best cultivated varieties have a chance to yield still better types, and that it is useless to select and sow the best heads of minor sorts. He further remarks that it is not probable that he found a new sport every time; on the contrary he assumes that his selections had been present in the field before, and during a series of succeeding generations. How many years old they were, was of course impossible to determine. But there is no reason to believe that the conditions in the fields of Scotland were different from those observed on the Isle of Jersey by Le Couteur.

In the year 1862 Shirreff devoted himself to the selection of oats, searching for the best panicles from the whole country, and comparing their offspring in his experimental-garden. " Early Fellow," " Fine Fellow," " Longfellow " and " Early Angus " are very notable varieties introduced into trade in this way.

Some years later Patrick Shirreff described his experiments and results in a paper entitled, "On the improvement of cereals," but the descriptions are very short, and give few details of systematic value. The leading principle, however, is clearly indicated, and anyone who studies with care his method of working, may confidently attempt to improve the varieties of his own locality in the same way.

This great principle of "variety-testing," as it has been founded by Le Couteur and Patrick Shirreff, has increased in importance ever since. Two main features are to be considered here. One is the production of local races, the other the choice of the best starting-point for hybridizing experiments, as is shown in California by the work of Luther Burbank in crossing different elementary species of *Lilium pardalinum* and others.

Every region and locality has its own conditions of climate and soil. Any ordinary mixed race will contain some elementary forms which are better adapted to a given district, while others are more suitable to divergent conditions. Hence it can readily be inferred that the choice cannot be the same for different regions. Every region should select its own type from among the various forms, and variety-testing therefore becomes a task which every one must undertake under his own conditions. Some varieties will prove, after isolation, to be profitable for large districts and perhaps for whole states. Others will be found to be of more local value, but in such localities to excel all others.

As an example we may take one of the varieties of wheat originated by the Minnesota Experiment Station. Hays described it as follows. It was originated from a single plant. From among 400 plants of "Blue stem" several of the best were chosen, each growing separately, a foot apart in every direction. Each of the selected plants yielded 500 or more grains of wheat, weighing 10 or more grams. The seeds from these selected plants were raised for a few years until sufficient was obtained to sow a plot. Then for several years the new strains were grown in a field beside the parent-variety. One of them was so much superior that all others were discarded. It was the one named "Minnesota No. 169." For a large area of Minnesota this wheat seems capable of yielding at least 1 or 2 bushels more grain per acre than its parent variety, which is the best kind commonly and almost universally found on the farms in southern and central Minnesota.

It would be quite superfluous for our present purpose to give more instances. The fact of the compound nature of so-called species of cultivated plants seems to be beyond all doubt, and its practical importance is quite obvious.

Acclimatization is another process, which is largely dependent on the choice of adequate varieties. This is shown on a large scale by the slow and gradual dispersion of the varieties of corn in this country. The largest types are limited to temperate and subtropical regions, while the varieties capable of cultivation in more northern latitudes are smaller in size and stature and require a smaller number of days to reach their full development from seed to seed. Northern varieties are small and short lived, but the "Forty-day-corn" or "Quarantino maize" is recorded to have existed in tropical America at the time of Columbus. In preference, or rather to the entire exclusion of taller varieties, it has thriven on the northern boundaries of the corn-growing states of Europe since the very beginning of its cultivation.

According to Naudin, the same rule prevails with melons, cucumbers and gherkins, and other instances could easily be given.

Referring now to the inferences that may be drawn from the experience of the breeders in order to elucidate the natural processes, we will return to the whitlow-grasses and pansies.

Nature has constituted them as groups of slightly different constant forms, quite in the same way as wheat and oats and corn. Assuming that this happened ages ago somewhere in central Europe, it is of course probable that the same differences in respect to the influence of climatic conditions will have prevailed as with cereals. Subsequent to the period which has produced the numerous elementary species of the whitlow-grass came a period of widespread distribution. The process must have been wholly comparable with that of acclimatization. Some species must have been more adapted to northern climates, others to the soils of western or eastern regions and so on. These qualities must have decided the general lines of the distribution, and the species must have been segregated according to their respective climatic qualities, and their adaptability to soil and weather. A struggle for life and a natural selection must have accompanied and guided the distribution, but there is no reason to assume that the various forms were changed by this process, and that we see them now endowed with other qualities than they had at the outset.

Natural selection must have played, in this and in a large number of other cases, quite the same part as the artificial method of variety-testing. Indeed it may be surmised that this has been its chief and prominent function. Taking up again our metaphor of the sieve we can assert that in such cases climate and soil exercise sifting action and in this way the application of the metaphor becomes more definite. Of course, next to the climate and soil in importance, come ecological conditions, the vegetable and animal enemies of the plants and other influences of the same nature.

In conclusion it is to be pointed out that this side of the problem of natural selection and the struggle for life appears to offer the best prospects for experimental, or for continued statistical inquiry. Direct observations are possible and any comparison of numerical proportions of species in succeeding years affords clear proof of the part it plays. And above all, such observations can be made quite independently of doubtful theoretical considerations about presumed changes of character.

The fact of natural selection is plain and it should be studied in its most simple conditions.

C. RETROGRADE VARIETIES

Lecture V

CHARACTERS OF RETROGRADE VARIETIES

Every one admires the luxuriance of garden-flowers, and their diversity of color and form. All parts of the world have contributed to their number and every taste can find its preference among them. New forms produced by the skill of the breeder are introduced every year. This has been done mostly by crossing and intermingling the characters of introduced species of the same genus. In some of the cases the history of our flowers is so old that their hybrid origin is forgotten, as in the case of the pansies. Hybridizations are still going on in other groups on a large scale, and new forms are openly claimed to be of hybrid origin.

Breeders and amateurs generally have more interest in the results than in the way in which they have been brought about. Excellent flowers and fruit recommend themselves and there seems to be no reason for inquiring about their origin. In some cases the name of the originator may be so widely known that it adds weight to the value of the new form, and therefore may advantageously be coupled with it. The origin and history of the greater part of our garden-flowers, fruits and vegetables are obscure; we see them as they are, and do not know from whence they came. The original habitat for a whole genus or for a species at large, may be known, but questions as to the origin of the single forms, of which it is built up, ordinarily remain unanswered.

For these reasons we are restricted in most cases to the comparison of the forms before us. This comparison has led to the general use of the term "variety" in opposition to "species." The larger groups of forms, which are known to have been introduced as such are called species. All forms which by their characters belong to such a species are designated as varieties, irrespective of their systematic relation to the form, considered as the ancestor of the group.

Hence, we distinguish between "hybrid varieties" and "pure varieties" according to their origin from different parents or from a single line of ancestors. Moreover, in both groups the forms may be propagated by seeds, or in the vegetative way by buds, by grafting or by cutting, and this leads to the distinction of " seed-varieties " and " vegetative varieties." In the first case the inheritance of the special characters through the seeds decides the status of the variety, in the latter case this point is left wholly out of consideration.

Leaving aside all these different types, we are concerned here only with the " seed-varieties " of pure origin, or at least with those, that are supposed to be so. Hybridization and vegetative multiplication of the hybrids no doubt occur in nature, but they are very rare, when compared with the ordinary method of propagation by seed. " Seed-varieties " may further be divided into constant and inconstant ones. The difference is very essential, but the test is not always easy to apply. Constant varieties are as sharply defined and as narrowly limited as are the best wild species, while inconstant types are cultivated chiefly on account of their wide range of form and color. This diversity is repeated yearly, even from the purest seed. We will now discuss the constant seed-varieties, leaving the inconstant and eversporting types to a subsequent lecture.

In this way we may make an exact inquiry into the departures from the species which are ordinarily considered to constitute the essential character of such a constant and pure seed-variety and need only compare these differences with those that distinguish the elementary species of one and the same group from each other.

Two points are very striking. By far the greatest part of the ordinary garden-varieties differ from their species by a single sharp character only. In derivative cases two, three or even more such characters may be combined in one variety, for instance, a dwarfed variety of the larkspur may at the same time bear white flowers, or even double white flowers, but the individuality of the single characters is not in the least obscured by such combinations.

The second point is the almost general occurrence of the same variety in extended series of species. White and double flowers, variegated leaves, dwarfs and many other instances may be cited. It is precisely this universal repetition of the same character that strikes us as the essential feature of a variety.

And again these two characteristics may now be considered separately. Let us begin with the sharpness of the varietal characters. In this respect varieties differ most obviously from elementary species. These are distinguished from their nearest allies in almost all organs. There is no prominent distinctive feature between the single forms of *Draba verna, Helianthemum* or of *Taraxacum;* all characters are almost equally concerned. The elementary species of *Draba* are characterized, as we have seen, by the forms and the hairiness of the leaves, the number and height of the flower-stalks, the breadth and incision of the petals, the forms of the fruits, and so on. Every one of the two hundred forms included in this collective species has its own type, which it is impossible to express by a single term. Their names are chosen arbitrarily. Quite the contrary is the case with most of the varieties, for which one word ordinarily suffices to express the whole difference.

White varieties of species with red or blue flowers are the most common instances. If the species has a compound color and if only one of the constituents is lost, partially colored types arise as in *Agrostemma Coronaria bicolor*. Or the spots may disappear and the color become uniform as in *Gentiana punctata concolor* and the spotless *Arum* or *Arum maculatum immaculatum*. Absence of hairs produces forms as *Biscutella lœvigata glabra;* lack of prickles gives the varieties known as *inermis*, as for instance, *Ranunculus arvensis inermis*. *Cytisus prostratus* has a variety *ciliata*, and *Solanum Dulcamara*, or the bitter-sweet, has a variety called *tomentosum*. The curious monophyllous variety of the strawberry and many other forms will be discussed later.

To enlarge this list it would only be necessary to extract from a flora, or from a catalogue of horticultural plants, the names of the varieties enumerated therein. In nearly every instance, where true varieties and not elementary species are concerned, a single term expresses the whole character.

Such a list would also serve to illustrate the second point since the same names would recur frequently. Long lists of varieties are called *alba*, or *inermis*, or *canescens* or *lutea*, and many genera contain the same appellations. In some instances the systematists use a diversity of names to convey exactly the same idea, as if to conceal the monotony of the character, as for instance in the case of the lack of hairs, which is expressed by the varietal names of *Papaver dubium glabrum*, *Arabis ciliata glabrata*, *Arabis hirsuta glaberrima*, *Veronica spicata nitens*, *Amygdalus persica laevis*, *Paeonia corallina leiocarpa*, &c.

On the contrary we find elementary species in different genera based on the greatest possible diversity of features. The forms of *Taraxacum* or *Helianthemum* do not repeat those of *Draba* or *Viola*. In roses and brambles the distinguishing features are characteristic of the type, as they are evidently derived from it and limited to it. And this is so true that nobody claims the grade of elementary species for white roses or white brambles, but everyone recognizes that forms diverging from the nearest species by a single character only, are to be regarded as varieties.

This general conviction is the basis on which we may build up a more sharply defined distinction between elementary species and varieties. It is an old rule in systematic botany, that no form is to be constituted a species upon the basis of a single character. All authors agree on this point; specific differences are derived from the totality of the attributes, not from one organ or one quality. This rule is intimately connected with the idea that varieties are derived from species. The species is the typical, really existing form from which the variety has originated by a definite change. In enumerating the different forms the species is distinguished by the term of genuine or typical, often only indicated as *a* or the first; then follow the varieties sometimes in order of their degree of difference, sometimes simply in alphabetical order. In the case of elementary species there is no real type; no one of them predominates because all are considered to be equal in rank, and the systematic species to which they are referred is not a really existing form, but is the abstraction of the common type of all, just as it is in the case of a genus or of a family.

Summarizing the main points of this discussion, we find that elementary species are of equal rank and together build up the collective or systematic ideal species. Varieties on the other hand are derived from a real and commonly, still existing type.

I hope that I have succeeded in showing that the difference between elementary species, or, as they are often called, smaller or subspecies, on the one hand and varieties on the other, is quite a marked one. However, in order to recognize this principle it is necessary to limit the term variety, to those propagating themselves by seed and are of pure and not of hybrid origin.

But the principle as stated here, does not involve an absolute contrast between two groups of characters. It is more a difference in our knowledge and appreciation of them than a difference in the things themselves. The characters of elementary species are, as a rule, new to us, while those of varieties are old and familiar. It seems to me that this is the essential point.

And what is it that makes us familiar with them? Obviously the continuous recurrence of the same changes, because by a constant repetition they must of course lose their novelty.

Presently we shall look into these characters more in detail and then we shall find that they are not so simple as might be supposed at first sight; but precisely because we are so familiar with them, we readily see that their different features really belong to a single character; while in elementary species everything is so new that it is impossible for us to discern the unities of the new attributes.

If we bear in mind all these difficulties we cannot wonder at the confusion on this question that seems to prevail everywhere. Some authors following Linnaeus simply call all the subdivisions of species, varieties; others follow Jordan and avoid the difficulty by designating all smaller forms directly as species. The ablest systematists prefer to consider the ordinary species as collective groups, calling their constituents "The elements of the species," as was done by A. P. De Candolle, Alph. De Candolle and Lindley.

By this method they clearly point out the difference between the subdivisions of wild species as they ordinarily occur, and the varieties in our gardens, which would be very rare, were they not singled out and preserved.

Our familiarity with a character and our grounds for calling it an old acquaintance may result from two causes, which in judging a new variety are essentially different. The character in question may be present in the given species or it may be lacking, but present in the other group. In the first case a variety can only be formed by the loss of the character, in the second case it arises by the addition of a new one.

The first mode may be called a negative process, while the second is then to be designated as positive. And as it is more easy to lose what one has than to obtain something new, negative varieties are much more common than are positive ones.

Let us now take an instance of a character that is apt to vary in both ways, for this is obviously the best way of making clear what is meant by a negative and a positive change.

In the family of the composites we find a group of genera with two forms of florets on each flower-head. The hermaphrodite ones are tubular with 5, or rarely 4, equal teeth, and occupy the center of the head. These are often called the flosculous florets or disk-florets. Those of the circumference are ligulate and ordinarily unisexual, without stamens. In many cases they are sterile, having only an imperfect ovary. They are large and brightly colored and are generally designated as ray-florets. As instances we may cite the camomile (*Anthemis nobilis*), the wild camomile (*Matricaria Cham-*

omilla), the yarrow (*Achillea Millefolium*), the daisies, the *Dahlia* and many others. Species occur in this group of plants from time to time that lack the ray-florets, as in the tansy (*Tanacetum vulgare*) and some artemisias. And the genus of the marigolds or *Bidens* is noted for containing both of these types. The smaller and the three-toothed marigold (*B. cernua* and *B. tripartita*) are very common plants of wet soil and swamps, ordinarily lacking the ray-florets, and in some countries they are very abundant and wholly constant in this respect, never forming radiate flower-heads. On the other hand the white-flowered and the purple marigold (*B. leucantha* and *B. atropurpurea*) are cultivated species of our gardens, prized for their showy flower-heads with large white or deeply colored, nearly black-purple florets.

Here we have opportunity to observe positive and negative varieties of the same character. The smaller, and the three-toothed marigold occur from time to time, provided with ray-florets, showing a positive variation. And the white marigold has produced in our gardens a variety without rays. Such varieties are quite constant, never returning to the old species.

Positive and negative varieties of this kind are by no means rare among the compositae.

In systematic works the positive ones are as a rule called "radiate," and the negative ones "discoid." Discoid forms of the ordinary camomile, of the daisy, of some asters (*Aster Tripolium*), and of some centauries have been described. Radiate forms have been observed in the tansy (*Tanacetum vulgare*), the common horse-weed or Canada fleabane (*Erigeron canadensis*) and the common groundsel (*Senecio vulgaris*). Taken broadly the negative varieties seem to be somewhat more numerous than the positive ones, but it is very difficult to come to a definite conclusion on this point.

Quite the contrary is the case with regard to the color-varieties of red and blue flowers. Here the loss of color is so common that every one could give long lists of examples of it. Linnaeus himself supposed that no blue or red-colored wild species would be without a white variety. It is well known that he founded his often criticized prescript never to trust to color in recognizing or describing a species, on this belief.

On the other hand there are some red varieties of white-flowered species. But they are very rare, and little is known about their characters or constancy. Blue varieties of white species are not found. The yarrow (*Achillea Millefolium*) has a red-flowered form, which occurs from time to time in sunny and sandy localities. I have isolated it and cultivated it during a series of years and during many generations. It is quite true to its character, but the degree of its coloring fluctuates between pink and white and is extremely variable. Perhaps it can be considered as an inconstant variety. A red-flowered form of the common *Begonia semperflorens* is cultivated under the name of "Vernon," the white hawthorn (*Crataegus Oxyacantha*) is often seen with red flowers, and a pink-flowered variety of the " Silverchain " or " Bastard acacia " (*Robinia Pseud-Acacia*) is not rarely cultivated. The " Crown " variety of the yellow wall-flower and the black varieties, are also to be considered as positive color-variations, the black being due in the latter cases to a very great amount of the red pigment.

Among fruits there are also some positive red varieties of greenish or yellowish species, as for instance the red gooseberry (*Ribes Grossularia*) and the red oranges. The red hue is far more common in leaves, as seen among herbs, in cultivated varieties of *Coleus* and in the brown-leaved form of the ordinary white clover, among trees and shrubs in the hazelnut (*Corylus*), the beach (*Fagus*), the birch (*Betula*), the barberry (*Berberis*) and many others. But though most of these forms are very ornamental and abundant in parks and gardens, little is as yet known concerning the origin of their varietal attributes and their constancy, when propagated by seeds. Besides the ray-florets and the colors, there are of course a great many other characters in which varieties may differ from their species. In most of the cases it is easy to discern whether the new character is a positive or a negative one. And it is not at all necessary to scrutinize very narrowly the list of forms to become convinced that the negative form is the one which prevails nearly everywhere, and that positive aberrations are in a general sense so rare that they might even be taken for exceptions to the rule.

Many organs and many qualities may be lost in the origination of a variety. In some instances the petals may disappear, as in *Nigella,* or the stamens, as in the Guelder rose (*Viburnum Opulus*) and the *Hortensia* and in some bulbs even the whole flowers may be wanting, as in the beautiful "Plumosa" form of the cultivated grape-hyacinth or *Muscari comosum.* Fruits of the pineapples and bananas without seeds are on record as well as some varieties of apples and pears, of raisins and oranges. And some years ago Mr. Rivière of Algeria described a date growing in his garden that forms fruit without pits. The stoneless plum of Mr.

Burbank of Santa Rosa, California, is also a very curious variety, the kernel of which is fully developed but naked, no hard substance intervening between it and the pulp.

More curious still are the unbranched varieties consisting of a single stem, as may be seen sometimes in the corn or maize and in the fir. Fir-trees of some three or four meters in height without a single branch, wholly naked and bearing leaves only on the shoots of the last year's growth at the apex of the tree, may be seen. Of course they cannot bear seed, and so it is with the sterile maize, which never produces any seed-spikes or staminate flowers. Other seedless varieties can be propagated by buds; their origin is in most cases unknown, and we are not sure as to whether they should be classified with the constant or with the inconstant varieties.

A very curious loss is that of starch in the grains of the sugar-corn and the sugar-peas. It is replaced by sugar or some allied substance (dextrine). Equally remarkable is the loss of the runners in the so-called "Gaillon" strawberries.

Among trees the pendulous or weeping, and the broomlike or fastigiate forms are very marked varieties, which occur in species belonging to quite different orders. The ash, the beach, some willows, many other trees and some finer species of garden-plants, as *Sophora japonica,* have given rise to weeping varieties, and the yew-tree or *Taxus* has a fastigiate form which is much valued because of its ascending branches and pyramidal habit. So it is with the pyramidal varieties of oaks, elms, the bastard-acacia and some others.

It is generally acknowledged that these forms are to be considered as varieties on the ground of their occurrence in so wide a range of species, and because they always bear the same attributes. The pendulous forms owe their peculiarity to a lengthening of the branches and a loss of their habit of growing upwards; they are too weak to retain a vertical position and the response to gravity, which is ordinarily the cause of the upright growth, is lacking in them. As far as we know, the cause of this weeping habit is the same in all instances. The fastigiate trees and shrubs are a counterpart of the weeping forms. Here the tendency to grow in a horizontal direction is lacking, and with it the bilateral and symmetric structure of the branches has disappeared. In the ordinary yew-tree the upright stem bears its needles equally distributed around its circumference, but on the branches the needles are inserted in two rows, one to the left and one to the right. All the needles turn their upper surfaces upwards, and their lower surfaces downwards, and all of them are by this means placed in a single horizontal plane, and branching takes place in the same plane. Evidently this general arrangement is another response to gravity, and it is the failure of this reaction which induces the branches to grow upwards and to behave like stems.

Both weeping and fastigiate characters are therefore to be regarded as steps in a negative direction, and it is highly important that even such marked departures occur without transitions or intermediate forms. If these should occur, though ever so rarely, they would probably have been brought to notice, on account of the great prospect the numerous instances would offer. The fact that they are lacking, proves that the steps, though apparently great, are in reality to be considered as covering single units, that cannot be divided into smaller parts. Unfortunately we are still in the dark as to the question of the inheritance of these forms, since in most cases it is difficult to obtain pure seed.

We now consider the cases of the loss of superficial organs, of which the nectarines are example. These are smooth peaches, lacking the soft hairy down, that is a marked peculiarity of the true peaches. They occur in different races of the peach. As early as the beginning of the past century, Gallesio described no less than eight subvarieties of nectarines, each related to a definite race of peach. Most of them reproduce themselves truly from seed, as is well known in this country concerning the clingstones, freestones and some other types. Nectarines have often varied, giving rise to new sorts, as in the case of the white nectarine and many others differing greatly in appearance and flavor. On the other hand it is to be remarked, that the trees do not differ in other respects and cannot be distinguished while young, the varietal mark being limited to the loss of the down on the fruit. Peaches have been known to produce nectarines, and nectarines to yield true peaches. Here we have another instance of positive and negative steps with reference to the same character, but I cannot withhold an expression of some doubt as to the possibility of crossing and subsequently splitting up of the hybrids as a more probable explanation of at least some of the cases quoted by various writers.

Smooth or glabrous varieties often occur, and some of them have already been cited as instances of the multiplication of varietal names. Positive aberrations are rather rare, and are mostly restricted to a greater density of the pubescence in some hairy species, as in *Galeopsis Ladanum canescens*, *Lotus corniculatus hirsutus* and so on. But *Veronica scutellata* is smooth and has a pubescent variety, and *Cytisus prostratus* and *C. spinescens* are each recorded to have a ciliate form.

Comparable with the occurrence and the lack of hairs, is the existence or deficiency of the glaucous effect in leaves, as is well known in the common *Ricinus*. Here the glaucous appearance is due to wax distributed in fine particles over the surface of the leaves, and in the green variety this wax is lacking. Other instances could be given as in the green varieties of *Papaver alpinum* and *Rumex scutatus*. No positive instances are recorded in this case.

Spines and prickles may often disappear and give rise to unarmed and defenceless types. Of the thorn-apples both species, the white-flowered *Datura Stramonium* and the purple *D. Tatula* have such varieties. Spinach has a variety called the "Dutch," which lacks the prickles of the fruit; it is a very old form and absolutely constant, as are also the thornless thorn-apples. Last year a very curious instance of a partial loss of prickles was discovered by Mr. Cockerell of East Las Vegas in New Mexico. It is a variety of the American cocklebur, often called sea-burdock, or the hedgehog-burweed, a stout and common weed of the western States. Its latin name is *Xanthium canadense* or *X. commune* and the form referred to is named by Mr. Cockerell *X. Wootoni*, in honor of Professor E. O. Wooton who described the first collected specimens.

The burs of the common species are densely covered with long prickles, which are slightly hooked at the apex. In the new form, which is similar in all other respects to the common cocklebur, the burs are more slender and the prickles much less numerous, about 25 to the bur and mostly stouter at the base. It occurs abundantly in New Mexico, always growing with the common species, and seems to be quite constant from seed. Mr. Cockerell kindly sent me some burs of both forms, and from these I raised in my garden last year a nice lot of the common, as well as of the *Wootoni* plants.

Spineless varieties are recorded for the bastard-acacia, the holly and the garden gooseberry (*Ribes Grossularia,* or *R. Uva-crispa*). A spineless sport of the prickly Broom (*Ulex europæus*) has been seen from time to time, but it has not been propagated.

Summarizing the foregoing facts, we have excellent evidence of varieties being produced either by the loss of some marked peculiarity or by the acquisition of others that are already present in allied species. There are a great many cases however, in which the morphologic cause of the dissimilarity is not so easily discerned. But there is no reason to doubt that most of them will be found to conform to the rule on closer investigation. Therefore we can consider the following as the principal difference between elementary species and varieties; that the first arise by the acquisition of entirely new characters, and the latter by the loss of existing qualities or by the gain of such peculiarities as may already be seen in other allied species.

If we suppose elementary species and varieties originated by sudden leaps or mutations, then the elementary species have mutated in the line of progression, some varieties have mutated in the line of retrogression, while others have diverged from their parental types in a line of degression, or in the way of repetition. This conception agrees quite well with the current idea that in the building up of the vegetable kingdom according to the theory of descent, it is species that form the links of the chain from the lower forms to the more highly organized later derivatives. Otherwise expressed, the system is built up of species, and varieties are only local and lateral, but never of real importance for the whole structure.

Heretofore we have generally assumed, that varieties differ from the parent-species in a single character only, or at least that only one need be considered. We now come to the study of those varieties, which differ in more than one character. Of these there are two types. In the first the points of dissimilarity are intimately connected with one another, in the second they are more or less independent.

The mutually related peculiarities may be termed correlative, and we therefore speak, in such cases, of correlative variability. This phenomenon is of the highest importance and is of general occurrence. But before describing some examples, it is as well to note that in the lecture on fluctuating variability, cases of a totally different nature will be dealt with, which unfortunately are designated by the same term. Such merely fluctuating variations are therefore to be left out of the present discussion.

The purple thorn-apple, which is considered by some writers as a variety of the white-flowered species or *Datura Stramonium,* and by others as a separate species, *D. Tatula,* will serve as an illustration. But as its distinguishing attributes, as far as we are concerned with them here, are of the nature described above as characteristic of varietal peculiarities no objection can be made to our using them as a case of correlative variability.

The essential character of the purple thorn-apple lies in the color of the flowers, which are of a very beautiful pale blue. But this color is not limited to the corolla. It is also to be seen in the stems and in the stalks and veins of the leaves, which are stained with a deep purple, the blue color being added to the original green. Even on the surface of the leaves it may spread into a purplish hue. On the stems it is to be met with everywhere, and even the young seedlings show it. This is of some importance, as the young plants when unfolding their cotyledons and primary leaves, may be distinguished by this means from the seedlings of the white-flowered species. In crossing experiments it is therefore possible to distinguish the whites and the blues, even in young seedlings, and experience shows that the correlation is quite constant. The color can always be relied upon; if lacking in the seedlings, it will be lacking in the stems and flowers also; but if the axis of the young plant is ever so slightly tinged, the color will show itself in its beauty in the later stages of the life of the plant.

This is what we term correlation. The colors of the different organs are always in agreement. It is true that they require the concurrence of light for development, and that in the dark or in a faint light the seedlings are apt to remain green when they should become purple, but aside from such consideration all organs always come true to their color, whether pure green and white, or whether these are combined with the blue tinge. This constancy is so absolute that the colors of the different organs convey the suggestion, that they are only separate marks of a single character.

It is on this suggestion that we must work, as it indicates the cause of the correlation. Once present, the faculty of producing the anthocyan, the color in question, will come into activity wherever and whenever opportunity presents itself. It is the cell-sap of the ordinary cell-tissue or parenchyma, which is colored by the anthocyan, and for this reason all organs possessing this tissue, may exhibit the color in question.

Thus the color is not a character belonging to any single organ or cell, nor is it bound to a morphologic unit; it is a free, physiologic quality. It is not localized, but belongs to the entire plant. If we wish to assume for its basis material representative particles, these particles must be supposed to be diffused throughout the whole body of the plant.

This conception of a physiologic unit as the

cause of colors and other qualities is evidently opposed to the current idea of the cells and tissues as the morphologic units of the plants. But I do not doubt, that in the long run it will recommend itself as much to the scientist as to the breeder. For the breeder, when desiring to keep his varieties up to their standard, or when breeding to a definite idea, obviously keeps his standard and his ideal for the whole plant, even if he breeds only for flowers or for fruit.

I have chosen the color of the purple thorn-apple as a first example, but the colors of other plants show so many diverging aspects, all pointing so clearly to the same conclusion, that it would be well to take a more extensive view of this interesting subject.

First we must consider the correlation in the colors of flowers and fruits. If both are colored in the species, whether red or brown or purple or nearly black, and a variety lacking this hue is known, it will be lacking in both organs. If the color is pure, the flowers and berries will become white, but such cases are rare. Ordinarily a yellowish or greenish tinge underlies the ornamental color, and if this latter disappears, the yellowish ground will become manifest. So for instance in the *Belladonna,* a beautiful perennial herb with great shiny black, but very poisonous, fruits. Its flowers are brown, but in some woods a variety with greenish flowers and bright yellow berries occurs, which is also frequently seen in botanic gardens. The anthocyan dye is lacking in both organs, and the same is the case with the stems and the leaves. The lady's laurel or *Daphne Mezereum* has red corollas, purple leaves and red fruits; its white-flowered variety may be distinguished by lack of the red hue in the stems and leaves, and by their beautiful yellow berries. Many other instances could be given, since the loss of color in berries is a very common occurrence, so common that for instance, in the heath-family or *Ericaceae,* with only a few exceptions, all berry-bearing species have white-fruited varieties.

The same correlation is observed in the seeds. The white-flowered flax may be seen to yield yellow and not brown seeds as in the blue species. Many varieties of flowers may be recognized by the color of their seeds, as in the poppies, stocks and others. Other white-flowered varieties may be distinguished when germinating, their young axes being of a pure instead of a purplish green. It is a test ordinarily used by gardeners, to purify their flower beds long before the blooming time, when thinning or weeding them. Even in wild plants, as in *Erodium, Calluna, Brunella* and others, a botanist may recognize the rare white-flowered variety by the pure green color of the leaves, at times when it is not in flower. Some sorts of peas bear colored flowers and a red mark on the stipules of their leaves. Among bulbous plants many varieties may be recognized even in the dry bulbs by the different tinges of the outer scales.

Leaving the colors, we come now to another instance of correlation, which is still more astonishing. For it is as rare, as color-varieties are common. It is afforded by some plants the leaves of which, instead of being entire or only divided into large parts, are cleft to a greater extent by repeated fissures of the marginal lobes. Such foliar variations are often seen in gardens, where they are cultivated for their beauty or singularity, as the laciniated alders, fern-leaved beeches and limes, oak-leaved laburnums, etc. Many of them are described under the varietal name of *laciniata*. In some cases this fissure extends to the petals of the flowers, and changes them in a way quite analogous to the aberrancy of the leaves. This is known to occur with a variety of brambles, and is often seen in botanic gardens in one of the oldest and most interesting of all anomalies, the laciniated variety of the greater celandine or *Chelidonium majus*. Many other instances could be given. Most of them belong to the group of negative variations, as we have defined them. But the same thing occurs also with positive varieties, though of course, such cases are very rare. The best known instance is that of the ever-flowering begonia, *Begonia semperflorens,* which has green leaves and white flowers, but which has produced garden varieties with a brown foliage and pink flowers. Here also the new quality manifests itself in different organs.

Enough has now been said on correlative changes, to convince us that they are as a rule to be considered as the expression of some general internal or physiologic quality, which is not limited to a single organ, but affects all parts of the organism, provided they are capable of undergoing the change. Such characters are therefore to be considered as units, and should be referred to the group of single characters.

Opposed to these are the true compound characters, which consist of different units. These may be segregated by the production of varieties, and thereby betray the separate factors of the complex group.

The most beautiful instances of such complex characters are offered by the colors of some of the most prized garden-flowers. Rarely these are of a single hue, often two or three shades contribute to the effect, and in some cases special spots or lines or tracings are to be seen on a white or on a colored background. That such spots and lines are separate units is obvious and is demonstrated by the fact that sometimes spotless varieties occur, which in all other respects have kept the colors of the species. The complexity of the color is equally evident, whenever it is built up of constituents of the anthocyan and of the yellow group. The anthocyan dye is limited to the sap-cavity of the cells, while the yellow and pure orange colors are fixed in special organs of the protoplasm. The observation under the microscope shows at once the different units, which though lying in the same cell and in almost immediate vicinity of each other are always wholly separated from one another by the wall of the vacuole or sap-filled cell-cavity.

The combination of red and yellow gives a brown tinge, as in the cultivated wall-flower, or those bright hues of a dark orange-red, which are so much sought in tulips. By putting such flowers for a short time in boiling water, the cells die and release the red pigment, which becomes diffused in the surrounding fluids and the petals are left behind with their yellow tinge. In this way it is easy to separate the constituents, and demonstrate the compound nature of the original colors.

But the diversity of the color patterns is far from being exhausted with these simple instances. Apart from them, or joined to them, other complications are frequently seen, which it is impossible to analyze in such an artificial way. Here we have to return to our former principle, the comparison of different varieties. Assuming that single units may be lost, irrespective of the others, we may expect to find them segregated by variation, wherever a sufficiently wide range of color-varieties is in cultivation. In fact, in most cases a high degree of dissimilarity may be reached in the simplest way by such a separation of the components, and by their combination into most diverse smaller groups. A very nice instance of such an analysis of flower-colors is afforded by the ordinary snapdragon. The beautiful brown-red color of this common garden plant is composed on one side of yellow elements, on the other of red units. Of the yellow there are two, one staining the whole corolla with a light hue, as is to be seen in the pure yellow variety called *luteum*. This form has been produced by the loss of the whole group of the red constituents. If the yellow tinge is also lost, there arises a white variety, but this is not absolutely colorless, but shows the other yellow constituent. This last stains only some small parts of the lips of the flower around the throat, brightening, as it seems, the entrance for the visiting insects. In many of the red or reddish varieties this one yellow patch remains, while the general yellow hue fails. In the variety called "Brilliant" the yellow ground makes the red color more shiny, and if it is absent the pure carmine tinge predominates.

It is readily seen, that in the ordinary form the lips are of a darker red than the tube. This evident dissimilarity indicates some complexity. And in fact we have two varieties which exhibit the two causes of this attribute separately. One of them is called "Delila," and has the red color limited to the lips, whilst the tube is pure white. The other is called "Fleshy," and is of a pale pink throughout the whole corolla. Adding these two units to one another, we get the original dark red of the wild type, and it may be briefly stated here, that the way of effecting such an addition is given us in the crossing of the "Fleshy" and the "Delila" variety, the hybrid showing the two colors and returning thereby to the old prototype.

Other cases of compound flower colors or of color patterns might be given as in the *Mimulus* and the poppy, and in most of these cases some varieties are to be seen in our gardens which show only the single constituents of the group.

Many dark flowers have an intermediate bright hued form besides the white variety, as in the case of roses, asters, *Nicandra* and so on.

Intermediate forms with respect to stature may also be seen. The opium-poppy, the snapdragon, peas, the *Nicandra*, and many other garden-plants have not only dwarf varieties, but also some of intermediate height. These, though they are intermediate between the tall and dwarf types, cannot be considered as transitions, as between them and the extremes, intermediates are, as a rule wholly lacking. Instances of the same occurrence of three types may be seen in the seeds of maize ("Cuzco," "Horse-dent" and "Gracillima") of beans and some other plants. The *Xanthium Wootoni*, above referred to, with only part of the prickles of *Xanthium commune* is also a very curious instance of the demonstration of the compound nature of a character.

Summarizing the conclusions that may be drawn from the evidence given in this lecture, we have seen that varieties differ from elementary species in that they do not possess anything really new. They originate for the greater part in a negative way, by the apparent loss of some quality, and rarely in a positive manner by acquiring a character, already seen in allied species. These characters are not of the nature of morphologic entities, but are to be considered as physiologic units, present in all parts of the organisms, and manifesting themselves wherever occasion is afforded. They are units in the sense that they may appear and disappear singly. But very often they are combined to yield compound characters, which are capable of analysis. Opportunities for such an analysis are afforded by these groups of cultivated varieties, of which some members show a single distinguishing quality, or a number of them.

Lecture VI

STABILITY AND REAL ATAVISM

It is generally believed that varieties are principally distinguished from species by their inconstancy. This conception is derived from some special cases and transferred to others, and in its common form this belief must have originated from the confusion which exists as to the meaning of the term variety. It is true that vegetative varieties as a rule run back, when propagated by seeds; they are an obvious instance of inconstancy. In the second place we have considered the group of inconstant or sporting varieties, which of course we must exclude when studying the stability of other types. However, even these sporting varieties are unstable only to a certain degree, and in a broader sense will prove to be as true to their character as the most constant types.

Having separated these two groups, which include also the wide range of hybrid forms, we may next consider only those varieties of pure origin, and ordinarily propagated by seeds, which have been discussed in former chapters. Their general character lies in their fidelity to type, and in the fact that this is single, and not double, as in the sporting varieties.

But the current belief is, that they are only true to their peculiarities to a certain degree, and that from time to time, and not rarely, they revert to the type from which they have arisen. Such reversion is supposed to prove that they are mere varieties, and at the same time to indicate empirically the species from which they have sprung.

In the next lecture we shall examine critically the evidence on which this assumption rests. Before doing so however, it will be necessary to collate the cases in which there is no reversion at all, or in which the reversion is absent at least in experimental and pure sowings.

In the present state of our knowledge it is very difficult to decide, whether or not true reversion occurs in constant varieties. If it does occur, it surely does so very rarely and only under unusual circumstances, or in particular individuals. However when such individuals are multiplied by buds and especially when they are the only representatives of their type, the reversion, though theoretically rare, will be shown by nearly every specimen of the variety. Examples of this will be given below.

They are generally called atavists or reversionists, but even these terms are sometimes used in a different sense.

Lastly it is to be said that the empirical and experimental evidence as to the question of constancy is not as extensive as it should be. The experimental conditions are seldom described, and it is only recently that an interest in the matter has been awakened. Much remains to be done. Among other things the innumerable varieties of trees, shrubs and perennial herbs should be tested as to their constancy when grown from purely fertilized seeds. Many of them may be included among the number that sport constantly.

Leaving aside the doubtful or insufficiently studied cases, we may now turn our attention to the facts that prove the absolute stability of a large number of varieties, at least as far as such completeness can be attained by experiment or observation.

The best proof is afforded by the varieties which grow wild in localities where they are quite isolated from the species, and where for this reason, no possibility of crossing disturbs the significance of the proof. As one instance the rayless form of the wild camomile, or the *Matricaria Chamomilla discoidea* may be mentioned. Many systematists have been so strongly impressed with its absolute constancy and its behavior as an ordinary species, that they have elevated it, as it is called, to the rank of a species. As such it is described under the name of *Matricaria discoidea DC.* It is remarkable for its rapid and widespread distribution, as of late years it has become naturalized in different parts of America and of Europe, where it is to be seen especially in France and in Norway. Experimentally I raised in succeeding years between 1000 and 2000 seedlings, but observed no trace of reversion, either in the strongest or in the numerous very small and weak individuals which appeared in the cultures.

The tansy-ragwort or *Senecio Jacobaea* may be chosen as a second instance. It is a perennial herb with short rootstocks and stout stems bearing numerous short-peduncled heads in a large compact corymb; it multiplies itself abundantly by seeds and is very common on the sand dunes of Holland. It has two forms, differing only in the occurrence or the lack of the ray florets. But these two varieties occupy different localities and are even limited to different provinces. As far as I have been able to ascertain on numerous excursions during a series of years, they never sport, and are only intermingled on the outskirts of their habitats. The rayless form is generally considered as the variety but it is quite as stable as the radiate species.

The radiate varieties of marigold, quoted in a former lecture, seem to be equally constant, when growing far away from their prototypes. I sowed the seeds of a single plant of the radiate form of *Bidens cernua,* and found all of the seedlings came true, and in the next year I had from their seed between 2000 and 3000 flowering individuals, all equally radiate. Many species of composites have been tried, and they are all constant. On the other hand rare sports of this kind have been observed by Murr and other authors.

Many kinds of vegetables and of fruits give instances of stability. White strawberries, green grapes, white currants, crisped lettuce, crisped parsley and some other crisped forms may be cited. The spinage without prickles is a widely known instance. White-flowered flax never reverts to the blue prototype, if kept pure. Sugar-peas and sugar-corn afford further instances. Strawberries without runners have come true from seed ever since their first appearance, over a hundred years ago.

Many garden-varieties, the stability of which under ordinary circumstances is doubtful, because of their being sown too close to other varieties of the same species, have been tested in respect to their stability by different writers and at different times. In doing this it is plain that it is very essential to be sure of the purity of the seed. Specimens must be grown in positions isolated from their allies, and if possible be pollinated artificially with the exclusion of the visits of insects. This may be done in different ways. If it is a rare species, not cultivated in the neighborhood, it is often sufficient to make sure of this fact. Pollen may be conveyed by bees from distances of some ten or twenty meters, or in rare cases from some hundred meters and more, but a greater distance is ordinarily sufficient for isolation. If the flowers fertilize themselves, as is more often the case than is generally supposed, or if it is easy to pollinate them artificially, with their own pollen or in small groups of similar individuals, the best way is to isolate them by means of close coverings. When flowering, the plants are as a rule too large to be put under bell-glasses, and moreover such coverings would keep the air moist, and cause the flower-buds to be thrown off. The best coverings are of netting, or of canvas of sufficiently wide mesh, although after a long experience I greatly prefer cages of fine iron-wire, which are put around and over the whole plant or group of plants, and fastened securely and tightly to the ground.

Paper bags also may be made use of. They are slipped over the flowering branches, and bound together around the twigs, thus enclosing the flowers. It is necessary to use prepared papers, in order that they may resist rain and wind. The best sort, and the one that I use almost exclusively in my fertilization-experiments, is made of parchment-paper. This is a wood-pulp preparation, freed artificially from the so-called wood-substance or lignin. Having covered the flowers with care, and having gathered the seeds free from intermixtures and if possible separately for each single individual, it only remains to sow them in quantities that will yield the greatest possible number of individuals. Reversions are supposed to be rare and small groups of seedlings of course would not suffice to bring them to light. Only sowings of many hundreds or thousands of individuals are decisive. Such sowings can be made in one year, or can be extended over a series of years and of generations. Hildebrand and Hoffman have preferred the last method, and so did Hofmeister and many others. Hildebrand sowed the white hyacinth, and the white varieties of the larkspur, the stock and the sweet pea. Hoffman cultivated the white flax and many other varieties and Hofmeister extended his sowings over thirty years with the white variety of the yellow foxglove (*Digitalis parviflora*).

White-flowered varieties of perennial garden-plants were used in my own experiments. I bought the plants, flowered them under isolation in the way described above, gathered the seeds from each individual separately and sowed them in isolated groups, keeping many hundreds and in some cases above a thousand plants up to the time of flowering. Among them I found only one inconstant variety, the white form of the yellow columbine, *Aquilegia chrysantha*. It evidently belonged to the group of sporting varieties already referred to. All others came absolutely true to type without any exception. The species experimented with, were *Campanula persicifolia, Hyssopus officinalis, Lobelia syphilitica, Lychnis chalcedonica, Polemonium dissectum, Salvia sylvestris* and some others. Tested in the same way I found the white varieties of the following annual plants also quite true: *Chrysanthemum coronarium, Godetia amoena, Linum usitatissimum, Phlox drummondi,* and *Silene Armeria*. To these may be added the white hemlock stork's-bill (*Erodium cicutarium album*) which grows very abundantly in some parts of my fatherland, and is easily recognizable by its pure green leaves and stems, even when not flowering. I cultivated it in large numbers during five succeeding generations, but was never able to find even the slightest indication of a reversion to the red prototype. The scarlet pimpernel or *Anagallis arvensis* has a blue variety which is absolutely constant. Even in Britton and Brown's "Flora," which rarely enumerates varieties, it is mentioned as being probably a distinct species. Eight hundred blooming seedlings were obtained from isolated parents, all of the same blue color. The New Zealand spinage (*Tetragonia expansa*) has a greenish and a brownish variety, the red color extending over the whole foliage, including the stems and the branches. I have tried both of them during several years, and they never sported into each other. I raised more than 5000 seedlings, from the different seeds of one lot of the green variety in succeeding years, but neither those germinating in the first year, nor the others coming into activity after two, three or four years of repose gave any sign of the red color of the original species.

It is an old custom to designate intermediate forms as hybrids, especially when both the types are widely known and the intermediates rare. Many persons believe that in doing so, they are giving an explanation of the rarer forms. But since the laws of hybridism are coming to be known we shall have to break with all such usages. So for instance there are numerous flowers which are of a dark red or a dark blue color, and which, besides a white variety, have a pink or a pale blue form. Such pale varieties are of exactly the same value as others, and on testing they are found to be equally stable. So for instance the pink variety of the Sweet William (*Silene Armeria rosea*), the *Clarkia pulchella carnea* and the pale variety of the corn-cockle, called usually *Agrostemma Githago nicaeensis* or even simply *A. nicaeensis*. The latter variety I found pure during ten succeeding generations. Another notable stable intermediate form is the poppy bearing the Danish flag (*Papaver somniferum Danebrog*). It is an old variety, and absolutely pure when cultivated separately. A long list of other instances might easily be given.

Many garden-varieties, that are still universally prized and cultivated are very old. It is curious to note how often such forms have been introduced as novelties. The common foxglove is one of the best examples. It has a monstrous variety, which is very showy because it bears on the summit of its raceme and branches, large erect cup-shaped flowers, which have quite a different aspect from the normal thimble-shaped side-blossoms. These flowers are ordinarily described as belonging to the anomaly known as "peloria," or regular form of a normally symmetric type; they are large and irregular on the stems and the vigorous branches but slender and quinate on the weaker twigs. Their beauty and highly interesting anomalous character has been the cause of their being described many times, and nearly always as a novelty; they have been recently re-introduced into horticulture as such, though they were already cultivated before the middle of the last century. About that time very good descriptions with plates were published in the journal "Flora" by Vrolik, but afterwards they seem to have been forgotten. The peloric variety of the foxglove always comes true from seed, though in the strict sense of the word which we have chosen for our discussion, it does not seem to be a constant and pure variety.

It is very interesting to compare old botanical books, or even old drawings and engravings containing figures of anomalous plants. The celebrated Pinacothec of Munich contains an old picture by Holbein (1495-1543) representing St. Sebastian in a flower-garden. Of the plants many are clearly recognizable, and among others there is one of the "one-leaved" variety of the strawberry, which may still be met with in botanical gardens. In the year 1671 a Dutch botanist, Abraham Munting published a large volume on garden-plants, containing a great number of very good engravings. Most of them of course show normal plants, but intermixed with these are varieties, that are still in cultivation and therefore must be at least two centuries old. Others, though not figured, are easily recognized by their names and descriptions. The cockscomb is the most widely known, but many white or double flowered varieties were already cultivated at that time. The striped *Jalappa,* the crested *Sedum,* the fasciated crown-imperial, white strawberries, red gooseberries and many others were known to Munting.

Some varieties are as old as culture itself, and it is generally known that the Romans cultivated the white form of the opium-poppy and used the foliage of the red variety of the sugar-beet as a vegetable.

In our time flowers and fruits are changing nearly as rapidly as the fancies and tastes of men. Every year new forms are introduced and usurp the place of older ones. Many are soon forgotten. But if we look at old country gardens, a goodly number of fine and valued old sorts are still to be found. It would be worth while to make special collections of living plants of old varieties, which surely would be a good and interesting work and bring about a conviction of the stability of pure strains. Coming now to the other side of the question, we may consider those cases of reversion which have been recorded from time to time, and which always have been considered as direct proofs of the varietal character of the reverting form. Reversion means the falling back or returning to another type, and the word itself expresses the idea that this latter type is the form from which the variety has arisen.

Some instances of atavism of this kind are well known, as they are often repeated by individuals that are multiplied by buds or by grafting. Before looking attentively into the different features of the many cases of rare reversions it will be advisable to quote a few examples.

The flowering-currant of the Pacific Coast or North American scarlet ribes (*Ribes san guineum*), a very popular ornamental shrub, will serve as a good example. It is prized because of its brilliant red racemes of flowers which blossom early in the spring, before the appearance of the leaves. From this species a white form has arisen, which is an old and widely cultivated one, but not so highly prized because of its pale flowers. These are not of a pure white, but have retained a faint reddish hue. The young twigs and the stalks of the leaves afford an instance of correlated variability since in the species the red color shows itself clearly mixed with the green, while in the variety this tinge is wholly wanting.

Occasionally this white-flowered currant reverts back to the original red type and the reversion takes place in the bud. One or two buds on a shrub bearing perhaps a thousand bunches of white flowers produce twigs and leaves in which the red pigment is noticeable and the flowers of which become brightly colored. If such a twig is left on the shrub, it may grow further, ramify and evolve into a larger group of branches. All of them keep true to the old type. Once reverted, the branches remain forever atavistic. It is a very curious sight, these small groups of red branches among the many white ones. And for this reason attention is often called to it, and more than once I myself have had the opportunity of noting its peculiarities. It seems quite certain that by planting such shrubs in a garden, we may rely upon seeing sooner or later some new buds reverting to the prototype.

Very little attention seems hitherto to have been given to this curious phenomenon, though in many respects it deserves a closer investigation. The variety is said to have originated from seed in Scotland, many years ago, and seems to be propagated only by cuttings or by grafting. If this is true, all specimens must be considered as constituting together only one individual, notwithstanding their wide distribution in the gardens and parks of so many countries. This induces me to suppose, that the tendency to reversion is not a character of the variety as such, but rather a peculiarity of this one individual. In other words it seems probable that when the whitish variety arises a second time from the red species, it is not at all necessary that it should exhibit this same tendency to revert. Or to put it still in another way, I think that we may suppose that a variety, which might be produced repeatedly from the same original stock, would only in rare individuals have a tendency to revert, and in most cases would be as absolutely constant as the species itself.

Such a conception would give us a distinct insight into the cause of the rarity of these reversions. Many varieties of shrubs and trees have originated but once or twice. Most of them must therefore, if our supposition is correct, be expected to be stable and only a few may be expected to be liable to reversions.

Among the conifers many very good cases of reversions by buds are to be found in gardens and glasshouses. They behave exactly like the whitish currant. But as the varietal characters are chiefly found in the foliage and in the branches, these aberrations are to be seen on the plants during the whole year. Moreover they are in some cases much more numerous than in the first instance. The *Cryptomeria* of Japan has a variety with twigs resembling ropes. This is not caused by a twisting, but only by a curvature of the needles in such a way that they seem to grow in spiral lines around the twigs. This variety often reverts to the type with widely spread, straight needles. And on many a specimen four, five, or more reverted branches may be seen on different parts of the same shrub. Still more widely cultivated is the shrub called *Cephalotaxus pedunculata fastigiata,* and more commonly known under its old name of *Podocarpus koraiana.* It is the broom-like variety of a species, nearly allied to the common American and European species of yew, (*Taxus minor* and *T. baccata*). It is a low shrub, with broadly linear leaves of a clear green. In the species the leaves are arranged in two rows, one to the left and one to the right of the horizontally growing and widely spreading branches. In the variety the branches are erect and the leaves inserted on all sides. When sporting, it returns to the bilateral prototype and flat wings of fan-shaped twigs are produced laterally on its dense broom-like tufts.

Wherever this variety is cultivated the same reversion may be seen; it is produced abundantly, and even under seemingly normal circumstances. But as in the case of the *Ribes* all the specimens are derived by buds from a single original plant. The variety was introduced from Japan about the year 1860, but is probably much older. Nothing is known as to its real origin. It never bears flowers or fruits. It is curious to note that the analogous variety of the European yew, *Taxus baccata fastigiata*, though much more commonly cultivated than the *Cephalotaxus*, never reverts, at least as far as I have been able to ascertain. This clearly corroborates the explanation given above.

After considering these rare instances of more widely known reversions, we may now examine the question of atavism from a broader point of view. But in doing so it should once more be remembered, that all cases of hybridism and also all varieties sporting annually or frequently, are to be wholly excluded. Only the very rare occurrence of instances of atavism in varieties that are for the rest known to be absolutely constant, is to be considered.

Atavism or reversion is the falling back to a prototype. But what is a prototype? We may take the word in a physiologic or in a systematic sense. Physiologically the signification is a very narrowly restricted one, and includes only those ancestors from which a form is known to have been derived. But such evidence is of course historic. If a variety has been observed to spring from a definite species, and if the circumstances have been sufficiently ascertained not to leave the slightest doubt as to its pure origin, and if moreover all the evidence has been duly recorded, we may say that the origin of the variety is historically known. In most cases we must be content with the testimony, given somewhat later, and recorded after the new variety had the opportunity of showing its greater merits.

If it now happens that such a variety of recorded origin should occasionally revert to its parent-species, we have all we can wish for, in the way of a thoroughly proved case of atavism. But such instances are very rare, as the birth of most varieties has only been very imperfectly controlled.

Next to this comes the systematic relation of a variety to its species. The historic origin of the variety may be obscure, or may simply be forgotten. But the distinguishing marks are of the order described in our last lecture, either in the positive or in the negative direction, and on this ground the rarer form is considered to be a variety of the more wide-spread one. If now the presumed variety sports and runs over to the presumed type, the probability of the supposed relation is evidently enhanced. But it is manifest that the explanation rests upon the results of comparative studies, and not upon direct observations of the phenomena themselves.

The nearer the relations between the two types in question, the less exposed to doubt and criticism are the conclusions. But the domain of atavism is not restricted to the cases described. Quite on the contrary the facts that strike us most forcibly as being reversions are those that are apt to give us an insight into the systematic affinity of a higher degree. We are disposed to make use of them in our attempts to perfect the natural system and to remould it in such a way as to become a pedigree of the related groups. Such cases of atavism no doubt occur, but the anomalies referred to them must be interpreted merely on the ground of our assumptions as to the relative places in the system to be assigned to the different forms.

Though such instances cannot be considered as belonging strictly to the subject we are dealing with, I think it may be as well to give an example, especially as it affords an occasion for referring to the highly important researches of Heinricher on the variability and atavistic tendencies of the pale blue flag or *Iris pallida.*

The flowers of the blue flags have a perianth of six segments united below into a tube. The three outer parts are dilated and spreading, or reflexed, while the three inner usually stand erect, but in most species are broad and colored like the outer ones. Corresponding to the outer perianth-segments are the three stamens and the three petal-like divisions of the style, each bearing a transverse stigma immediately above the anther. They are pollinated by humble-bees, and in some instances by flies of the genus *Rhingia,* which search for the honey, brush the pollen out of the anthers and afterwards deposit it on the stigma. According to systematic views of the monocotyledons the original prototype of the genus *Iris* must have had a whorl of six equal, or nearly equal perianth-segments and six stamens, such as are now seen in the more primitive types of the family of the lilies, as for instance in the lilies themselves, the tulips, hyacinths and others. As to the perianth this view is supported by the existence of one species, the *Iris falcifolia,* the perianth of which consists of six equal parts. But species with six stamens are wholly lacking. Heinricher however, in cultivating some anomalous forms of *Iris pallida,* succeeded in filling out this gap and in producing flowers with a uniform perianth and six stamens, recalling thereby the supposed ancestral type. The way in which he got these was as follows: he started from some slight deviations observed in the flowers of the pale species, sowed the seeds in large numbers and selected from the seedlings only those, which clearly showed anomalies in the expected atavistic direction. By repeating this during several generations he at last reached his goal and was able to give reality to the prototype, which formerly was only a hypothetical one. The *Iris kaempferi,* a large-flowered Japanese species much cultivated in gardens, is very variable in the number of the different parts of its flowers, and may in some instances be seen even with six stamens. If studied in the same way as Heinricher's iris, it no doubt will yield highly interesting and confirmatory results.

Many other instances of such systematic atavism could be given, and every botanist can easily add some from memory. Many anomalies, occurring spontaneously, are evidently due to the same principle, but it would take too long to describe them.

Reversion may occur either by buds or by seeds. It is highly probable that it occurs more readily by sexual than by asexual propagation. But if we restrict the discussion to the limits hitherto observed, seed-reversions must be said to be extremely rare. Or rather cases which are sufficiently certain to be relied upon, are very rare, and perhaps wholly lacking. Most of the instances, recorded by various writers, are open to question. Doubts exist as to the purity of the seeds and the possibility of some unobserved cross disturbing the results.

In the next lecture we shall deal in general with the ordinary causes and results of such crosses. We shall then see that they are so common and occur so regularly under ordinary circumstances that we can never rely on the absolute purity of any seeds, if the impossibility of an occasional cross has not been wholly excluded, either by the circumstances themselves, or by experimental precautions taken during the flowering period.

For these reasons cases of atavism given without recording the circumstances, or the precautions that guarantee the purity of the fertilization, should always be disregarded. And moreover another proof should always be demanded. The parent which yielded the seeds might be itself a hybrid and liable to reversions by the ordinary laws of the splitting up of hybrids. Such cases should likewise be discarded, since they bring in confusing elements. If we review the long list of recorded cases by these strict methods of criticism very few instances will be found that satisfy legitimate demands. On this ground it is by far safer in the present state of our knowledge, to accept bud-variations only as direct proofs of true atavism. And even these may not always be relied on, as some hybrids are liable to split up in a vegetative way, and in doing so to give rise to bud-variations that are in many respects apparently similar to cases of atavism. But fortunately such instances are as yet very rare.

After this discussion it would be bold indeed to give instances of seed-atavism, and I believe that it will be better to refrain wholly from doing so.

Many instances of so-called atavism are of purely morphologic nature. The most interesting cases are those furnished by the forms which some plants bear only while young, and which evidently connect them with allied species, in which the same features may be seen in the adult state. Some species of the genus *Acacia* bear bipinnate leaves, while others have no leaves at all, but bear broadened and flattened petioles instead. The second type is presumed to be descended from the first by the loss of the leaflets and the modification of the stalks into flat and simple phyllodes. But many of them are liable to recall this primitive form when very young, in the first two or three, or sometimes in eight or ten primary leaves. These leaves are small because of the weakness of the young plant and therefore often more or less reduced in structure. But they are usually strictly bipinnate and thereby give testimony as to their descent from species which bear such leaves throughout their life.

Other similar cases could be given, but this will suffice. They once more show how necessary it is to separate the different cases, thrown together until now, under this general name of atavism. It would be far better to give them all special names, and as long as these are not available we must be cautious not to be misguided by the name, and especially not to confuse different phenomena with one another, because at the present time they bear the same names.

Taking into consideration the relatively numerous restrictions resulting from this discussion, we will now make a hasty survey of some of the more notable and generally acknowledged cases of atavism by bud-propagation. But it should be repeated once more that most of the highly cultivated plants, grown as vegetables or for their fruit or flowers, have so many crosses in their ancestry, that it seems better to exclude them from all considerations, in which purity of descent is a requisite. By so doing, we exclude most of the facts which were until now generally relied upon. For the roses, the hyacinths, the tulips, the chrysanthemums always have furnished the largest contributions to the demonstrations of bud-variation. But they have been crossed so often, that doubt as to the purity of the descent of any single form may recur, and may destroy the usefulness of their many recorded cases of bud-variation for the demonstration of real atavism. The same assertion holds good in many other cases, as with *Azalea* and *Camellia*. And the striped varieties of these genera belong to the group of ever-sporting forms, and therefore will be considered later on. So it is with carnations and pinks, which occasionally vary by layering, and of which some kinds are so uncertain in character that they are called by floriculturists "catch-flowers." On the other hand there is a larger group of cases of reversion by buds, which is probably not of hybrid nature, nor due to innate inconstancy of the variety, but must be considered as pure atavism. I refer to the bud-variations of so many of our cultivated varieties of shrubs and trees. Many of them are cultivated because of their foliage. They are propagated by grafting, and in most cases it is probable that all the numerous specimens of the same variety have been derived in this way from one primitive, aberrant individual. We may disregard variegated leaves, spotted or marked with white or yellow, because they are too inconstant types.

We may next turn our attention to the varieties of trees with cut leaves, as the oak-leaved *Laburnum,* the parsley-leaved vine and the fern-leaved birch. Here the margin of the leaves is deeply cut and divided by many incisions, which sometimes change only the outer parts of the blade, but in other cases may go farther and reach, or nearly reach, the midvein, and change the simple leaf into a seemingly compound structure. The anomaly may even lead to the almost complete loss of all the chorophyll-tissue and the greater part of the lateral veins, as in the case of the cut-leaved beech or *Fagus sylvatica pectinata.*

Such varieties are often apt to revert by buds to the common forms. The cut-leaved beech sometimes reverts partially only, and the branches often display the different forms of cut-leaved, fern-like, oak-leaved and other variously shaped leaves on the same twigs. But this is merely due to the wide variability of the degree of fissure and is to be considered only as a fluctuation between somewhat widely distant extremes, which may even apparently include the form of the common beech-leaves. It is not a bud-variation at all, and it is to be met with quite commonly while the true reversions by buds are very rare and are of the nature of sports appearing suddenly and remaining constant on the same twig. Analogous phenomena of wide variability with true reversion may be seen in the variety of the European hornbeam called *Carpinus Betulus heterophylla*. The leaves of this tree generally show the greatest diversity in form. Some other cases have been brought together by Darwin. In the first place a subvariety of the weeping-willow with leaves rolled up into a spiral coil. A tree of this kind kept true for twenty-five years and then threw out a single upright shoot bearing flat leaves. The barberry (*Berberis*) offers another case; it has a well known variety with seedless fruit, which can be propagated by cuttings or layers, but its runners are said always to revert to the common form, and to produce ordinary berries with seeds. Most of the cases referred to by Darwin, however, seem to be doubtful and cannot be considered as true proofs of atavism until more is known about the circumstances under which they were produced.

Red or brown-leaved varieties of trees and shrubs also occasionally produce green-leaved branches, and in this way revert to the type from which they must evidently have arisen. Instances are on record of the hazel, *Corylus Avellana,* of the allied *Corylus tubulosa,* of the red beech, the brown birch and of some other purple varieties. Even the red bananas, which bear fruits without seeds and therefore have no other way of being propagated than by buds, have produced a green variety with yellow fruits. The *Hortensia* of our gardens is another instance of a sterile form which has been observed to throw out a branch with cymes bearing in their center the usual small staminate and pistillate flowers instead of the large radiate and neutral corollas of the variety, thereby returning to the original wild type. Crisped weeping-willows, crisped parsley and others have reverted in a similar manner.

All such cases are badly in need of a closer investigation. And as they occur only occasionally, or as it is commonly stated, by accident, the student of nature should be prepared to examine carefully any case which might present itself to him. Many phases of this difficult problem could no doubt be solved in this way. First of all the question arises as to whether the case is one of real atavism, or is only seemingly so, being due to hybrid or otherwise impure descent of the varying individual, and secondly whether it may be only an instance of the regularly occurring so-called atavism of the sporting varieties with which we shall deal in a later lecture. If it proves to be real atavism and rare, the case should be accurately described and figured, or photographed if possible; and the exact position of the reverting bud should be ascertained. Very likely the so-called dormant or resting buds are more liable to reversions than the primary ones in the axils of the leaves of young twigs. Then the characters of the atavistic branches should be minutely compared with those of the presumed ancestor; they may be quite identical with them or slightly divergent, as has been asserted in some instances. The atavism may be complete in one case, but more or less incomplete in others.

By far the most interesting point is the question, as to what is to be expected from the seeds of such an atavistic branch. Will they keep true to the reverted character, or return to the characters of the plant which bears the retrograde branch? Will all of them do so, or only part of them, and how large a part? It is very astonishing that this question should still be unsolved where so many individual trees bear atavistic branches that remain on them through long series of years. But then many such branches do not flower at all, or if they flower and bear seed, no care is taken to prevent cross-fertilization with the other flowers of the same plant, and the results have no scientific value. For anyone who cares to work with the precautions prescribed by science, a wide field is here open for investigation, because old reverted branches may be met with much less rarely than new ones.

Finally the possibility is always to be considered that the tendency to bud-reversions may be a special feature of some individuals, and may not be met with in others of the same variety. I have spoken of this before. For the practical student it indicates that a specimen, once observed to produce atavistic buds, may be expected to do the same thing again. And then there is a very good chance that by combining this view with the idea that dormant buds are more apt to revert than young ones, we may get at a method for further investigation, if we recur to the practice of pruning. By cutting away the young twigs in the vicinity of dormant buds, we may incite these to action. Evidently we are not to expect that in so doing they will all become atavistic. For this result is not at all assured; on the contrary, all that we might hope to attain would be the possibility of some of them being induced to sport in the desired direction.

Many questions in scientific research can only

be answered by long and arduous work in well-equipped laboratories; they are not to be attempted by every one. But there are other problems which the most complete of institutions are not able to study if opportunity is not offered them, and such opportunities are apt to occur more often in fields, gardens, parks, woods and plains, than in the relatively small experimental gardens of even the largest institution. Therefore, whosoever has the good fortune to find such sports, should never allow the occasion to pass without making an investigation that may bring results of very great importance to science.

Lecture VII

FALSE ATAVISM OR VICINISM

About the middle of the last century Louis de Vilmorin showed that it was possible to subject plants to the methods of amelioration of races then in use for domestic animals, and since that time atavism has played a large part in all breeding-processes. It was considered to be the greatest enemy of the breeder, and was generally spoken of as a definite force, working against and protracting the endeavors of the horticulturist.

No clear conception as to its true nature had been formulated, and even the propriety of designating the observed phenomena by the term atavism seemed doubtful. Duchesne used this word some decades ago to designate those cases in which species or varieties revert spontaneously, or from unknown internal causes, to some long-lost characters of their ancestors. Duchesne's definition was evidently a sharp and useful one, since it developed for the first time the idea of latent or dormant qualities, formerly active, and awaiting probably through centuries an occasion to awaken, and to display the lost characters.

Cases of apparent reversion were often seen in nurseries, especially in flower culture, which under ordinary circumstances are rarely wholly pure, but always sport more or less into the colors and forms of allied varieties. Such sporting individuals have to be extirpated regularly, otherwise the whole variety would soon lose its type and its uniformity and run over to some other form in cultivation in the vicinity. For this reason atavism in nurseries causes much care and labor, and consequently is to be dealt with as a very important factor.

From time to time the idea has suggested itself to some of the best authorities on the amelioration of plants, that this atavism was not due to an innate tendency, but, in many cases at least, was produced by crosses between neighboring varieties. It is especially owing to Verlot that this side of the question was brought forward. But breeders as a rule have not attached much importance to this supposition, chiefly because of the great practical difficulties attending any attempt to guard the species of the larger cultures against intermixture with other varieties. Bees and humble-bees fly from bud to bud, and carry the pollen from one sort to another, and separation by great distances would be required to avoid this source of impurity. Unfortunately the arrangements and necessities of large cultures make it impossible to isolate the allied varieties from each other.

From a theoretical point of view the origin of these impurities is a highly important question. If the breeders' atavism is due to crosses, and only to this cause, it has no bearing at all on the question of the constancy of varieties. And the general belief, that varieties are distinguished from true species by their repeated reversion and that even such reversibility is the real distinction of a variety, would not hold.

For this reason I have taken much trouble in ascertaining the circumstances which attend this form of atavism. I have visited a number of the leading nurseries of Europe, tested their products in various ways, and made some experiments on the unavoidable conditions of hybridizing and on their effect on the ensuing generations. These investigations have led me to the conclusion, that atavism, as it is generally described, always or nearly always is due to hybridization, and therefore it is to be considered as untrue or false atavism.

True atavism, or reversion caused by an innate latent tendency, seems to be very rare, and limited to such cases as we have spoken of under our last heading. And since the definition, given to this term by its author, Duchesne, is generally accepted in scientific works, it seems better not to use it in another sense, but rather to replace it in such cases by another term. For this purpose I propose the word *vicinism,* derived from the Latin *vicinus* or neighbor, as indicating the sporting of a variety under the influence of others in its vicinity. Used in this way, this term has the same bearing as the word atavism of the breeders, but it has the advantage of indicating the true cause thereof.

It is well known that the term variability is commonly employed in the broadest possible sense. No single phenomenon can be designated by this name, unless some primary restriction be given. Atavism and vicinism are both cases of variability, but in wholly different sense. For this reason it may be as well, to insert here a short survey of the general meanings to be conveyed by the term variation. It implies in the first place the occurrence of a wide range of forms and types, irrespective of their origin, and in the second place the process of the change in such forms. In the first signification it is nearly identical with polymorphy, or richness of types, especially so when these types are themselves quite stable, or when it is not at all intended to raise the question of their stability. In scientific works it is commonly used to designate the occurrence of subspecies or varieties, and the same is the case in the ordinary use of the term when dealing with cultivated plants. A species may consist of larger or smaller groups of such units, and they may be absolutely constant, never sporting if hybridization is precluded, and nevertheless it may be called highly variable. The opium-poppy affords a good instance. It "varies" in height, in color of foliage and flowers; the last are often double or laciniated; it may have white or bluish seeds, the capsules may open themselves or remain closed and so on. But every single variety is absolutely constant, and never runs into another, when the flowers are artificially pollinated and the visits of insects excluded. So it is with many other species. They are at the same time wholly stable and very variable.

The terms variation and variety are used frequently when speaking of hybrids. By crossing forms, which are already variable in the sense just mentioned, it is easy to multiply the number of the types, and even in crossing pure forms the different characters may be combined in different ways, the resulting combinations yielding new, and very often, valuable varieties. But it is manifest that this form of variation is of quite another nature from the variations of pure races. Many hybrid varieties are quite constant, and remain true to their type if no further crosses are made; many others are artificially propagated only in a vegetative way, and for this reason are always found true. Hybrid varieties as a rule were formerly confused with pure varieties, and in many instances our knowledge as to their origin is quite insufficient for sharp distinctions. To every student of nature it is obvious, that crossing and pure variability are wholly distinct groups of phenomena, which should never be treated under the same head, or under the same name.

Leaving aside polymorphy, we may now discuss those cases of variability, in which the changes themselves, and not only their final results play a part. Of such changes two types exist. First, the ever-recurring variability, never absent in any large group of individuals, and determining the differences which are always to be seen between parents and their children, or between the children themselves. This type is commonly called "individual variability" and since this term also has still other meanings, it has of late become customary to use instead the term "fluctuating variability." And to avoid the repetition of the latter word it is called "fluctuation." In contrast to these fluctuations are the so-called sports or single varieties, not rarely denominated spontaneous variations, and for which I propose to use the term "mutations." They are of very rare occurrence and are to be considered as sudden and definite steps.

Lastly, we have to consider those varieties, which vary in a much wider range than the ordinary ones, and seem to fluctuate between two opposite extremes, as for instance variegated leaves, cultivated varieties with variegated or striped flowers, double flowers and some other anomalies. They are ever-sporting and ever-returning from one type to the other. If however, we take the group of these extremes and their intermediates as a whole, this group remains constant during the succeeding generations. Here we find once more an instance of the seemingly contradictory combination of high variability and absolute constancy. It means that the range of variability has quite definite limits, which in the common course of things, are never transgressed.

We may infer therefore that the word variability has such a wide range of meanings that it ought never be used without explanation.

Nothing indeed, is more variable than the signification of the term variable itself.

For this reason, we will furthermore designate all variations under the influence of neighbors with the new and special term "vicinism." It always indicates the result of crossing.

Leaving this somewhat lengthy terminological discussion, we now come to the description of the phenomenon itself. In visiting the plantations of the seedsmen in summer and examining the large fields of garden-flowers from which seed is to be gathered, it is very rare to find a plot quite pure. On the contrary, occasional impurities are the rule. Every plot shows anomalous individuals, red or white flowers among a field of blue, normal among laciniated, single among double and so on. The most curious instance is afforded by dwarf varieties, where in the midst of hundreds and thousands of small individuals of the same height, some specimens show twice their size. So for instance, among the dwarfs of the larkspur, *Delphinium Ajacis*.

Everywhere gardeners are occupied in destroying these "atavists," as they call them. When in full bloom the plants are pulled up and thrown aside. Sometimes the degree of impurity is so high, that great piles of discarded plants of the same species lie about the paths, as I have seen at Erfurt in the case of numerous varieties of the Indian cress or *Tropaeolum*.

Each variety is purified at the time when it shows its characters most clearly. With vegetables, this is done long before flowering, but with flowers only when in full bloom, and with fruits, usually after fertilization has been accomplished. It needs no demonstration to show that this difference in method must result in very diverging degrees of purity.

We will confine ourselves to a consideration of the flowers, and ask what degree of purity may be expected as the result of the elimination of the anomalous plants during the period of blooming.

Now it is evident that the colors and forms of the flowers can only be clearly distinguished, when they are fully displayed. Furthermore it is impossible to destroy every single aberrant specimen as soon as it is seen. On the contrary, the gardener must wait until all or nearly all the individuals of the same variety have displayed their characters, as only in this way can all diverging specimens be eliminated by a single inspection. Unfortunately the insects do not wait for this selection. They fertilize the flowers from the beginning, and the damage will have been done long before the day of inspection comes around. Crosses are unavoidable and hybrid seeds will unavoidably come into the harvest. Their number may be limited by an early eradication of the vicinists, or by the elimination of the first ripe seeds before the beginning of the regular harvest, or by other devices. But some degree of impurity will remain under ordinary circumstances.

It seems quite superfluous to give more details. In any case in which the selection is not done before the blooming period, some impurities must result. Even if it is done before that time, errors may occur, and among hundreds and thousands of individuals a single anomalous one may escape observation.

The conclusion is, that flower seeds as they are offered in commerce, are seldom found absolutely pure. Every gardener knows that he will have to weed out aberrant plants in order to be sure of the purity of his beds. I tested a large number of samples of seeds for purity, bought directly from the best seed-growers. Most of them were found to contain admixtures and wholly pure samples were very rare.

I will now give some illustrative examples. From seeds of a yellow snapdragon, I got one red-flowered specimen among half a hundred yellow ones, and from the variety " Delila " of the same species two red ones, a single white and two belonging to another variety called " Firefly." *Calliopsis tinctoria* has three varieties, the ordinary type, a brown-flowered one and one with tubular rays. Seeds of each of these three sorts ordinarily contain a few belonging to the others. *Iberis umbellata rosea* often gives some white and violet examples. The " Swan " variety of the opium-poppy, a dwarfish double-flowered form of a pure white, contained some single-flowered and some red-flowered plants, when sown from commercial seed are said to be pure. But these were only occasional admixtures, since after artificial fertilization of the typical specimens the strain at once became absolutely pure, and remained so for a series of generations, as long as the experiment was continued. Seeds of trees often contain large quantities of impurities, and the laciniated varieties of birch, elder and walnut have often been observed to come true only in a small number of seedlings.

In the case of new or young varieties, seed-merchants often warn their customers as to the probable degree of purity of the seeds offered, in order to avoid complaints. For example the snow-white variety of the double daisy, *Bellis perennis plena,* was offered at the start as containing as much as 20% of red-flowered specimens.

Many fine varieties are recorded to come true from seed, as in the case of the holly with yellow fruits, tested by Darwin. Others have been found untrue to a relatively high degree, as is notorious in the case of the purple beech. Seeds of the laciniated beech gave only 10% of laciniated plants in experiments made by Strasburger; seeds of the monophyllous acacia, *Robinia Pseud-Acacia monophylla,* were found to be true in only 30% of the seedlings. Weeping ashes often revert to the upright type, red May-thorns (*Crataegus*) sometimes revert nearly entirely to the white species and the yellow cornel berry is recorded to have reverted in the same way to the red berries of the *Cornus Mas.*

Varieties have to be freed by selection from all such impurities, since isolation is a means which is quite impracticable under ordinary circumstances. Isolation is a scientific requirement that should never be neglected in experiments, indeed it may be said to be the first and most important requisite for all exact research in questions of variability and inheritance. But in cultivating large fields of allied varieties for commercial purposes, it is impossible to grow them at such distances from each other as to prevent cross-pollination by the visits of bees.

This purification must be done in nearly every generation. The oldest varieties are to be subjected to it as well as the latest. There is no regular amelioration, no slow progression in the direction of becoming free from these admixtures. Continuous selection is indispensable to maintain the races in the degree of purity which is required in commerce, but it does not lead to any improvement. Nor does it go so far as to become unnecessary in the future. This shows that there must be a continuous source of impurities, which in itself is not neutralized by selection, but of which selection can only eliminate the deteriorating elements.

The same selection is usually applied to new varieties, when they occasionally arise. In this case it is called "fixing," as gardeners generally believe that through selection the varieties are brought to the required degree of purity. This belief seems to rest mainly on observations made in practice, where, as we have seen, isolation is of very rare application. Most varieties would no doubt be absolutely pure from the first moment of their existence, if it were only possible to have them purely fertilized. But in practice this is seldom to be obtained. Ordinarily the breeder is content with such slow improvement as may be obtained with a minimum of cost, and this mostly implies a culture in the same part of the nursery with older varieties of the same species. Three, four or five years are required to purify the novelty, and as this same length of time is also required to produce sufficient quantities of seed for commercial purposes, there is no strong desire to shorten the period of selection and fixation. I had occasion to see this process going on with sundry novelties at Erfurt in Germany. Among them a chamois-colored variety of the common stock, a bluish *Clarkia elegans* and a curiously colored opium-poppy may be mentioned. In some cases the cross-fertilization is so overwhelming, that in the next generation the novelty seems entirely to have disappeared.

The examples given may suffice to convey a general idea of the phenomenon, ordinarily called atavism by gardeners, and considered mostly to be the effect of some innate tendency to revert to the ancestral form. It is on this conception that the almost universal belief rests, that varieties are distinguished, as such, from species by their inconstancy. Now I do not deny the phenomenon itself. The impurity of seeds and cultures is so general and so manifest, and may so easily be tested by every one that it cannot reasonably be subjected to any doubt. It must be conceded to be a fact, that varieties as a rule revert to their species under the ordinary circumstances of commercial culture. And I cannot see any reason why this fact should not be considered as stating a principal difference between varieties and species, since true species never sport into one another.

My objection only refers to the explanation of the observed facts. According to my view nearly all these ordinary reversions are due to crosses, and it is for this reason that I proposed to call them by a separate name, that of " vicinists." Varieties then, by means of such spontaneous intercrossing sport into one another, while species either do not cross, or when crossing produce hybrids that are otherwise constituted and do not give the impression of atavistic reversion.

I must not be content with proposing this new conception, but must give the facts on which this assumption rests. These facts are the results of simple experiments, which nevertheless are by no means easy to carry out, as they require the utmost care to secure the absolute purity of the seeds that are employed. This can only be guaranteed by previous cultures of isolated plants or groups of plants, or by artificial pollination.

Once sure of this preliminary condition, the experiment simply consists in growing a variety at a given distance from its species and allowing the insects to transfer the pollen. After harvesting the seed thus subjected to the presumed cause of the impurities, it must be sown in quantities, large enough to bring to light any slight anomaly, and to be examined during the period of blooming.

The wild seashore aster, *Aster Tripolium*, will serve as an example. It has pale violet or bluish rays, but has given rise to a white variety, which on testing, I have found pure from seed. Four specimens of this white variety were cultivated at a distance of nearly 100 meters from a large lot of plants of the bluish species. I left fertilization to the bees, harvested the seeds of the four whites separately and had from them the following year more than a thousand flowering plants. All of them were of the purest white, with only one exception, which was a plant with the bluish rays of the species, wholly reverting to its general type. As the variety does not give such reversions when cultivated in isolation, this sport was obviously due to some cross in the former year. In the same way I tried the white Jacob's ladder, *Polemonium coeruleum album* in the neighborhood of the blue-flowered species, the distance in this case being only 40 meters. Of two hundred seeds one became a blue atavist, or rather vicinist, while all others remained true to the white type. The same was observed in the white creeping thyme, or *Thymus Serpyllum album,* and the white self-heal, *Brunella vulgaris alba,* gave even so much as 28% seedlings with purple corollas out of some 400 specimens, after being cultivated in close proximity to its parent-species. I have tried many other species, but always with the same result. Such atavists only arise by cultivation in the proximity of allied varieties, never in isolation. They are not real atavists, but only vicinists.

In order to show this yet more clearly, I made another experiment with the white self-heal. I had a lot of the pinnate-leaved variety with purple flowers and somewhat stouter stems, and cultivated single plants of the white-flowering sort at distances that varied from 2 – 16 meters. The seeds of each plant were collected and sown separately, those of the nearest gave up to 5 or 6 hybrids from the seeds of one parent, while those of the farthest gave only one purple-flowered plant for each parent. Evidently the chance of the pollen being carried by bees is much greater on short than on longer distances.

True hybrids between species may arise in

quite the same way, and since it is obviously impossible to attribute them to an innate tendency to reversion, they afford an absolutely irrefutable proof of the assertion that pollen is often brought by insects from one lot of plants to another. In this way I obtained a hybrid between the common Jacob's ladder and the allied species *Polemonium dissectum*. With a distance of 100 meters between them I had two hybrid seeds among a hundred of pure ones. At a similar distance pollen was carried over from the wild radish, *Raphanus Raphanistrum*, to the allied *Raphanus caudatus*, and I observed the following year some very nice hybrids among my seedlings. A hybrid-bean between *Phaseolus nanus* and *P. multiflorus*, and some hybrids between the yellow daisy, *Chrysanthemum segetum* and the allied *Chrysanthemum coronarium* or ox-eye daisy which also arose spontaneously in my garden between parents cultivated at recorded distances, might further be noted. Further details of these experiments need not be given. Suffice to say, that occasional crosses between species do occur, and not even rarely, that they are easily recognized as such and cannot be confused with cases of atavism, and that therefore they give proof to the assumption that in the same way crosses ordinarily occur also between varieties of the same species, if cultivated at small distances apart, say 40 – 50 meters or even more.

Vicinism therefore, may play a part in all such cultures, enough to account for all the impurities observed in the nurseries or in commercial seed-samples.

Of course this whole discussion is limited to such species as are not only as a rule visited by insects, but are dependent on these visits for their fertilization. Most of our garden-flowers are included in this category. If not then we may expect to find the cultures and seeds pure, irrespective of the distances between allied varieties, as for instance with peas, which are known to be self-fertilizing. Another instance is given by the barley. One of the most curious anomalous varieties of this cereal, is the "Nepaul-barley," with its small adventitious flowers on the palets or inner scales. It is a very old, widely cultivated sort, which always comes true from seed, and which has been tested in repeated experiments in my garden. The spikelets of this curious plant are one-flowered and provided with two linear glumes or outer scales. Of the inner scales or palets, the outer one is three-lobed at the summit, hence the varietal name of *Hordeum vulgare trifurcatum*. The central lobe is oblong and hollow, covering a small supernumerary floret inserted at its base. The two lateral lobes are narrower, sometimes linear, and are often prolonged into an awn, which is generally turned away from the center of the spike. The central lobe sometimes bears two florets at its base, although but one is usually present and it may be incomplete.

I might give one more instance from my own experience. A variety of the evening-primrose with small linear petals was once found by one of my sons growing wild near Amsterdam. It was represented by only one individual, flowering among a great many of the ordinary type with broad petals. But the evening-primroses open their anthers in the morning, fertilize themselves during the day, and only display their beautiful flowers in the evening, after the pollination has been accomplished. They then allure evening moths, such as *Agrotis* and *Plusia,* by their bright color, their sweet honey-smell and their nectar. Since the fertilization is accomplished many hours before opening, crosses are effected only in rare instances, and the seeds commonly remain true to the parent-type. The seeds of this one plant, when sown separately in my garden, produced exclusively flowers with the small linear petals of their parent. Although I had a hundred individuals bearing many thousands of flowers, there was not an instance of reversion. And such would immediately have been observed, had it occurred, because the hybrids between the cruciate and the normal flowers are not intermediate, but bear the broad petals of the *O. biennis*.

We may now take up another phase of the question, that of the running out of new varieties, shortly after their introduction into a new country, or later.

The most widely known instance of this is that of the American corn in Baden, recorded by Metzger and quoted by Darwin as a remarkable instance of the direct and prompt action of climate on a plant. It has since been considered as a reversion to the old type. Such reversions invariably occur, according to Wallace, in cases of new varieties, which have been produced quickly. But as we now know, such reversions are due to spontaneous crosses with the old form, and to the rule, that the hybrids of such origin are not intermediate, but assume the features of the older of the two parents. In the light of this experience, Metzger's observation becomes a typical instance of vicinism. It relates to the " Tuscarora " corn of St. Louis, a variety with broad and flat white seeds.

About the year 1840, this corn was introduced into Baden in Germany, and cultivated by Metzger. In the first year it came true to type, and attained a height of 12 feet, but the season did not allow its seeds to ripen normally. Only a few kernels were developed before the winter. From this seed plants of a wholly different type came the next year, of smaller stature, and with more brownish and rounded kernels. They also flowered earlier and ripened a large number of seeds. The depression on the outer side of the seed had almost disappeared, and the original white had become darker. Some of the seeds had even become yellow and in their rounded form they approached the common European maize. Obviously they were hybrids, assuming the character of their pollen-parent, which evidently was the ordinary corn, cultivated all around. The observation of the next year showed this clearly, for in the third generation nearly all resemblance to the original and very distinct American species was lost. If we assume that only those seeds ripened which reverted to the early-ripening European type, and that those that remained true to the very late American variety could not reach maturity, the case seems to be wholly comprehensible, without supposing any other factors to have been at work than those of vicinism, which though unknown at the period of Metzger's and Darwin's writings, seems now to be fully understood. No innate tendency to run out and no changing influence of the climate are required for an adequate explanation of the facts.

In the observation quoted, what astonishes us most, is the great rapidity of the change, and the short time necessary for the offspring of the accidental crosses to completely supplant the introduced type. In the lecture on the selection of elementary species, closely analogous cases were described. One of them was the wild oat or *Avena fatua* which rapidly supplants the cultivated oats in bad years in parts of the fields. Other instances were the experiments of Risler with the " Galland " wheat and the observation of Rimpau on " Rivett's bearded " wheat.

Before leaving the question of vicinism and its bearing on the general belief of the instability of varieties, which when tested with due care, prove to be quite stable, it may be as well to consider the phenomena from another point of view. Our present knowledge of the effects of crosses between varieties enables us to formulate some general rules, which may be used to calculate, and in some way to predict, the nature of the impurities which necessarily attend the cultivation of allied species in close vicinity. And this mode of cultivation being in almost universal use in the larger nurseries, we may, by this discussion, arrive at a more scientific estimation of the phenomena of vicinism, hitherto described.

The simplest case that may be given, is when an ordinary retrograde variety is cultivated with the species to which it belongs. For instance, if dwarfs are cultivated next to the taller type, or a white variety next to the red or blue-flowering species, or thornless forms in neighboring beds with the armed species. Bees and humble-bees, butterflies and moths are seen flying from flower to flower, collecting the honey and carrying pollen. I frequently saw them cross the limits of the neighboring beds. Loaded with the pollen of the variety they visit the flowers of the different species and impregnate the stigma with it. And returning to the variety they bring about similar crosses in the flowers of the latter. Hybrid seeds will develop in both cases and become mixed with the crop. We now have to ask the question, what sort of plants will arise from these hybrid seeds. As a general rule we may state, first, that the hybrids of either form of cross are practically the same, secondly that they are not intermediate, but that the character of one parent prevails to the almost absolute exclusion of the other and in the third place that the older character dominates the younger.

The hybrid offspring will therefore, in the main, have the character of the species and be indistinguishable from it, or show only such differences as escape ordinary observation. When occurring in the seeds of the variety they betray themselves as soon as the differential characters are displayed. Between the thousands of flowering plants of a white variety the hybrids will instantly catch the eye by their red or blue corollas. Quite the contrary effect results from the admixture of hybrids with the seeds of the species itself. Here no difference will show itself, even in the fullest bloom. The effect of the spontaneous crosses will pass unobserved. The strain, if pure in the first year, will seem to be still in the same condition. Or in other terms, the unavoidable spontaneous crosses will disturb the purity of the variety in the second year, while they do not seem to interfere at all with the uniformity of the species. The direct effect of the visits of the insects is evident in the first case, but passes unobserved in the latter.

From this it would seem, that spontaneous crosses are hurtful to varieties, but are innocuous to true species. Certainly this would be so, were there no selection. But it is easily seen, that through this operation the effect becomes quite the opposite. For when the fields are inspected at the time of the fullest display of the varietal characters, the obvious hybrids will be eliminated, but the hidden ones will of necessity be spared, as they are concealed among the species by the similarity of their type. Hence, the harvest of the variety may be rendered pure or nearly so, while the harvest of the species will retain the seeds of the hybrids. Moreover it will contain seeds originated by the spontaneous but numerous crosses of the true plants with the sparsely intermingled hybrids.

This brings us to the question, as to what will be the visible consequences of the occurrence of such invisible hybrids in the following generation. In opposition to the direct effects just described, we may call them indirect. To judge of their influence, we must know how hybrid seeds of the first generation behave.

In one of our lectures we will deal with the laws that show the numerical relations known as the laws of Mendel. But for our present purpose, these numerical relations are only of subordinate importance. What interests us here is the fact that hybrids of varieties do not remain constant in the second generation but usually split as it is said, remaining hybrid only in part of their offspring, the other portion returning to the parental types. This however, will show itself only in those individuals which reassume the character of the varietal parent, all the others apparently remaining true to the type of the species. Now it is easy to foresee what must happen in the second generation if the first generation after the cross is supposed to be kept free from new vicinistic influences, or from crosses with neighboring varieties.

We may limit ourselves in the first place to the seeds of the unobserved hybrids. For the greater part they will repeat the character of their parents and still remain concealed. But a small number will display the varietal marks, as for example showing white flowers in a field of blue ones. Hence, the indirect consequence of the spontaneous crosses will be the same in the species, as was the direct effect in the variety, only, that it appears a year later. It will then be eliminated in the process of selection.

Obviously, this elimination conduces only to a partial purification. The conspicuous plants will be destroyed, but a greater number of hybrids will remain, still concealed by their resemblance to the general type and will be spared to repeat the same process next year. So while the variety may be freed every year from the impurities brought into it in the preceeding summer, the admixtures of the species will continue during a number of years, and it may not be possible to get rid of them at all.

It is an often recurring assertion that white varieties of colored species are the most stable of all horticultural races. They are often said to be at least as constant as the species itself, and even to surpass it in this quality. With our present state of knowledge, the explanation of this general experience is easily given. For selection removes the effect of spontaneous crosses from the variety in each year, and renders it practically pure, while it is wholly inadequate to produce the same effects on the species, because of the concealed hybrids.

The explanation given in this simple instance may be applied to the case of different varieties of the same species, when growing together and crossed naturally by insects.

It would take too long to go into all the details that present themselves here to the student of nature and of gardens. I will only state, that since varieties differ principally from their species by the lack of some sharp character, one variety may be characterized by the lack of color of the flowers, another by the lack of pubescence, a third by being dwarfed, and so on. Every character must be studied separately in its effects on the offspring of the crosses. And it is therefore easily seen, that the hybrids of two varieties may resemble neither of them, but revert to the species itself. This is necessarily and commonly the case, since it is always the older or positive characters that prevail in the hybrids and the younger or negative that lie hidden. So for instance, a blue dwarf larkspur, crossed with a tall white variety, must give a tall blue hybrid, reassuming in both characters the essentials of the species.

Keeping this rule in view, it will be easy to calculate what may be expected from spontaneous crosses for a wide range of occurrences, and thus to find an explanation of innumerable cases of apparent variability and reversion in the principle of vicinism. Students have only to recollect that specific characters prevail over varietal ones, and that every character competes only with its own antagonist. Or to give a sharper distinction: whiteness of flowers cannot be expected to be interchanged with pubescence of leaves.

In concluding I will point out another danger which in the principle of vicinism may be avoided. If you see a plant in a garden with all the characteristics of its species, how can you be sure that it is truly a representative of the species, and not a hybrid? The prevailing characters are in either case the same. Perhaps on close inspection you may find in some cases a slight difference, some character being not as fully developed in the hybrid as in the species. But when such is not the case, or where the opportunity for such a closer examination is wanting, a hybrid may easily be taken for a specimen of the pure race. Now take the seeds of your plant and sow them. If you had not supposed it to be hybrid you will be astonished at finding among its progeny some of a wholly different type. You will be led to conclude that you are observing a sudden change in structure such as is usually called a sport.

Or in other words you may think that you are assisting at the origination of a new variety. If you are familiar with the principle of vicinism, you will refrain from such an inference and consider the supposition of a hybrid origin. But in former times, when this principle was still unknown and not even guessed at, it is evident that many mistakes must have been made, and that many an instance, which until now has been considered reliable proof of a so-called single variation, is in fact only a case of vicinism. In reading the sparse literature on sports, numerous cases will be found, which cannot stand this test. In many instances crossing must be looked to as an explanation, and in other cases the evidence relied upon does not suffice to exclude this assumption. Many an old argument has of late lost its force by this test.

Returning to our starting point we may now state that regular reversions to a specific type characterize a form as a variety of that species. These reversions, however, are **not due to an** innate tendency, but to unobserved spontaneous crosses.

Lecture VIII

LATENT CHARACTERS

No organism exhibits all of its qualities at any one time. Many of them are generally dormant and await a period of activity. For some of them this period comes regularly, while in others the awakening depends upon external influences, and consequently occurs very irregularly. Those of the first group correspond to the differences in age; the second constitute the responses of the plant to stimuli including wound-injuries.

Some illustrative examples may be quoted in order to give a precise idea of this general conception of dormant or latent characters. Seed-leaves are only developed in the seed and the seedling; afterwards, during the entire lifetime of the plant, the faculty of producing them is not made use of. Every new generation of seeds however, bears the same kind of seed-leaves, and hence it is manifest that it is the same quality, which shows itself from time to time.

The primary leaves, following the seed-leaves, are different in many species from the later ones, and the difference is extremely pronounced in some cases of reduction. Often, when leaves are lacking in the adult plant, being replaced by flattened stalks as in the case of the acacias, or by thorns, or green stems and twigs as in the prickly broom or *Ulex europaeus,* the first leaves of the young plant may be more highly differentiated, being pinnate in the first case and bearing three leaflets in the second instance. This curious behavior which is very common, brings the plants, when young, nearer to their allies than in the adult state, and manifestly implies that the more perfect state of the leaves is latent throughout the life of the plant, with the exception of the early juvenile period.

Eucalyptus Globulus, the Australian gum-tree, has opposite and broadly sessile leaves during the first years of its life. Later these disappear and are replaced by long sickle-shaped foliage organs, which seem to be scattered irregularly along the branches. The juvenile characters manifestly lie dormant during the adult period, and that this is so, may be shown artificially by cutting off the whole crown of the tree, when the stem responds by producing numerous new branches, which assume the shape proper to the young trees, bearing sessile and opposite leaves.

It seems quite unnecessary to give further instances. They are familiar to every student. It is almost safe to say that every character has its periods of activity and of inactivity, and numbers of flowers and fruits can be mentioned as illustrations. One fact may be added to show that nearly every part of the plant must have the power of producing all or nearly all the characters of the individual to which it belongs. This proof is given by the formation of adventitious buds. These, when once formed, may grow out into twigs, with leaves and flowers and roots. They may even be separated from the plants and used as cuttings to reproduce the whole. Hence we may conclude that all tissues, which possess the power of producing adventitious buds, must conceal in a latent state, all the numerous characters required for the full development of the whole individual.

Adventitious buds may proceed from specialized cells, as on the margin of the leaves of *Bryophyllum calycinum;* or from the cells of special tissues, as in the epidermis of the begonias; or they may be provoked by wounds in nearly every part of the plant, provided it be able to heal the wound by swelling tissues or callus. The best instance is afforded by elms and by the horse-chestnut. If the whole tree is hewn down the trunk tries to repair the injury by producing small granulations of tissue between the wood and the bark, which gradually coalesce while becoming larger. From this new ring of living matter innumerable buds arise, that expand into leafy branches, showing clearly that the old trunk possesses, in a latent state, all the qualities of the whole crown. Indeed, such injured stumps may be used for the production of copses and hedges.

All the hitherto recorded cases of latency have this in common, that they may become active during the life-time of any given individual once, or oftener. This may be called the ordinary type of latency.

Besides this there is another form of latent characters, in which this awakening power is extremely limited, or wholly absent. It is the systematic latency, which may be said to belong to species and varieties in the same way as the ordinary latency belongs to individuals. As this individual latency may show itself from time to time during the life of a given plant, the first may only become active from time to time during the whole existence of the variety or the species. It has no regular period of activity, nor may it be incited by artificial stimulation.

It emerges from concealment only very rarely and only on its own initiative. Such instances of atavism have been described in previous lectures, and their existence has been proved beyond doubt.

Systematic latency explains the innumerable instances in which species are seen to lack definite characteristics which ordinarily do not fail, either in plants at large, or in the group or family to which the plant belongs. If we take for instance the broom-rape or *Orobanche,* or some other pale parasite, we explain their occurrence in families of plants with green leaves, by the loss of the leaves and of the green color. But evidently this loss is not a true one, but only the latency of those characters. And even this latency is not a complete one, as little scales remind us of the leaves, and traces of chlorophyll still exist in the tissues. Numerous other cases will present themselves to every practical botanist.

Taking for granted that characters, having once been acquired, may become latent, and that this process is of universal occurrence throughout the whole vegetable and animal kingdom, we may now come to a more precise and clear conception of the existing differences between species and varieties.

For this purpose we must take a somewhat

broader view of the whole evolution of the vegetable kingdom. It is manifest that highly developed plants have a larger number of characters than the lower groups. These must have been acquired in some way, during preceding times. Such evolution must evidently be called a process of improvement, or a progressive evolution. Contrasted to this is the loss, or the latency of characters, and this may be designated retrogressive or retrograde evolution. But there is still a third possibility. For a latent character may reassume its activity, return to the active state, and become once more an important part of the whole organization. This process may be designated as degressive evolution; it obviously completes the series of the general types of evolution.

Advancement in general in living nature depends on progressive evolution. In different parts of the vegetable kingdom, and even in different families this progression takes place on different lines. By this means it results in an ever increasing divergency between the several groups. Every step is an advance, and many a step must have been taken to produce flowering plants from the simplest unicellular algae.

But related to, and very intimately connected with this advancement is the retrogressive evolution. It is equally universal, perhaps never failing. No great changes have been attained, without acquiring new qualities on one side, and reducing others to latency. Everywhere such retrogressions may be seen. The polypetalous genera *Pyrola, Ledum,* and *Monotropa* among the sympetalous heaths, are a remarkable instance of this. The whole evolution of the monocotyledons from the lowest orders of dicotyledons implies the seeming loss of cambial growth and many other qualities. In the order of aroids, from the calamus-root or sweet flag, with its small but complete flowers, up to the reduced duckweeds (*Lemna*), almost an unbroken line of intermediate steps may be traced showing everywhere the concurrence of progressive and retrogressive evolution.

Degressive evolution is not so common by far, and is not so easy to recognize, but no doubt it occurs very frequently. It is generally called atavism, or better, systematic atavism, and the clearest cases are those in which a quality which is latent in the greater part of a family or group, becomes manifest in one of its members. Bracts in the inflorescence of crucifers are ordinarily wanting, but may be seen in some genera, *Erucastrum pollichii* being perhaps the most widely known instance, although other cases might easily be cited.

For our special purpose we may take up only the more simple cases that may be available for experimental work. The great lines of evolution of whole families and even of genera and of many larger species obviously lie outside the limits of experimental observation. They are the outcome of the history of the ancestors of the present types, and a repetition of their history is far beyond human powers. We must limit ourselves to the most recent steps, to the consideration of the smallest differences. But it is obvious that these may be included under the same heads as the larger and older ones. For the larger movements are manifestly to be considered only as groups of smaller steps, going in the same direction.

Hence we conclude, that even the smallest steps in the evolution of plants which we are able to observe, may be divided into progressive, retrogressive and degressive ones. The acquisition of a single new quality is the most simple step in the progressive line, the becoming latent and the reactivating of this same quality are the prototypes of the two other classes.

Having taken this theoretical point of view, it remains to inquire, how it concurs with the various facts, given in former lectures and how it may be of use in our further discussions.

It is obvious that the differences between elementary species and varieties on the one hand, and between the positive and negative varieties as distinguished above, are quite comparable with our theoretical views. For we have seen that varieties can always be considered as having originated by an apparent loss of some quality of the species, or by the resumption of a quality which in allied species is present and visible. In our exposition of the facts we have of course limited ourselves to the observable features of the phenomena without searching for a further explanation. For a more competent inquiry however, and for an understanding of wider ranges of facts, it is necessary to penetrate deeper into the true nature of the implied causes.

Therefore we must try to show that elementary species are distinguished from each other by the acquisition of new qualities, and that varieties are derived from their species either by the reduction of one or more characteristics to the latent state, or by the energizing of dormant characters.

Here we meet with a great difficulty. Hitherto varieties and subspecies have never been clearly defined, or when they have been, it was not by physiological, but only by morphological research. And the claims of these two great lines of inquiry are obviously very diverging. Morphological or comparative studies need a material standard, by which it may be readily decided whether certain groups of animals and plants are to be described or denominated as species, as subspecies or as varieties. To get at the inner nature of the differences is in most cases impossible, but a decision must be made. The physiological line of inquiry has more time at its disposal; it calls for no haste. Its experiments ordinarily cover years, and a conclusion is only to be reached after long and often weary trials. There is no making a decision on any matter until all doubtful points have been cleared up. Of course, large groups of facts remain uncertain, awaiting a closer inquiry, and the teacher is constrained to rely on the few known instances of thoroughly investigated cases. These alone are safe guides, and it seems far better to trust to them and to make use of them for the construction of sharp conceptions, which may help us to point out the lines of inquiry which are still open.

Leaving aside all such divisions and definitions, as were stamped with the name of provisional species and varieties by the great systematist, Alphonse De Candolle, we may now try to give the proofs of our assertion, by using only those instances that have been thoroughly tested in every way.

We may at once proceed to the retrogressive or negative varieties. The arguments for the assumption that elementary species owe their origin to the acquisition of new qualities may well be left for later lectures when we shall deal with the experimental proofs in this matter.

There are three larger groups of facts, on which the assumption of latent characters in ordinary varieties rests. These are true atavism, incomplete loss of characters, and systematic affinity. Before dealing with each of these separately, it may be as well to recall once more that in former lectures we have treated the apparent losses only as modifications in a negative way, without contemplating the underlying causes.

Let us recall the cases of bud-atavism given by the whitish variety of the scarlet *Ribes*, by peaches and nectarines, and by conifers, including *Cephalotaxus* and *Cryptomeria*. These and many other analogous facts go to prove the relation of the variety to the species. Two assumptions are allowable. In one the variety differs from the species by the total loss of the distinctive character. In the other this character is simply reduced to an inactive or dormant state. The fact of its recurrence from time to time, accompanied by secondary characters previously exhibited, is a manifest proof of the existence of some relation between the lost and the resumed peculiarity. Evidently this relation cannot be accounted for on the assumption of an absolute disappearance; something must remain from which the old features may be restored.

This lengthy discussion may be closed by the citation of the cases, in which plants not only show developmental features of a former state, but also reproduce the special features they formerly had, but seemingly have lost. Two good illustrative examples may be given. One is afforded by the wheat-ear carnation, the other by the green dahlias, and both have occurred of late in my own cultures.

A very curious anomaly may from time to time be observed in large beds of carnations. It bears no flowers, but instead of them small green ears, which recall the ears of wheat. Thence the name of "Wheat-ear" carnation. On closer inspection it is easily seen how they originate. The normal flowers of the carnations are preceded by a small group of bracts, which are arranged in opposite pairs and therefore constitute four rows.

In this variety the flower is suppressed and this loss is attended by a corresponding increase of the number of the pairs of bracts. This malformation results in square spikes or somewhat elongated heads consisting only of the greenish bracts. As there are no flowers, the variety is quite sterile, and as it is not regarded by horticulturists as an improvement on the ordinary bright carnations, it is seldom multiplied by layering. Notwithstanding this, it appears from time to time and has been seen in different countries and at different periods, and, what is of great importance for us, in different strains of carnations. Though sterile, and obviously dying out as often as it springs into existence, it is nearly two centuries old. It was described in the begining of the 18th century by Volckamer, and afterwards by Jaeger, De Candolle, Weber, Masters, Magnus and many other botanists. I have had it twice, at different times and from different growers.

So far as I have been able to ascertain reversions of this curious carnation to normal flowers have not yet been recorded. Such a modification occurred last summer in my garden on a plant which had not been divided or layered, but on which the slender branches had been left on the stem. Some of them remained true to the varietal type and bore only green spikes. Others reverted wholly or partially to the production of normal flowers. Some branches bore these only, others had spikes and flowers on neighboring twigs, and in still other instances little spikes had been modified in such manner that a more or less well developed flower was preceded by some part of an ear.

The proof that this retrograde modification was due to the existence of a character in the latent state was given by the color of the flowers. If the reverted bud had only lost the power of producing spikes, they would evidently simply have returned to the characteristics of the ordinary species, and their color would have been a pale pink. Instead of this, all flowers displayed corollas of a deep brown. They obviously reverted to their special progenitor, the chance variety from which they had sprung, and not to the common prototype of the species. Of course it was not possible to ascertain from which variety the plant had really originated, but the reproduction of any one clearly defined varietal mark is in itself proof enough of their origin, and of the latency of the dark brown flower-color in this special case.

A still better proof is afforded by a new type of green dahlia. The ordinary green dahlia has large tufts of green bracts instead of flowering heads, the scales of the receptacle having assumed the texture and venation of leaves, and being in some measure as fleshy. But the green heads retain the form of the ordinary flower-heads, and as they have no real florets that may fade away, they remain unchanged on the plants, and increase in number through the whole summer. The new types of green dahlia however, with which I have now to deal, are distinguished by the elongation of the axis of the head, which is thereby changed into a long leafy stalk, attaining a length of several inches. These stalks continue growing for a very long time, and for the most part die without producing anything else than green fleshy scales.

This long-headed green dahlia originated at Haarlem some years ago, in the nursery of Messrs. Zocher & Co. It was seen to arise twice, from different varieties. Both of these were double-flowered, one a deep carmine with white tips on the rays, the other of a pale orange tint, known by the name of " Surprise." As they did not bear any florets or seeds, they were quite sterile. The strain arising from the carmine variety was kindly given to me by Messrs. Zocher & Co., and was propagated in my garden, while the other was kept in the nursery. In the earlier cultures both remained true to their types, never producing true florets. No mark of the original difference was to be seen between them. But last summer (1903) both reverted to their prototypes, bearing relatively large numbers of ordinary double flower-heads among the great mass of green stalks. Some intermediate forms also occurred consisting of green-scaled stalks ending in small heads with colored florets.

Thus far we have an ordinary case of reversion. But the important side of the phenomenon was, that each plant exactly " recollected " from which parent it had sprung. All of those in my garden reverted to the carmine florets with white tips, and all of those in the nursery to the pale orange color and the other characteristics of the " Surprise " variety.

It seems absolutely evident, that no simple loss can account for this difference. Something of the character of the parent-varieties must have remained in the plant. And whatever conception we may formulate of these vestigial characters it is clear that the simplest and most obvious idea is their preservation in a dormant or latent state. Assuming that the distinguishing marks have only become inactive by virescence, it is manifest that on returning each will show its own peculiarities, as recorded above.

Our second point was the incomplete loss of

the distinguishing quality in some varieties. It is of general occurrence, though often overlooked. Many white varieties of colored flowers give striking instances, among them many of the most stable and most prized garden-flowers. If you look at them separately or in little bouquets they seem to be of irreproachable purity. But if you examine large beds a pale hue will become visible. In many cases this tinge is so slight as to be only noticeable in a certain illumination, or by looking in an oblique direction across the bed; in others it is at once evident as soon as it has been pointed out. It always reminds the observer of the color of the species to which the variety belongs, being bluish in violets and harebells, reddish in godetias and phloxes, in *Silene Armeria* and many others. It proves that the original color-quality of the species has not wholly, but only partly disappeared. It is dormant, but not entirely obliterated; latent, but not totally concealed; inactive, but only partially so. Our terminology is an awkward one; it practically assumes, as it so often does in other cases, a conventional understanding, not exactly corresponding to the simple meaning of the words. But it would be cumbrous to speak always of partial inactivity, incomplete latency or half awakening qualities. Even such words as sublatent, which would about express the real state of things, would have little chance of coming into general use.

Such sub-latent colors are often seen on special parts in white varieties of flowers. In many cases it is the outer side of the petals which recalls the specific color, as in some white roses. In violets it is often on the spur that the remains of the original pigment are to be seen. In many instances it is on the tips of the petals or of the segments of the corolla, and a large number of white or yellow flowers betray their affinity to colored species by becoming red or bluish at the edges or on the outer side.

The reality of such very slight hues, and their relation to the original pigment of the species may in some cases be proved by direct experiment. If it is granted that latency is not an absolute quality, then it will be readily accepted, that even latency must be subjected to the laws of gradual variation or fluctuating variability. We will deal with these laws in a later lecture but every one knows that greater deviations than the ordinary may be attained by sowing very large numbers and by selecting from among them the extreme individuals and sowing anew from their seed. In this way the slightest tinge of any latent color may be strengthened, not indeed to the restoration of the tinge of the species, but at least so far as to leave no doubt as to the identity of the visible color of the species and the latent or sublatent one of the variety.

I made such an experiment with the peach-leaved harebell or *Campanula persicifolia*. The white variety of this species, which is often met with in our gardens, shows a very pale bluish hue when cultivated in large quantities, which however is subject to individual variations. I selected some plants with a decided tinge, flowered them separately, sowed their seeds, and repeated this during two generations. The result was an increase of the color on the tips of the segments of the corolla in a few individuals, most of them remaining as purely white as the original strain. But in those few plants the color was very manifest, individually variable in degree, but always of the same blue as in the species itself.

Many other instances could be given. Smooth varieties are seldom absolutely so, and if scattering hairs are found on the leaves or only on some more or less concealed parts, they correspond in their character to those of the species. So it is with prickles, and even the thornless thorn-apple has fruits with surfaces far from smooth. The thornless horse-chestnut has in some instances such evident protuberances on the valves of its fruits, that it may seem doubtful whether it is a pure and stable variety.

Systematic latency may betray itself in different ways, either by normal systematic marks, or by atavism. With the latter I shall deal at length on another occasion, and therefore I will give here only one very clear and beautiful example. It is afforded by the common red clover. Obviously the clovers, with their three leaflets in each leaf, stand in the midst of the great family of papilionaceous plants, the leaves of which are generally pinnate. Systematic affinity suggests that the "three-leaved" forms must have been derived from pinnate ancestors, evidently by the reduction of the number of the leaflets. In some species of clover the middle of the three is more or less stalked, as is ordinarily the case in pinnate leaves; in others it is as sessile as are its neighbors. In a subsequent chapter I will describe a very fine variety, which sometimes occurs in the wild state and may easily be isolated and cultivated. It is an ordinary red clover with five leaflets instead of three, and with this number varying between three and seven, instead of being nearly wholly stable as in the common form. It produces from time to time pinnate leaves, very few indeed, and only rarely, but then often two or three or even more on the same individual. Intermediate stages are not wanting, but are of no consequence here. The pinnate leaves obviously constitute a reversion to some prototype, to some ancestor with ordinary papilionaceous leaves. They give proof of the presence of the common character of the family, concealed here in a latent state. Any other explanation of this curious anomaly would evidently be artificial. On the other hand nothing is really known about the ancestors of clover, and the whole conception rests only on the prevailing views of the systematic relationships in this family. But, as I have already said, further proof must be left for a subsequent occasion.

Many instances, noted in our former lectures, could be quoted here. The systematic distribution of rayed and rayless species and varieties among the daisy-group of the composites affords a long series of examples. Accidental variations in both directions occur. The Canada fleabane or *Erigeron canadensis,* the tansy or *Tanacetum vulgare* and some others may at times be seen with ray-florets, and according to Murr, they may sometimes be wanting in *Aster Tripolium, Bellis perennis,* some species of *Anthemis, Arnica montana* and in a number of other well-known rayed species. Another instance may be quoted; it has been pointed out by Grant Allen, and refers to the dead-nettle or *Lamium album*. Systematically placed in a genus with red-flowering species, we may regard its white color as due to the latency of the general red pigment. But if the flower of this plant is carefully examined, it will be found in most cases not to be purely white, but to have some dusky lines and markings on its lower lip. Similar devices are observed on the lip of the allied *Lamium maculatum,* and in a less degree on the somewhat distant *Lamium purpureum*. With *Lamium maculatum* or spotted dead-nettle, the affinity is so close that even Bentham united the two in a single species, considering the ordinary dead-nettle only as a variety of the dappled purple type. For the support of this conception of a specific or varietal retrograde change many other facts are afforded by the distribution of the characteristic color and of the several patterns of the lips of other labiates, and our general understanding of the relationships of the species and genera in this family may in a broad sense be based on the comparison of these seemingly subordinate characteristics.

The same holds good in many other cases, and systematists have often become uncertain as to the true value of some form, by its relationship to the allied types in the way of retrogressive modification. Color-differences are so showy, that they easily overshadow other characters. The white and the blue thorn-apple, the white and the red campion (*Lychnis vespertina* and *diurna*) and many other illustrative cases could be given, in which two forms are specifically separated by some authors, but combined by others on the ground of the retrograde nature of some differentiating mark.

Hitherto we have dealt with negative characters and tried to prove that the conception of latency of the opposite positive characteristics is a more natural explanation of the phenomenon than the idea of a complete loss. We have now to consider the positive varieties, and to show that it is quite improbable that here the species have struck out for themselves a wholly new character. In some instances such may have been the case, but then I should prefer to treat these rather as elementary species. But in the main we will have to assume the latency of the character in the species and its reassumption by the variety when originating, as the most probable explanation.

Great stress is laid upon this conception by the fact, that positive varieties are so excessively rare when compared with the common occurrence of negative ones. Indeed, if we put aside the radiate and the color-varieties of flowers and foliage, hardly any cases can be cited. We have dealt with this question in a former lecture, and may now limit ourselves to the positive color-varieties.

The latency of the faculty of producing the red pigment in leaves must obviously be accepted for nearly the whole vegetable kingdom. Oaks and elms, the beautiful climbing species of *Ampelopsis,* many conifers, as for instance *Cryptomeria japonica,* some brambles, the Guelder-rose (*Viburnum Opulus*) and many other trees and shrubs assume a more or less bright red color in the fall. During summer this tendency must have been dormant, and that this is so, is shown by the young leaves of oaks and others, which, when unfolding in the spring show a similar but paler hue. Moreover, there is a way of awakening the concealed powers at any time. We have only to inflict small wounds on the leaves, or to cut through the nerves or to injure them by a slight bruising, and the leaves frequently respond with an intense reddening of the living tissues around and especially above the wounds. *Azolla caroliniana,* a minute moss-like floating plant allied to the ferns, responds to light and cold with a reddish tinge, and to shade or warmth with a pure green. The foliage of many other plants behaves likewise, as also do apples and peaches on the insolated sides of the fruits. It is quite impossible to state these groups of facts in a more simple way than by the statement that the tendency to become red is almost generally present, though latent in leaves and stems, and that it comes into activity whenever a stimulus provokes it.

Now it must be granted that the energizing of such a propensity under ordinary circumstances is quite another thing from the origination of a positive variety by the evolution of the same character. In the variety the activity has become independent of outer influences or dependent upon them in a far lesser degree. The power of producing the red pigments is shown to be latent by the facts given above, and we see that in the variety it is no longer latent but is in perfect and lasting activity throughout the whole life of the plant.

Red varieties of white flowers are much more rare. Here the latency of the red pigment may be deduced partly from general arguments like those just given, partly from the special systematic relations in the given cases. Hildebrand has clearly worked out this mode of proof. He showed by the critical examination of a large number of instances that the occurrence of the red-flowered varieties is contingent upon the existence of red species in the same genus, or in some rare cases, in nearly allied genera. Colors that are not systematically present in the group to which a white species belongs are only produced in its varieties in extremely rare cases.

We may quote some special rules, indicated by Hildebrand. Blue species are in the main very rare, and so are blue varieties of white species also. Carnations, Asiatic or cultivated buttercups (*Ranunculus asiaticus*), *Mirabilis,* poppies, *Gladiolus, Dahlia,* and some other highly cultivated or very old garden-plants have not been able to produce true blue flowers. But the garden-anemone (*Anemone coronaria*) has allies with very fine blue flowers. The common stock has bluish varieties and is allied to *Aubretia* and *Hesperis,* and gooseberries have a red form, recalling the ordinary currant. In nearly all other instances of blue or red varieties every botanist will be able to point out some allied red or blue species, as an indication of the probable source of the varietal character.

Dark spots on the lower parts of the petals of some plants afford another instance, as in poppies and in the allied *Glaucium,* where they sometimes occur as varietal and in other cases as specific marks.

The yellow fails in many highly developed

flowers, which are not liable to produce yellow variations, as in *Salvia, Aster, Centaurea, Vinca, Polygala* and many others. Even the rare pale yellowish species of some of these genera have no tendency in this direction. The hyacinths are the most remarkable, if not the sole known instance of a species having red and blue and white and yellow varieties, but here the yellow is not the bright golden color of the buttercups.

The existence of varietal colors in allied species obviously points to a common cause, and this cause can be no other than the latency of the pigment in the species that do not show it.

The conception of latency of characters as the common source of the origination of varieties, either in the positive or in the negative way, leads to some rules on variability, which are known under the names given to them by Darwin. They are the rules of repeated, homologous, parallel and analogous variability. Each of them is quite general, and may be recognized in instances from the most widely distant families. Each of them is quite evident and easily understood on the principle of latency.

By the term of repeated variability is meant the well-known phenomenon, that the same variety has sprung at different times and in different countries from the same species. The repetition obviously indicates a common internal cause. The white varieties of blue- and red-flowered plants occur in the wild state so often, and in most of the instances in so few individuals that a common pedigree is absolutely improbable. In horticulture this tendency is widely and vexatiously known, since the repetition of an old variety does not bring any advantage to the breeder. The old name of "conquests," given by the breeders of hyacinths, tulips and other flower-bulbs to any novelty, in disregard of the common occurrence of repetitions, is an indication of the same experience in the repeated appearance of certain varieties.

The rule of parallel variations demands that the same character occasionally makes its appearance in the several varieties or races, descended from the same species, and even in widely distinct species. This is a rule, which is very important for the general conception of the meaning of the term variety as contrasted with elementary species. For the recurrence of the same deviation always impresses us as a varietal mark. Laciniated leaves are perhaps the most beautiful instance, since they occur in so many trees and shrubs, as the walnut tree, the beech, the birch, the hazelnut, and even in brambles and some garden-varieties of the turnip (*Brassica*).

In such cases of parallel variations the single instances obviously follow the same rules and are therefore to be designated as analogous. Pitchers or ascidia, formed by the union of the margins of a leaf, are perhaps the best proof. They were classified by Morren under two heads, according to their formation from one or more leaves. Monophyllous pitchers obey the same law, viz.: that the upper side of the leaf has become the inner side of the pitcher. Only one exception to this rule is known to me. It is afforded by the pitchers of the banyan or holy fig-tree, *Ficus religiosus,* but it does not seem to belong to the same class as other pitchers, since as far as it has been possible to ascertain the facts, these pitchers are not formed by a few leaves as in all other cases, but by all the leaves of the tree.

In some cases pitchers are only built up of part of the leaf-blade. Such partial malformations obey a rule, that is common to them and to other foliar enations, viz.: that the side of the leaf from which they emerge, is always their outer side. The inner surface of these enations corresponds to the opposite side of the leaf, both in color and in anatomical structure.

The last of the four rules above mentioned is

that of the homologous variability. It asserts that the same deviation may occur in different, but homologous parts of the same plant. We have already dealt with some instances, as the occurrence of the same pigment in the flowers and foliage, in the fruits and seeds of the same plant, as also illustrated by the loss of the red or blue tinge by flowers and berries. Other instances are afforded by the curious fact that the division of the leaves into numerous and small segments is repeated by the petals, as in the common celandine and some sorts of brambles.

It would take too long to make a closer examination of the numerous cases which afford proof of these statements. Suffice it to say that everywhere the results of close inspection point to the general rule, that the failure of definite qualities both in species and in varieties must, in a great number of cases, be considered as only apparent. Hidden from view, occasionally reappearing, or only imperfectly concealed, the same character must be assumed to be present though latent.

In the case of negative or retrogressive varieties it is the transition from the active into a dormant state to which is due the origin of the variety. Positive varieties on the contrary owe their origin to the presence of some character in the species in the latent state, and to the occasional re-energizing thereof.

Specific or varietal latency is not the same thing as the ordinary latency of characters that only await their period of activity, or the external influence which will awake them. They are permanently latent, and could well be designated by the word *perlatent*. They spring into activity only by some sudden leap, and then at once become independent of ordinary external stimulation.

Lecture IX

CROSSES OF SPECIES AND VARIETIES

In the foregoing lectures I have tried to show that there is a real difference between elementary species and varieties. The first are of equal rank, and together constitute the collective or systematic species. The latter are usually derived from real and still existing types. Elementary species are in a sense independent of each other, while varieties are of a derivative nature.

Furthermore I have tried to show that the ways in which elementary or minor species must have originated from their common ancestor must be quite different from the mode of origin of the varieties. We have assumed that the first come into existence by the production of something new, by the acquirement of a character hitherto unnoticed in the line of their ancestors. On the contrary, varieties, in most cases, evidently owe their origin to the loss of an already existing character, or in other less frequent cases, to the re-assumption of a quality formerly lost. Some may originate in a negative, others in a positive manner, but in both cases nothing really new is acquired.

This distinction holds good for all cases in which the relationship between the forms in question is well known. It seems entirely justifiable therefore to apply it also to cases in which the systematic affinity is doubtful, as well as to instances in which it is impossible to arrive at any taxonomic conclusions. The extreme application of the principle would no doubt disturb the limits between many species and varieties as now recognized. It is not to be forgotten however that all taxonomic distinctions, which have not been confirmed by physiologic tests are only provisional, a view acknowledged by the best systematists. Of course the description of newly discovered forms can not await the results of physiologic inquiries, but it is absolutely impossible to reach definite conclusions on purely morphologic evidence. This is well illustrated by the numerous discords of opinion of different authors on the systematic worth of many forms.

Assuming the above mentioned principle as established, and disregarding doubtful cases as indicated, the term progressive evolution is used to designate the method in which elementary species must have originated. It is the manner in which all advance in the animal and vegetable kingdoms must have taken place; continuously adding new characters to the already existing number. Contrasted with this method of growing differentiation, are the retrogressive modifications, which simply retrace a step, and the degressive changes in which a backward step is retraced and old characters revived. No doubt both of these methods have been operative on a large scale, but they are evidently not in the line of general advancement.

In all of these directions we see that the differentiating marks show more or less clearly that they are built up of units. Allied forms are separated from each other without intermediates. Transitions are wholly wanting, although fallaciously apparent in some instances owing to the wide range of fluctuating variability of the forms concerned, or to the occurrence of hybrids and subvarieties.

These physiologic units, which in the end must be the basis for the distinction of the systematic units, may best be designated by the term of "unit-characters." Their internal nature is as yet unknown to us, and we will not now look into the theories, which have been propounded as to the probable material basis underlying them. For our present purpose the empirical evidence of the general occurrence of sharp limits between nearly related characters must suffice. As Bateson has put it, species are discontinuous, and we must assume that their characters are discontinuous also.

Moreover there is as yet no reason for trying to make a complete analysis of all the characters of a plant. No doubt, if attained, such an analysis would give us a deep insight into the real internal construction of the intricate properties of organisms in general. But taxonomic studies in this direction are only in their infancy and do not give us the material required for such an analysis. Quite on the contrary, they compel us to confine our study to the most recently acquired, or youngest characters, which constitute the differentiating marks between nearly allied forms.

Obviously this is especially the case in the realm of the hybrids, since only nearly related forms are able to give hybrid offspring. In dealing with this subject we must leave aside all questions concerning more remote relationships.

It is not my purpose to treat of the doctrine of hybridization at any length. Experience is so rapidly increasing both in a practical and in a purely scientific direction that it would take an entire volume to give only a brief survey of the facts and of all the proposed theories.

For our present purposes we are to deal with hybrids only in so far as they afford the means of a still better distinction between elementary species and varieties. I will try to show that these two contrasting groups behave in quite a different manner, when subjected to crossing experiments, and that the hope is justified that some day crosses may become the means of deciding in any given instance, what is to be called a species, and what a variety, on physiologic grounds. It is readily granted that the labor required for such experiments, is perhaps too great for the results to be attained, but then it may be possible to deduce rules from a small series of experiments, which may lead us to a decision in wider ranges of cases.

To reach such a point of view it is necessary to compare the evidence given by hybrids, with the conclusions already attained by the comparison of the differentiating characteristics of allied forms.

On this ground we first have to inquire what may be expected respecting the internal nature and the outcome of the process of crossing in the various cases cited in our former discussion.

We must always distinguish the qualities, which are the same in both parents, from those that constitute the differentiating marks in every single cross. In respect to the first group the cross is not at all distinguished from a normal fertilization, and ordinarily these characters are simply left out of consideration. But it should never be forgotten that they constitute the enormous majority, amounting to hundreds and thousands, whereas the differentiating marks in each case are only one or two or a few at most. The whole discussion is to be limited to these last-named exceptions. We must consider first what would be the nature of a cross when species are symmetrically combined, and what must be the case when varieties are subjected to the same treatment. In so doing, I intend to limit the discussion to the most typical cases. We may take the crosses between elementary species of the same or of very narrowly allied systematic species on the one side, and on the other, limit treatment to the crossing of varieties with the species, from which they are supposed to have sprung by a retrograde modification. Crosses of different varieties of the same species with one another obviously constitute a derivative case, and should only be discussed secondarily. And crosses of varieties with positive or degressive characters have as yet so rarely been made that we may well disregard them.

Elementary species differ from their nearest allies by progressive changes, that is by the acquirement of some new character. The derivative species has one unit more than the parent. All other qualities are the same as in the parent. Whenever such a derivative is combined with its parent the result for these qualities will be exactly as in a normal fertilization. In such ordinary cases it is obvious that each character of the pollen-parent is combined with the same character of the pistil-parent. There may be slight individual differences, but each unit-character will become opposed to, and united with, the same unit-character in the other parent. In the offspring the units will thus be paired, each pair consisting of two equivalent units. As to their character the units of each single pair are the same, only they may exhibit slight differences as to the degree of development of this character.

Now we may apply this conception to the sexual combination of two different elementary species, assuming one to be the derivative of the other. The differentiating mark is only present in one of the parents and wanting in the other. While all other units are paired in the hybrid, this one is not. It meets with no mate, and must therefore remain unpaired. The hybrid of two such elementary species is in some way incomplete and unnatural. In the ordinary course of things all individuals derive their qualities from both parents; for each single mark they possess at least two units. Practically but not absolutely equal, these two opponents always work together and give to the offspring a likeness to both parents. No unpaired qualities occur in normal offspring; these constitute the essential features of the hybrids of species and are at the same time the cause of their wide deviations from the ordinary rules.

Turning now to the varieties, we likewise need discuss their differentiating marks only. In the negative types, these consist of the apparent loss of some quality which was active in the species. But it was pointed out in our last lecture that such a change is an apparent loss. On a closer inquiry we are led to the assumption of a latent or dormant state. The presumably lost characters have not absolutely, or at least not permanently disappeared. They show their presence by some slight indication of the quality they represent, or by occasional reversions. They are not wanting, but only latent.

Basing our discussion concerning the process of crossing on this conception, and still limiting the discussion to one differentiating mark, we come to the inference, that this mark is present and active in the species, and present but dormant in the variety. Thus it is present in both, and as all other characters not differentiating find their mates in the cross, so these two will also meet one another. They will unite just as well as though they were both active or both dormant. For essentially they are the same, only differing in their degree of activity. From this we can infer, that in the crossing of varieties, no unpaired remainder is left, all units combining in pairs exactly as in ordinary fertilization.

Setting aside the contrast between activity and latency in this single pair, the procedure in the inter-crossing of varieties is the same as in ordinary normal fertilization.

Summarizing this discussion we may conclude that in normal fertilization and in the inter-crossing of varieties all characters are paired, while in crosses between elementary species the differentiating marks are not mated.

In order to distinguish these two great types of fertilization we will use the term bisexual for the one and unisexual for the other. The term *balanced crosses* then conveys the idea of complete bisexuality, all unit-characters combining in pairs. *Unbalanced crosses* are those in which one or more units do not find their mates and therefore remain unpaired. This distinction was proposed by Macfarlane when studying the minute structure of plant-hybrids in comparison with that of their parents (1892).

In the first place it shows that a species-hybrid may inherit the distinguishing marks of both parents. In this way it may become intermediate between them, having some characters in common with the pollen-parent and others with the pistil-parent. As far as these characters do not interfere with each other, they may be fully developed side by side, and in the main this is the way in which hybrid characters are evolved. But in most cases our existing knowledge of the units is far too slender to give a complete analysis, even of these distinguishing marks alone. We recognize the parental marks more or less clearly, but are not prepared for exact delimitations. Leaving these theoretical considerations, we will pass to the description of some illustrative examples.

In the first place I will describe a hybrid between two species of *Oenothera*, which I made some years ago. The parents were the common evening-primrose or *Oenothera biennis* and of its small-flowered congener, *Oenothera muricata*. These two forms were distinguished by Linnaeus as different species, but have been considered by subsequent writers as elementary species or so-called systematic varieties of one species designated with the name of the presumably older type, the *O. biennis*. Varietal differences in a physiologic sense they do not possess, and for this reason afford a pure instance of unbalanced union, though differing in more than one point.

I have made reciprocal crosses, taking at one time the small-flowered and at the other the common species as pistillate parent. These crosses do not lead to the same hybrid as is ordinarily observed in analogous cases; quite on the contrary, the two types are different in most features, both resembling the pollen-parent far more than the pistil-parent. The same curious result was reached in sundry other reciprocal crosses between species of this genus. But I will limit myself here to one of the two hybrids.

In the summer of 1895 I castrated some flowers of *O. muricata,* and pollinated them with *O. biennis,* surrounding the flowers with paper bags so as to exclude the visits of insects. I sowed the seeds in 1896 and the hybrids were biennial and flowered abundantly the next year and were artificially fertilized with their own pollen, but gave only a very small harvest. Many capsules failed, and the remaining contained only some few ripe seeds.

From these I had in the following year the second hybrid generation, and in the same way I cultivated also the third and fourth. These were as imperfectly fertile as the first, and in some years did not give any seed at all, so that the operation had to be repeated in order to continue the experiment. Last summer (1903) I had a nice lot of some 25 biennial specimens blooming abundantly. All in all I have grown some 500 hybrids, and of these about 150 specimens flowered.

These plants were all of the same type, resembling in most points the pollen-parent, and in some others the pistil-parent of the original cross. The most obvious characteristic marks are afforded by the flowers, which in *O. muricata* are not half so large as in *biennis*, though borne by a calyx-tube of the same length. In this respect the hybrid is like the *biennis* bearing the larger flowers. These may at times seem to deviate a little in the direction of the other parent, being somewhat smaller and of a slightly paler color. But it is very difficult to distinguish between them, and if *biennis* and hybrid flowers were separated from the plants and thrown together, it is very doubtful whether one would succeed in separating them.

The next point is offered by the foliage. The leaves of *O. biennis* are broad, those of *O. muricata* narrow. The hybrid has the broad leaves of *O. biennis* during most of its life and at the time of flowering. Yet small deviations in the direction of the other parent are not wanting, and in winter the leaves of the hybrid rosettes are often much narrower than those of *O. biennis,* and easily distinguishable from both parents. A third distinction consists in the density of the spike. The distance between the insertion of the flowers of *O. biennis* is great when compared with that of *O. muricata.* Hence the flowers of the latter species are more crowded and those of *O. biennis* more dispersed, the spikes of the first being densely crowned with flowers and flower-buds while those of *O. biennis* are more elongated and slender. As a further consequence the *O. biennis* opens on the same evening only one, two or three flowers on the same spike, whereas *O. muricata* bears often eight or ten or more flowers at a time. In this respect the hybrid is similar to the pistil-parent, and the crowding of the broad flowers at the top of the spikes causes the hybrids to be much more showy than either of the parent types.

Other distinguishing marks are not recorded by the systematists, or are not so sharply separated as to allow of the corresponding qualities of the hybrids being compared with them.

This hybrid remains true to the description given. In some years I cultivated two generations so as to be able to compare them with one another, but did not find any difference. The most interesting point however, is the likeness between the first generation, which obviously must combine in its internal structure the units of both parents, and the second and later generations which are only of a derivative nature. Next to this stands the fact that in each generation all individuals are alike. No reversion to the parental forms either in the whole type or in the single characteristics has ever been observed, though the leaves of some hundreds, and the spikes and flowers of some 150 individual plants have been carefully examined. No segregation or splitting up takes place.

Here we have a clear, undoubted and relatively simple, case of a true and pure species-hybrid. No occurrence of possible varietal characteristics obscures the result, and in this respect this hybrid stands out much more clearly than all those between garden-plants, where varietal marks nearly always play a most important part.

From the breeder's point of view our hybrid *Oenothera* would be a distinct gain, were it not for the difficulty of its propagation. But to enlarge the range of the varieties this simple and stable form would need to be treated anew, by crossing it with the parent-types. Such experiments however, have miscarried owing to the too stable nature of the unit-characters.

This stability and this absence of the splitting shown by varietal marks in the offspring of hybrids is one of the best proofs of unisexual unions. It is often obscured by the accompanying varietal marks, or overlooked for this reason. Only in rare cases it is to be met with in a pure state and some examples are given of this below.

Before doing so, I must call your attention to another feature of the unbalanced unions. This is the diminution of the fertility, a phenomenon universally known as occurring in hybridizations. It has two phases. First, the diminished chance of the crosses themselves of giving full crops of seed, as compared with the pure fertilization of either parent. And, secondly, the fertility of the hybrids themselves. Seemingly, all grades of diminished fertility occur and the oldest authors on hybrids have pointed out that a very definite relation exists between the differences of the parents and the degree of sterility, both of the cross and of the hybrid offspring. In a broad sense these two factors are proportionate to each other, the sterility being the greater, the lesser the affinity between the parents. Many writers have tried to trace this rule in the single cases, but have met with nearly unsurmountable difficulties, owing chiefly to our ignorance of the units which form the differences between the parents in the observed cases.

In the case of *Oenothera muricata* x *biennis* the differentiating units reduce the fertility to a low degree, threatening the offspring with almost complete infertility and extinction. But then we do not know whether these characters are really units, or perhaps only seemingly so and are in reality composed of smaller entities which as yet we are not able to segregate. And as long as we are devoid of empirical means of deciding such questions, it seems useless to go farther into the details of the question of the sterility. It should be stated here however, that pure varietal crosses, when not accompanied by unbalanced characters, have never showed any tendency to diminished fertility. Hence there can be little doubt that the unpaired units are the cause of this decrease in reproductive power.

The genus *Oenothera* is to a large degree devoid of varietal characteristics, especially in the subgenus *Onagra*, to which *biennis, muricata, lamarckiana* and some others belong. On the other hand it seems to be rich in elementary species, but an adequate study of them has as yet not been made. Unfortunately many of the better systematists are in the habit of throwing all these interesting forms together, and of omitting their descriptive study. I have made a large number of crosses between such undescribed types and as a rule got constant hybrid races. Only one or two exceptions could be quoted, as for instance the *Oenothera brevistylis*, which in its crosses always behaves as a pure retrogressive variety. Instead of giving an exhaustive survey of hybrids, I simply cite my crosses between *lamarckiana* and *biennis*, as having nearly the aspect of the last named species, and remaining true to this in the second generation without any sign of reversion or of splitting. I have crossed another elementary species, the *Oenothera hirtella* with some of my new and with some older Linnean species, and got several constant hybrid races. Among these the offspring of a cross between *muricata* and *hirtella* is still in cultivation. The cross was made in the summer of 1897 and last year (1903) I grew the fourth generation of the hybrids. These had the characters of the *muricata* in their narrow leaves, but the elongated spikes and relatively large flowers of the *hirtella* parent, and remained true to this type, showing only slight fluctuations and never reverting or segregating the mixed characters. Both parents bear large capsules with an abundance of seed, but in the hybrids the capsules remain narrow and weak, ripening not more than one-tenth the usual quantity of seed. Both parents are easily cultivated in annual generations and the same holds good for the hybrid. But whereas the hybrid of *muricata* and *biennis* is a stout plant, this type is weak with badly developed foliage, and very long strict spikes. Perhaps it was not able to withstand the bad weather of the last few years.

A goodly number of constant hybrids are described in literature, or cultivated in fields and gardens. In such cases the essential question is not whether they are now constant, but whether they have been so from the beginning, or whether they prove to be constant whenever the original cross is repeated. For constant hybrids may also be the issue of incipient splittings, as we shall soon see.

Among other examples we may begin with the hybrid alfalfa or hybrid lucerne (*Medicago media*). It often originates spontaneously between the common purple lucerne or alfalfa and its wild ally with yellow flowers and procumbent stems, the *Medicago falcata*. This hybrid is cultivated in some parts of Germany on a large scale, as it is more productive than the ordinary lucerne. It always comes true from seed and may be seen in a wild state in parks and on lawns. It is one of the oldest hybrids with a pure and known lineage. The original cross has been repeated by Urban, who found the hybrid race to be constant from the beginning.

Another very notorious constant hybrid race is the *Aegilops speltaeformis*. It has been cultivated in botanic gardens for more than half a century, mostly in annual or biennial generations. It is sufficiently fertile and always comes true. Numerous records have been made of it, since formerly it was believed by Fabre and others to be a spontaneous transition from some wild species of grass to the ordinary wheat, not a cross. Godron, however, showed that it can be produced artificially, and how it has probably sprung into existence wherever it is found wild. The hybrid between *Aegilops ovata,* a small weed, and the common wheat is of itself sterile, producing no good pollen. But it may be fertilized by the pollen of wheat and then gives rise to a secondary hybrid, which is no other than the *Aegilops speltaeformis*. This remained constant in Godron's experiments during a number of generations, and has been constant up to the present time.

Constant hybrids have been raised by Millardet between several species of strawberries. He combined the old cultivated forms with newly discovered types from American localities. They ordinarily showed only the characteristics of one of their parents and did not exhibit any new combination of qualities, but they came true to this type in the second and later generations.

In the genus *Anemone,* Janczewski obtained the same results. Some characters of course may split, but others remain constant, and when only such are present, hybrid races result with new combinations of characters, which are as constant as the best species of the same genus. The hybrids of Janczewski were quite fertile, and he points out that there is no good reason why they should not be considered as good new species. If they had not been produced artificially, but found in the wild state, their origin would have been unknown, and there can be no doubt that they would have been described by the best systematists as species of the same value as their parents. Such is especially the case with a hybrid between *Anemone magellanica* and the common *Anemone sylvestris*.

Starting from similar considerations Kerner von Marilaun pointed out the fact long ago that many so-called species, of rare occurrence, standing between two allied types, may be considered to have originated by a cross. Surely a wide field for abuse is opened by such an assertion, and it is quite a common habit to consider intermediate forms as hybrids, on the grounds afforded by their external characters alone, and without any exact knowledge of their real origin and often without knowing anything as to their constancy from seed. All such apparent explanations are now slowly becoming antiquated and obsolete, but the cases adduced by Kerner seem to stand this test.

Kerner designates a willow, *Salix ehrhartiana* as a constant hybrid between *Salix alba* and *S. pentandra*. *Rhododendron intermedium* is an intermediate form between the hairy and the rusty species from the Swiss Alps, *R. hirsutum* and *R. ferrugineum,* the former growing on chalky, and the other on silicious soils. Wherever both these types of soil occur in the same valley and these two species approach one another, the hybrid *R. intermedium* is produced, and is often seen to be propagating itself abundantly. As is indicated by the name, it combines the essential characters of both parents.

Linaria italica is a hybrid toad-flax between *L. genistifolia* and *L. vulgaris,* a cross which I have repeated in my garden. *Drosera obovata* is a hybrid sundew between *D. anglica* and *D. rotundifolia*. *Primula variabilis* is a hybrid between the two common primroses, *P. officinalis* and *P. grandiflora*. The willow-herb (*Epilobium*), the self-heal (*Brunella*) and the yellow pond-lilies (*Nuphar*) afford other instances of constant wild hybrids.

Macfarlane has discovered a natural hybrid between two species of sundew in the swamps near Atco, N. J. The parents, *D. intermedia* and *D. filiformis,* were growing abundantly all around, but of the hybrid only a group of eleven plants was found. A detailed comparison of the hybrid with its parents demonstrated a minute blending of the anatomical peculiarities of the parental species.

Luther Burbank of Santa Rosa, California, has produced a great many hybrid brambles, the qualities of which in many respects surpass those of the wild species. Most of them are only propagated by cuttings and layers, not being stable from seed. But some crosses between the blackberry and the raspberry (*R. fruticosus* and *R. idaeus*) which bear good fruit and have become quite popular, are so fixed in their type as to reproduce their composite characters from seed with as much regularity as the species of *Rubus* found in nature. Among them are the " Phenomenal " and the

"Primus." The latter is a cross between the Californian dewberry and the Siberian raspberry and is certainly to be regarded as a good stable species, artificially produced. Bell Salter crossed the willow-herbs *Epilobium tetragonum* and *E. montanum,* and secured intermediate hybrids which remained true to their type during four successive generations.

Other instances might be given. Many of them are to be found in horticultural and botanical journals which describe their systematic and anatomical details. The question of stability is generally dealt with in an incidental manner, and in many cases it is difficult to reach conclusions from the facts given. Especially disturbing is the circumstance that from a horticultural point of view it is quite sufficient that a new type should repeat itself in some of its offspring to be called stable, and that for this reason absolute constancy is rarely proved.

The range of constant hybrids would be larger by far were it not for two facts. The first is the absolute sterility of so many beautiful hybrids, and the second is the common occurrence of retrogressive characters among cultivated plants. To describe the importance of both these groups of facts would take too much time, and therefore it seems best to give some illustrative examples instead.

Among the species of *Ribes* or currant, which are cultivated in our gardens, the most beautiful are without doubt the Californian and the Missouri currant, or *Ribes sanguineum* and *R. aureum*. A third form, often met with, is "Gordon's currant," which is considered to be a hybrid between the two. It has some peculiarities of both parents. The leaves have the general form of the Californian parent, but are as smooth as the Missouri species. The racemes or flower-spikes are densely flowered as in the red species, but the flowers themselves are of a yellow tinge, with only a flesh-red hue on the outer side of the calyx. It grows vigorously and is easily multiplied by cuttings, but it never bears any fruit. Whether it would be constant, if fertile, is therefore impossible to decide.

Berberis ilicifolia is considered as a hybrid between the European barberry (*B. vulgaris*) and the cultivated shrub *Mahonia aquifolia*. The latter has pinnate leaves, the former undivided ones. The hybrid has undivided leaves which are more spiny than those of the European parent, and which are not deciduous like them, but persist during the winter, a peculiarity inherited from the *Mahonia*. As far as I have been able to ascertain, this hybrid never produces seed.

Another instance of an absolutely sterile hybrid is the often quoted *Cytisus adami*. It is a cross between the common laburnum (*Cytisus Laburnum*) and another species of the same genus, *C. purpureus,* and has some traits of both. But since the number of differentiating marks is very great in this case, most of the organs have become intermediate. It is absolutely sterile. But it has the curious peculiarity of splitting in a vegetative way. It has been multiplied on a large scale by grafting, and was widely found in the parks and gardens of Europe during the last century. Nearly all these specimens reverted from time to time to the presumable parents. Not rarely a bud of Adam's laburnum assumed all the qualities of the common laburnum, its larger leaves, richer flowered racemes, large and brightly yellow flowers and its complete fertility. Other buds on the same tree reverted to the purple parent, with its solitary small flowers, its dense shrublike branches and very small leaves. These too are fertile, though not producing their seeds as abundantly as the *C. Laburnum* reversions. Many a botanist has sown the seeds of the latter and obtained only pure common *C. Laburnum* plants. I had a lot of nearly a hundred seedlings myself, many of which have already flowered, bearing the leaves and flowers of the common species. Seeds of the purple reversions have also been sown, and also yielded the parental type only.

Why this most curious hybrid sports so regularly and why others always remain true to their type is as yet an open question.

But recalling our former consideration of this subject the supposition seems allowable that the tendency to revert is not connected with the type of the hybrid, but is apt to occur in some rare individuals of every type. But since most of the sterile hybrids are only known to us in a single individual and its vegetative offspring, this surmise offers an explanation of the rare occurrence of sports.

Finally, we must consider some of the so called hybrid races or strains of garden-plants. *Dahlia, Gladiolus, Amaryllis, Fuchsia, Pelargonium* and many other common flowers afford the best known instances. Immeasurable variability seems here to be the result of crossing. But on a closer inspection the range of characters is not so very much wider in these hybrid races than in the groups of parent-species which have contributed to the origin of the hybrids. Our tuberous begonias owe their variability to at least seven original parent species, and to the almost incredible number of combinations which are possible between their characters. The first of these crosses was made in the nursery of Veitch and Sons near London by Seden, and the first hybrid is accordingly known as *Begonia sedeni* and is still to be met with. It has been superseded by subsequent crosses between the *sedeni* itself and the *veitchi* and *rosiflora,* the *davisii,* the *clarkii* and others. Each of them contributed its advantageous qualities, such as round flowers, rosy color, erect flower stalks, elevation of the flowers above the foliage and others. New crosses are being made continuously, partly between the already existing hybrids and partly with newly introduced wild species. Only rarely is it possible to get pure seeds, and I have not yet been able to ascertain whether the hybrids would come true from seed. Specific and varietal characters may occur together in many of the several forms, but nothing is as yet accurately known as to their behavior in pure fertilizations. Constancy and segregation are thrown together in such a manner that extreme variability results, and numerous beautiful types may be had, and others may be expected from further crosses. For a scientific analysis, however, the large range of recorded facts and the written history, which at first sight seems to have no lacunae, are not sufficient. Most of the questions remain open and need investigation. It would be a capital idea to try to repeat the history of the begonias or any other hybrid race, making all the described crosses and then recording the results in a manner requisite for complete and careful scientific investigations.

Many large genera of hybrid garden-flowers owe their origin to species rich in varieties or in elementary subspecies. Such is the case with the gladiolus and the tulips. In other cases the original types have not been obtained from the wild state but from the cultures of other countries.

The dahlias were cultivated in Mexico when first discovered by Europeans, and the chrysanthemums have been introduced from the old gardens of Japan. Both of them consisted of various types, which afterwards have been increased chiefly by repeated intercrossing.

The history of many hybrid races is obscure, or recorded by different authorities in a different way. Some have derived their evidence from one nursery, some from another, and the crosses evidently may have been different in different places. The early history of the gladiolus is an instance. The first crosses are recorded to have been made between *Gladiolus psittacinus* and *G. cardinalis,* and between their hybrid, which is still known under the name of *gandavensis* and the *purpureo-auratus.* But other authors give other lines of descent. So it is with *Amaryllis,* which is said by De Graaff to owe its stripes to *A. vittata,* its fine form to *A. brasiliensis,* the large petals to *A. psittacina,* the giant flowers to *A. leopoldi,* and the piebald patterns to *A. pardina.* But here, too, other authors give other derivations.

Summarizing the results of our inquiry we see in the first place how very much remains to be done. Many old crosses must be repeated and studied anew, taking care of the purity of the cross as well as of the harvesting of the seeds. Many supposed facts will be shown to be of doubtful validity. New facts have to be gathered, and in doing so the distinction between specific and varietal marks must be taken strictly into account. The first have originated as progressive mutations; they give unbalanced crosses with a constant offspring, as far as experience now goes. The second are chiefly due to retrograde modifications, and will be the subject of the next lecture.

Lecture X

MENDEL'S LAW OF BALANCED CROSSES

In the scientific study of the result of crosses, the most essential point is the distinction of the several characters of the parents in their combination in the hybrids and their offspring. From a theoretical point of view it would be best to choose parents which would differ only in a single point. The behavior of the differentiating character might then easily be seen.

Unfortunately, such simple cases do not readily occur. Most species, and even many elementary species are distinguished by more than one quality. Varieties deviating only in one unit-character from the species, are more common. But a closer inspection often reveals some secondary characters which may be overlooked in comparative or descriptive studies, but which reassume their importance in experimental crossings.

In a former lecture we have dealt with the qualities which must be considered as being due to the acquisition of new characters. If we compare the new form in this case with the type from which it has originated, it may be seen that the new character does not find its mate, or its opposite, and it will be unpaired in the hybrid.

In the case of retrogressive changes the visible modification is due, at least in the best known instances, to the reduction of an active quality to a state of inactivity or latency. Now if we make a cross between a species and its variety, the differentiating character will be due to the same internal unit, with no other difference than that it is active in the species and latent in the variety. In the hybrid these two corresponding units will make a pair. But while all other pairs in the same hybrid individuals consist of like antagonists, only this pair consists of slightly unlike opponents.

This conception of varietal crosses leads to three assertions, which seem justifiable by actual experience.

First, there is no reason for a diminution of the fertility, as all characters are paired in the hybrid, and no disturbance whatever ensues in its internal structure. Secondly, it is quite indifferent, how the two types are combined, or which of them is chosen as pistillate and which as staminate parent. The deviating pair will have the same constitution in both cases, being built up of one active and one dormant unit.

Thirdly this deviating pair will exhibit the active unit which it contains, and the hybrid will show the aspect of the parent in which the character was active and not that of the parent in which it was dormant. Now the active quality was that of the species, and its latent state was found in the variety. Hence the inference that hybrids between a species and its retrograde variety will bear the aspect of the species. This attribute may be fully developed, and then the hybrid will not be distinguishable from the pure species in its outer appearance. Or the character may be incompletely evolved, owing to the failure of cooperation of the dormant unit. In this case the hybrid will be in some sense intermediate between its parents, but these instances are more rare than the alternate ones, though presumably they may play an important part in the variability of many hybrid garden-flowers.

All of these three rules are supported by a large amount of evidence. The complete fertility of varietal hybrids is so universally acknowledged that it is not worth while to give special instances. With many prominent systematists it has become a test between species and varieties, and from our present point of view this assumption is correct. Only the test is of little use in practice, as fertility may be diminished in unbalanced unions in all possible degrees, according to the amount of difference between the parents. If this amount is slight, if for instance, only one unit-character causes the difference, the injury to fertility may be so small as to be practically nothing. Hence we see that this test would not enable us to judge of the doubtful cases, although it is quite sufficient as a proof in cases of wider differences.

Our second assertion related to the reciprocal crosses. This is the name given to two sexual combinations between the same parents, but with interchanged places as to which furnishes the pollen. In unbalanced crosses of the genus *Oenothera* the hybrids of such reciprocal unions are often different, as we have previously shown. Sometimes both resemble the pollen-parent more, in other instances the pistil-parent. In varietal crosses no such divergence is as yet known. It would be quite superfluous to adduce single cases as proofs for this rule, which was formerly conceived to hold good for hybrids in general. The work of the older hybridists, such as Koelreuter and Gaertner affords numerous instances.

Our third rule is of a wholly different nature. Formerly the distinction between elementary species and varieties was not insisted upon, and the principle which stamps retrograde changes as the true character of varieties is a new one. Therefore it is necessary to cite a considerable amount of evidence in order to prove the assertion that a hybrid bears the active character of its parent-species and not the inactive character of the variety chosen for the cross.

We may put this assertion in a briefer form, stating that the active character prevails in the hybrid over its dormant antagonist. Or as it is equally often put, the one dominates and the other is recessive. In this terminology the character of the species is dominant in the hybrid while that of the variety is recessive. Hence it follows that in the hybrid the latent or dormant unit is recessive, but it does not follow that these three terms have the same meaning, as we shall see presently. The term recessive only applies to the peculiar state into which the latent character has come in the hybrid by its pairing with the antagonistic active unit.

In the first place it is of the highest importance to consider crosses between varieties of recorded origin and the species from which they have sprung. When dealing with mutations of celandine we shall see that the laciniated form originated from the common celandine in a garden at Heidelberg about the year 1590. Among my oenotheras one of the eldest of the recent productions is the *O. brevistylis* or short-styled species which was seen for the first time in the year 1889. The third example offered is a hairless variety of the evening campion, *Lychnis vespertina*, found the same year, which hitherto had not been observed.

For these three cases I have made the crosses of the variety with the parent-species, and in each case the hybrid was like the species, and not like the variety. Nor was it intermediate. Here it is proved that the older character dominates the younger one.

In most cases of wild, and of garden-varieties, the relation between them and the parent-species rests upon comparative evidence. Often the variety is known to be younger, in other cases it may be only of local occurrence, but ordinarily the historic facts about its origin have never been known or have long since been forgotten.

The easiest and most widely known varietal crosses are those between varieties with white flowers and the red- or blue-flowered species. Here the color prevails in the hybrid over the lack of pigment, and as a rule the hybrid is as deeply tinted as the species itself, and cannot be distinguished from it, without an investigation of its hereditary qualities. Instances may be cited of the white varieties of the snapdragon, of the red clover, the long-spurred violet (*Viola cornuta*) the sea-shore aster (*Aster Tripolium*), corn-rose (*Agrostemma Githago*), the Sweet William (*Silene Armeria*), and many garden flowers, as for instance, the *Clarkia pulchella,* the *Polemonium coeruleum,* the *Veronica longifolia,* the gloxinias and others. If the red hue is combined with a yellow ground-color in the species, the variety will be yellow and the hybrid will have the red and yellow mixture of the species as for instance, in the genus *Geum.* The toad-flax has an orange-colored palate, and a variety occurs in which the palate is of the same yellow tinge as the remaining parts of the corolla. The hybrid between them is in all respects like the parent-species.

Other instances could be given. In berries the same rule prevails. The black nightshade has a variety with yellow berries, and the black color returns in the hybrid. Even the foliage of some garden-plants may afford instances, as for instance, the purplish amaranth (*Amaranthus caudatus*). It has a green variety, but the hybrid between the two has the red foliage of the species.

Special marks in leaves and in flowers follow the same rule. Some varieties of the opium-poppy have large black patches at the basal end of the petals, while in others this pattern is entirely white. In crossing two such varieties, for instance, the dark " Mephisto " with the white-hearted " Danebrog," the hybrid shows the active character of the dark pattern.

Hairy species crossed with their smooth varieties produce hairy hybrids, as in some wheats, in the campion (*Lychnis*), in *Biscutella* and others. The same holds good for the crosses between spiny species and their unarmed derivatives, as in the thorn-apple, the corn-crowfoot (*Ranunculus arvensis*) and others.

Lack of starch in seeds is observed in some varieties of corn and of peas. When such derivatives are crossed with ordinary starch-producing types, the starch prevails in the hybrid.

It would take too much time to give further examples. But there is still one point which should be insisted upon. It is not the systematic relation of the two parents of a cross, that is decisive, but only the occurrence of the same quality, in the one in an active, and in the other in an inactive condition. Hence, whenever this relation occurs between the parents of a cross, the active quality prevails in the hybrid, even when the parents differ from each other in other respects so as to be distinguished as systematic species. The white and red campions give a red hybrid, the black and pale henbane (*Hyoscyamus niger* and *H. pallidus*) give a hybrid with the purple veins and center in the corolla of the former, the white and blue thornapple produce a blue hybrid, and so on. Instances of this sort are common in cultivated plants.

Having given this long list of examples of the rule of the dominancy of the active character over the opposite dormant unit, the question naturally arises as to how the antagonistic units are combined in the hybrid. This question is of paramount importance in the consideration of the offspring of the hybrids. But before taking it up it is as well to learn the real signification of recessiveness in the hybrids themselves.

Recessive characters are shown by those rare cases, in which hybrids revert to the varietal parent in the vegetative way. In other words by bud-variations or sports, analogous to the splitting of Adam's laburnum into its parents, by means of bud-variation already described. But here the wide range of differentiating characters of the parents of this most curious hybrid fail. The illustrative examples are extremely simple, and are limited to the active and inactive condition of only one quality.

An instance is given by the long-leaved veronica (*Veronica longifolia*), which has bluish flowers in long spikes. The hybrid between this species and its white variety has a blue corolla. But occasionally it produces some purely white flowers, showing its power of separating the parental heritages, combined in its internal structures. This reversion is not common, but in thousands of flowering spikes one may expect to find at least one of them. Sometimes it is a whole stem springing from the underground system and bearing only white flowers on all its spikes. In other instances it is only a side branch which reverts and forms white flowers on a stem, the other spikes of which remain bluish. Sometimes a spike even differentiates longitudinally, bearing on one side blue and on the other white corollas, and the white stripe running over the spike may be seen to be long and large, or narrow and short in various degrees. In such cases it is evident that the heritages of the parents remain uninfluenced by each other during the whole life of the hybrid, working side by side, but the active element always prevails over its latent opponent which is ready to break free whenever an opportunity is offered.

It is now generally assumed that this incomplete mixture of the parental qualities in a hybrid, this uncertain and limited combination is the true cause of the many deviations, exhibited by varietal hybrids when compared with their parents. Partial departures are rare in the hybrids themselves, but in their offspring the divergence becomes the rule.

Segregation seems to be a very difficult process in the vegetative way, but it must be very easy in sexual reproduction, indeed so easy as to show itself in nearly every single instance.

Leaving this first generation, the original hybrids, we now come to a discussion of their offspring. Hybrids should be fertilized either by their own pollen, or by that of other individuals born from the same cross. Only in this case can the offspring be considered as a means of arriving at a decision as to the internal nature of the hybrids themselves. Breeders generally prefer to fertilize hybrids with the pollen of their parents. But this operation is to be considered as a new cross, and consequently is wholly excluded from our present discussion. Hence it follows that a clear insight into the heredity of hybrids may be expected only from scientific experiments. Furthermore some of the diversity observed as a result of ordinary crosses, may be due to the instability of the parents themselves or at least of one of them, since breeders ordinarily choose for their crosses some already very variable strain. Combining such a strain with the desirable qualities of some newly imported species, a new strain may result, having the new attribute in addition to all the variability of the old types. In scientific experiments made for the purpose of investigating the general laws of hybridity, such complex cases are therefore to be wholly excluded. The hereditary purity of the parents must be considered as one of the first conditions of success.

Moreover the progeny must be numerous, since neither constancy, nor the exact proportions in the case of instability, can be determined with a small lot of plants.

Finally, and in order to come to a definite choice of research material, we should keep in mind that the chief object is to ascertain the relation of the offspring to their parents. Now in nearly all cases the seeds are separated from the fruits and from one another, before it becomes possible to judge of their qualities. One may open a fruit and count the seeds, but ordinarily nothing is noted as to their characters. In this respect no other plant equals the corn or maize, as the kernels remain together on the spike, and as it has more than one variety characterized by the color, or constitution, or other qualities of the grains. A corn-grain, however, is not a seed, but a fruit containing a seed. Hence the outer parts pertain to the parent plant and only the innermost ones to the seedling and therefore to the following generation. Fruit-characters thus do not offer the qualities we need, only the qualities resulting from fertilizations are characteristic of the new generation. Such attributes are afforded in some cases by the color, in others by the chemical constitution.

We will choose the latter, and take the sugar-corn in comparison with the ordinary or starch-producing forms for our starting point. Both sugar- and starch-corns have smooth fruits when ripening. No difference is to be seen in the young ripe spikes. Only the taste, or a direct chemical analysis might reveal the dissimilarity. But as soon as the spikes are dried, a diversity is apparent. The starchy grains remain smooth, but the sugary kernels lose so much water that they become wrinkled. The former becomes opaque, the latter more or less transparent. Every single kernel may instantly be recognized as belonging to either of the types in question, even if but a single grain of the opposite quality might be met with on a spike. Kernels can be counted on the spike, and since ordinary spikes may bear from 300–500 grains and often more, the numerical relation of the different types may be deduced with great accuracy.

Coming now to our experiment, both starchy

and sugary varieties are in this respect wholly constant, when cultivated separately. No change is to be seen in the spikes. Furthermore it is very easy to make the crosses. The best way is to cultivate both types in alternate rows and to cut off the staminate panicles a few days before they open their first flowers. If this operation is done on all the individuals of one variety, sparing all the panicles of the other, it is manifest that all the plants will become fertilized by the latter, and hence that the castrated plants will only bear hybrid seeds.

The experiment may be made in two ways; by castrating the sugary or the starchy variety. In both cases the hybrid kernels are the same. As to their composition they repeat the active character of the starchy variety. The sugar is only accumulated as a result of an incapacity of changing it into starch, and the lack of this capacity is to be considered as a retrogressive varietal mark. The starch-producing unit-character, which is active in the ordinary sorts of corns, is therefore latent in sugar-corn.

In order to obtain the second generation, the hybrid grains are sown under ordinary conditions, but sufficiently distant from any other variety of corn to insure pure fertilization. The several individuals may be left to pollinate

each other, or they may be artificially pollinated
with their own pollen.

The outcome of the experiments is shown by
the spikes, as soon as they dry. Each spike
bears two sorts of kernels irregularly dispersed
over its surface. In this point all the spikes
are alike. On each of them one may see on the
first inspection that the majority of the kernels
are starch-containing seeds, while a minor part
becomes wrinkled and transparent according to
the rule for sugary seeds. This fact shows at
once that the hybrid race is not stable, but has
differentiated the parental characters, bringing
those of the varietal parent to perfect purity
and isolation. Whether the same holds good
for the starchy parent, it is impossible to judge
from the inspection of the spikes, since it has
been seen in the first generation that the hybrid
kernels are not visibly distinguished from those
of the pure starch-producing grains.

It is very easy to count the number of both
sorts of grains in the spike of such a hybrid.
In doing so we find, that the proportion is
nearly the same on all the spikes, and only
slight variations would be found in hundreds
of them. One-fourth of the seeds are wrinkled
and three-fourths are always smooth. The
number may vary in single instances and be a
little more or a little less than 25%, ranging, for

instance, from 20 to 27%, but as a rule, the average is found nearly equal to 25%.

The sugary kernels, when separated from the hybrid spikes and sown separately, give rise to a pure sugary race, in no degree inferior in purity to the original variety. But the starchy kernels are of different types, some of them being internally like the hybrids of the first generation and others like the original parent. To decide between these two possibilities, it is necessary to examine their progeny.

For the study of this third hybrid generation we will now take another example, the opium-poppies. They usually have a dark center in the flowers, the inferior parts of the four petals being stained a deep purple, or often nearly black. Many varieties exhibit this mark as a large black cross in the center of the flower. In other varieties the pigment is wanting, the cross being of a pure white. Obviously it is only reduced to a latent condition, as in so many other cases of loss of color, since it reappears in a hybrid with the parent-species.

For my crosses I have taken the dark-centered "Mephisto" and the "Danebrog," or Danish flag, with a white cross on a red field. The second year the hybrids were all true to the type of "Mephisto." From the seeds of each artificially self-fertilized capsule, one-fourth (22.5%)

in each instance reverted to the varietal mark of the white cross, and three-fourths (77.5%) retained the dark heart. Once more the flowers were self-pollinated and the visits of insects excluded. The recessives now gave only recessives, and hence we may conclude that the varietal marks had returned to stability. The dark-hearted or dominants behaved in two different ways. Some of them remained true to their type, all their offspring being dark-hearted. Evidently they had returned to the parent with the active mark, and had reassumed this type as purely as the recessives had reached theirs. But others kept true to the hybrid character of the former generation, repeating in their progeny exactly the same mixture as their parents, the hybrids of the first generation, had given.

This third generation therefore gives evidence, that the second though apparently showing only two types, really consists of three different groups. Two of them have reassumed the stability of their original grandparents, and the third has retained the instability of the hybrid parents.

The question now arises as to the numerical relation of these groups. Our experiments gave the following results:

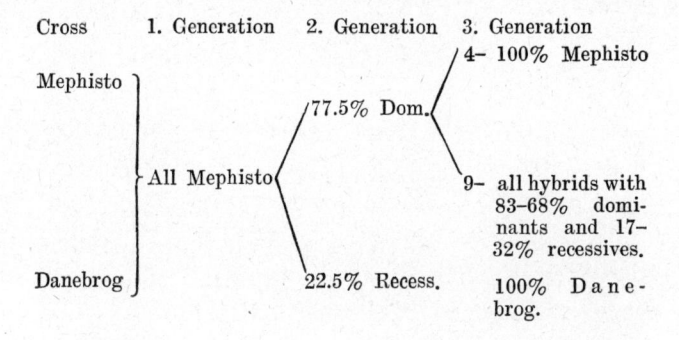

Cross	1. Generation	2. Generation	3. Generation
Mephisto ⎤			4— 100% Mephisto
	All Mephisto	77.5% Dom.	
			9— all hybrids with 83–68% dominants and 17–32% recessives.
Danebrog ⎦		22.5% Recess.	100% Danebrog.

Examining these figures we find one-fourth of constant recessives, as has already been said, further one-fourth of constant dominants, and the rest or one half as unstable hybrids. Both of the pure groups have therefore reappeared in the same numbers. Calling A the specimens with the pure active mark, L those with the latent mark, and H the hybrids, these proportions may be expressed as follows:

$$1 A + 2 H + 1 L.$$

This simple law for the constitution of the second generation of varietal hybrids with a single differentiating mark in their parents is called the law of Mendel. Mendel published it in 1865, but his paper remained nearly unknown to scientific hybridists. It is only of late years that it has assumed a high place in scientific literature, and attained the first rank as an investigation on fundamental questions of heredity. Read in the light of modern ideas on unit-characters it is now one of the most important works on heredity and has already widespread and abiding influence on the philosophy of hybridism in general.

But from its very nature and from the choice of the material made by Mendel, it is restricted to balanced or varietal crosses. It assumes pairs of characters and calls the active unit of the pair dominant, and the latent recessive, without further investigations of the question of latency. It was worked out by Mendel for a large group of varieties of peas, but it holds good, with only apparent exceptions, for a wide range of cases of crosses of varietal characters. Recently many instances have been tested, and even in many cases third and later generations have been counted, and whenever the evidence was complete enough to be trusted, Mendel's prophecy has been found to be right.

According to this law of Mendel's the pairs of antagonistic characters in the hybrid split up in their progeny, some individuals reverting to the pure parental types, some crossing with each other anew, and so giving rise to a new generation of hybrids. Mendel has given a very suggestive and simple explanation of his formula. Putting this in the terminology of to-day, and limiting it to the occurrence of only one differential unit in the parents, we may give it in the following manner. In fertilization, the characters of both parents are not uniformly mixed, but remain separated though most intimately combined in the hybrid throughout life. They are so combined as to work together nearly always, and to have nearly equal influence on all the processes of the whole individual evolution. But when the time arrives to produce progeny, or rather to produce the sexual cells through the combination of which the offspring arises, the two parental characters leave each other, and enter separately into the sexual cells. From this it may be seen that one-half of the pollen-cells will have the quality of one parent, and the other the quality of the other. And the same holds good for the egg-cells. Obviously the qualities lie latent in the pollen and in the egg, but ready to be evolved after fertilization has taken place.

Granting these premises, we may now ask as to the results of the fertilization of hybrids, when this is brought about by their own pollen. We assume that numerous pollen grains fertilize numerous egg cells. This assumption at once allows of applying the law of probability, and to infer that of each kind of pollen grains one-half will reach egg-cells with the same quality and the other half ovules with the opposite character.

Calling P pollen and O ovules, and representing the active mark by P and O, the latent qualities by P' and O', they would combine as follows:

P + O giving uniform pairs with the active mark,
P + O' giving unequal pairs,
P' + O giving unequal pairs,
P' + O' giving uniform pairs with the latent mark.

In this combination the four groups are obviously of the same size, each containing one-fourth of the offspring. Manifestly they correspond exactly to the direct results of the experiments, P + O representing the individuals which reverted to the specific mark, P'+O' those who reassumed the varietal quality and P+O' and P+O' those who hybridized for the second time. These considerations lead us to the following form of Mendel's formula:

$$P + O = 1/4\text{-Active} \quad \text{or } 1\,\text{A,}$$
$$\left.\begin{matrix} P + O' \\ P' + O \end{matrix}\right\} = 1/2\text{-Hybrid} \quad \text{or } 2\,\text{H,}$$
$$P' + O' = 1/4\text{-Latent} \quad \text{or } 1\,\text{L,}$$

Which is evidently the same as Mendel's empirical law given above.

To give the proof of these assumptions Mendel has devised a very simple crossing experiment, which he has effected with his varieties of peas. I have repeated it with the sugar-corn, which gives far better material for demonstration. It starts from the inference that if dissimilarity among the pollen grains is excluded, the diversity of the ovules must at once become manifest and vice versa. In other terms, if a hybrid of the first generation is not allowed to fertilize itself, but is pollinated by one of its parents, the result will be in accordance with the Mendelian formula.

In order to see an effect on the spikes produced in this way, it is of course necessary to fertilize them with the pollen of the variety, and not with that of the specific type. The latter would give partly pure starchy grains and partly hybrid kernels, but these would assume the same type. But if we pollinate the hybrid with pollen of a pure sugar-corn, we may predict the result as follows.

If the spike of the hybrid contains dormant paternal marks in one-half of its flowers and in the other half maternal latent qualities, the sugar-corn pollen will combine with one-half of the ovules to give hybrids, and with the other half so as to give pure sugar-grains. Hence we see that it will be possible to count out directly the two groups of ovules on inspecting the ripe and dry spikes. Experience teaches us that both are present, and in nearly equal numbers; one-half of the grains remaining smooth, and the other half becoming wrinkled.

The corresponding experiment could be made with plants of a pure sugar-race by pollination with hybrid pollen. The spikes would show exactly the same mixture as in the above case, but now this may be considered as conclusive proof that half the pollen-grains represent the quality of one parent and the other half the quality of the other.

Another corollary of Mendel's law is the following. In each generation two groups return to purity, and one-half remains hybrid. These last will repeat the same phenomenon of splitting in their progeny, and it is easily seen that the same rule will hold good for all succeeding generations. According to Mendel's principle, in each year there is a new hybridization, differing in no respect from the first and original one. If the hybrids only are propagated, each year will show one-fourth of the offspring returning to the specific character, one-fourth assuming the type of the variety and one-half remaining hybrid. I have tested this with a hybrid between the ordinary nightshade with black berries, and its variety, *Solanum nigrum chlorocarpum,* with pale yellow fruits.

Eight generations of the hybrids were cultivated, disregarding always the reverting offspring. At the end I counted the progeny of the sixth and seventh generations and found figures for their three groups of descendants, which exactly correspond to Mendel's formula.

Until now we have limited ourselves to the consideration of single differentiating units. This discussion gives a clear insight into the fundamental phenomena of hybrid fertilization. It at once shows the correctness of the assumption of unit-characters, and of their pairing in the sexual combinations.

But Mendel's law is not at all restricted to these simple cases. Quite on the contrary, it explains the most intricate questions of hybridization, providing they do not transgress the limits of symmetrical unions. But in this realm nearly all results may be calculated beforehand, on the ground of the principle of probability. Only one more assumption need be discussed. The several pairs of antagonistic characters must be independent from, and uninfluenced by, one another. This premise seems to hold good in the vast majority of cases, though rare exceptions seem to be not entirely wanting. Hence the necessity of taking all predictions from Mendel's law only as probabilities, which will prove true in most, but not necessarily in all cases.

But here we will limit ourselves to normal cases.

The first example to be considered is obviously the assumption that the parents of a cross differ from each other in respect to two characters. A good illustrative example is afforded by the thorn-apple. I have crossed the blue-flowered thorny form, usually known as *Datura Tatula,* with the white thornless type, designated as *D. Stramonium inermis.* Thorns and blue pigment are obviously active qualities, as they are dominant in the hybrids. In the second generation both pairs of characters are resolved into their constituents and paired anew according to Mendel's law. After isolating my hybrids during the period of flowering, I counted among their progeny:

```
128 individuals with blue flowers and thorns
 47     "      "    "     "   without  "
 54     "      "  white   "    and     "
 21     "      "    "     "   without  "
───
250
```

The significance of these numbers may easily be seen, when we calculate what was to be expected on the assumption that both characters follow Mendel's law, and that both are independent from each other. Then we would have three-fourths blue offspring and one-fourth individuals with white flowers. Each of these two groups would consist of thorn-bearing and thornless plants, in the same numerical relation. Thus, we come to the four groups observed in our experiment, and are able to calculate their relative size in the following way:

		Proportion
Blue with thorns......	$3/4 \times 3/4 = 9/16 = 56.25\%$	9
Blue, unarmed	$3/4 \times 1/4 = 3/16 = 18.75\%$	3
White with thorns.....	$1/4 \times 3/4 = 3/16 = 18.75\%$	3
White, unarmed	$1/4 \times 1/4 = 1/16 = 6.25\%$	1

In order to compare this inference from Mendel's law and the assumption of independency, with the results of our experiments, we must calculate the figures of the latter in percentages. In this way we find:

	Found.	Calculated.
Blue with thorns.....	$128 = 51\%$	56.25%
Blue unarmed	$47 = 19\%$	18.75%
White with thorns....	$54 = 22\%$	18.75%
White unarmed	$21 = 8\%$	6.25%

The agreement of the experimental and the theoretical figures is as close as might be expected.

This experiment is to be considered only as an illustrative example of a rule of wide application. The rule obviously will hold good in all such cases as comply with the two conditions already premised, viz.: that each character agrees with Mendel's law, and that both are wholly independent of each other. It is clear that our figures show the numerical composition of the hybrid offspring for any single instance, irrespective of the morphological nature of the qualities involved.

Mendel has proved the correctness of these deductions by his experiments with peas, and by combining their color (yellow or green) with the chemical composition (starch or sugar) and other pairs of characters. I will now give two further illustrations afforded by crosses of the ordinary campion. I used the red-flowered or day-campion, which is a perennial herb, and a smooth variety of the white evening-campion, which flowers as a rule in the first summer. The combination of flower-color and pubescence gave the following composition for the second hybrid generation:

	Number	%	Calculation
Hairy and red.......	70	44	56.25%
Hairy and white.....	23	14	18.75%
Smooth and red......	46	23	18.75%
Smooth and white....	19	12	6.25%

For the combination of pubescence and the capacity of flowering in the first year I found:

	Number	%	Calculated
Hairy, flowering......	286	52	56.25%
Hairy, without stem..	128	23	18.75%
Smooth, flowering....	96	17	18.75%
Smooth, without stem	42	8	6.25%

Many other cases have been tested by different writers and the general result is the applicability of Mendel's formula to all cases complying with the given conditions.

Intentionally I have chosen for the last example two pairs of antagonisms, relating to the same pair of plants, and which may be tested in one experiment and combined in one calculation.

For the latter we need only assume the same conditions as mentioned before, but now for three different qualities. It is easily seen that the third quality would split each of our four groups into two smaller ones in the proportion of $3/4 : 1/4$.

We would then get eight groups of the following composition:

$$9/16 \times 3/4 = 27/64 \text{ or } 42.2\%$$
$$9/16 \times 1/4 = 9/64 \text{ `` } 14.1\%$$
$$3/16 \times 3/4 = 9/64 \text{ `` } 14.1\%$$
$$3/16 \times 1/4 = 3/64 \text{ `` } 4.7\%$$
$$3/16 \times 3/4 = 9/64 \text{ `` } 14.1\%$$
$$3/16 \times 1/4 = 3/64 \text{ `` } 4.7\%$$
$$1/16 \times 3/4 = 3/64 \text{ `` } 4.7\%$$
$$1/16 \times 1/4 = 1/64 \text{ `` } 1.6\%$$

The characters chosen for our experiment include the absence of stem and flowers in the first year, and therefore would require a second year to determine the flower-color on the perennial specimens. Instead of doing so I have taken another character, shown by the teeth of the capsules when opening. These curve outwards in the red campion, but lack this capacity in the evening-campion, diverging only until an upright position is reached. The combination of hairs, colors and teeth gives eight groups, and the counting of their respective numbers of individuals gave the following result:

Hairs	Flowers	Teeth of capsules	Number	%	Calculated
Hairy	red	curved	91	47	42.2%
Hairy	red	straight	15	7.5	14.1%
Hairy	white	curved	23	12	14.1%
Hairy	white	straight	17	8.5	4.7%
Smooth	red	curved	23	12	14.1%
Smooth	red	straight	9	4.5	4.7%
Smooth	white	curved	5	2.5	4.7%
Smooth	white	straight	12	6	1.6%

The agreement is as comprehensive as might be expected from an experiment with about 200 plants, and there can be no doubt that a repetition on a larger scale would give still closer agreement.

In the same way we might proceed to crosses with four or more differentiating characters. But each new character will double the number of the groups. Four characters will combine into 16 groups, five into 32, six into 64, seven into 128, etc. Hence it is easily seen that the size of the experiments must be made larger and larger in the same ratio, if we intend to expect numbers equally trustworthy. For seven differentiating marks 16,384 individuals are required for a complete series. And in this set the group with the seven attributes all in a latent condition would contain only a single individual.

Unfortunately the practical value of these calculations is not very great. They indicate the size of the cultures required to get all the possible combinations, and show that in ordinary cases many thousands of individuals have to be cultivated, in order to exhaust the whole range of possibilities. They further show that among all these thousands, only very few are constant in all their characters; in fact, it may easily be seen that with seven differentiating points among the 16,384 named above, only one individual will have all the seven qualities in pure active, and only one will have them all in a purely dormant condition. Then there will be some with some attributes active and others latent, but their numbers will also be very small. All others will split up in the succeeding generation in regard to one or more of their apparently active marks. And since only in very rare cases the stable hybrids can be distinguished by external characters from the unstable ones, the stability of each individual bearing a desired combination of characters would have to be established by experiment after pure fertilization. Mendel's law teaches us to predict the difficulties, but hardly shows any way to avoid them. It lays great stress on the old prescript of isolation and pure fertilization, but it will have to be worked out and applied to a large number of practical cases before it will gain a preeminent influence in horticultural practice.

Or, as Bailey states it, we are only beginning to find a pathway through the bewildering maze of hybridization.

This pathway is to be laid out with regard to the following considerations. We are not to cross species or varieties, or even accidental plants. We must cross unit-characters, and consider the plants only as the bearers of these units. We may assume that these units are represented in the hereditary substance of the cell-nucleus by definite bodies of too small a size to be seen, but constituting together the chromosomes. We may call these innermost representatives of the unit-characters pangenes, in accordance with Darwin's hypothesis of pangenesis, or give them any other name, or we may even wholly abstain from such theoretical discussion, and limit ourselves to the conception of the visible character-units. These units then may be present, or lacking and in the first case active, or latent.

True elementary species differ from each other in a number of unit-characters, which do not contrast. They have arisen by progressive mutation. One species has one kind of unit, another species has another kind. On combining these, there can be no interchange. Mendelism assumes such an interchange between units of the same character, but in a different condition. Activity and latency are such conditions, and therefore Mendel's law obviously applies to them. They require pairs of antagonistic qualities, and have no connection whatever with those qualities which do not find an opponent in the other parent. Now, only pure varieties afford such pure conditions. When undergoing further modifications, some of them may be in the progressive line and others in the retrogressive. Progressive modifications give new units, which are not in contrast with any other, retrograde changes turn active units into the latent condition and so give rise to pairs. Ordinary species generally originate in this way, and hence differ from each other partly in specific, partly in varietal characters. As to the first, they give in their hybrids stable peculiarities, while as to the latter, they split up according to Mendel's law.

Unpaired or unbalanced characters lie side by side with paired or balanced qualities, and they do so in nearly all the crosses made for practical purposes, and in very many scientific experiments. Even Mendel's peas were not pure in this respect, much less do the campions noted above differ only in Mendelian characters.

Comparative and systematic studies must be made to ascertain the true nature of every unit in every single plant, and crossing experiments must be based on these distinctions in order to decide what laws are applicable in any case.

D. EVER-SPORTING VARIETIES

Lecture XI

STRIPED FLOWERS

Terminology is an awkward thing. It is as disagreeable to be compelled to make new names, as to be constrained to use the old faulty ones. Different readers may associate different ideas with the same terms, and unfortunately this is the case with much of the terminology of the science of heredity and variability. What are species and what are varieties? How many different conceptions are conveyed by the terms constancy and variability? We are compelled to use them, but we are not at all sure that we are rightly understood when we do so.

Gradually new terms arise and make their way. They have a more limited applicability than the old ones, and are more narrowly circumscribed. They are not to supplant the older terms, but permit their use in a more general way.

One of these doubtful terms is the word *sport*. It often means bud-variation, while in other cases it conveys the same idea as the old botanical term of mutation. But then all sorts of seemingly sudden variations are occasionally designated by the same term by one writer or another, and even accidental anomalies, such as teratological ascidia, are often said to arise by sports.

If we compare all these different conceptions, we will find that their most general feature is the suddenness and the rarity of the phenomenon. They convey the idea of something unexpected, something not always or not regularly occurring. But even this demarcation is not universal, and there are processes that are regularly repeated and nevertheless are called sports. These at least should be designated by another name.

In order to avoid confusion as far as possible, with the least change in existing terminology, I shall use the term " ever-sporting varieties " for such forms as are regularly propagated by seed, and of pure and not hybrid origin, but which sport in nearly every generation. The term is a new one, but the facts are for the most part new, and require to be considered in a new light. Its meaning will become clearer at once when the illustrations afforded by striped flowers are introduced. In the following discussion it will be found most convenient to give a summary of what is known concerning them, and follow this by a consideration of the detailed evidence obtained experimentally, which supports the usage cited.

The striped variety of the larkspur of our gardens is known to produce monochromatic flowers, in addition to striped ones. They may be borne by the same racemes, or on different branches, or some seedlings from the same parent-plant may bear monochromatic flowers while others may be striped. Such deviations are usually called sports. But they occur yearly and regularly and may be observed invariably when the cultures are large enough. Such a variety I shall call "ever-sporting."

The striped larkspur is one of the oldest garden varieties. It has kept its capacity of sporting through centuries, and therefore may in some sense be said to be quite stable. Its changes are limited to a rather narrow circle, and this circle is as constant as the peculiarities of any other constant species or variety. But within this circle it is always changing from small stripes to broad streaks, and from them to pure colors. Here the variability is a thing of absolute constancy, while the constancy consists in eternal changes! Such apparent contradictions are unavoidable, when we apply the old term to such unusual though not at all new cases. Combining the stability and the qualities of sports in one word, we may evidently best express it by the new term of ever-sporting variety.

We will now discuss the exact nature of such varieties, and of the laws of heredity which govern them. But before doing so, I might point out, that this new type is a very common one. It embraces most of the so-called variable types in horticulture, and besides these a wide range of anomalies.

Every ever-sporting variety has at least two different types, around and between which it varies in numerous grades, but to which it is absolutely limited. Variegated leaves fluctuate between green and white, or green and yellow, and display these colors in nearly all possible patterns. But there variability ends, and even the patterns are ordinarily narrowly prescribed in the single varieties. Double flowers afford a similar instance. On one side the single type, on the other the nearly wholly double model are the extreme limits, between which the variability is confined. So it is also with monstrosities. The race consists of anomalous and normal individuals, and displays between them all possible combinations of normal and monstrous parts. But its variability is restricted to this group. And large as the group may seem on first inspection, it is in reality very narrow. Many monstrosities, such as fasciated branches, pitchers, split leaves, peloric flowers, and others constitute such ever-sporting varieties, repeating their anomalies year by year and generation after generation, changing as much as possible, but remaining absolutely true within their limits as long as the variety exists.

It must be a very curious combination of the unit-characters which causes such a state of continuous variability. The pure quality of the species must be combined with the peculiarity of the variety in such a way, that the one excludes the other, or modifies it to some extent, although both never fully display themselves in the same part of the same plant. A corolla cannot be at once monochromatic and striped, nor can the same part of a stem be twisted and straight. But neighboring organs may show the opposite attributes side by side.

In order to look closer into the real mechanism of this form of variability, and of this constant tendency to occasional reversions, it will be best to limit ourselves first to a single case, and to try to gather all the evidence, which can be obtained by an examination of the hereditary relations of its sundry constituents.

This may best be done by determining the degree of inheritance for the various constituents of the race during a series of years. It is only necessary to apply the two precautions of excluding all cross-fertilization, and of gathering the seeds of each individual separately. We do not need to ascertain whether the variety as such is permanent; this is already clear from the simple fact of its antiquity in so many cases. We wish to learn what part each individual, or each group of individuals with similar characters, play in the common line of inheritance. In other words, we must build up a genealogical tree, embracing several generations and a complete set of the single cases occurring within the variety, in order to allow of its being considered as a part of the genealogy of the whole. It should convey to us an idea of the hereditary relations during the life-time of the variety.

It is manifest that the construction of such a genealogical tree requires a number of separate experiments. These should be extended over a series of years. Each should include a number of individuals large enough to allow the determination of the proportion of the different types among the offspring of a single plant. A species which is easily fertilized by its own pollen, and which bears capsules with large quantities of seeds, obviously affords the best opportunities. As such, I have chosen the common snapdragon of the gardens, *Antirrhinum majus*. It has many striped varieties, some tall, others of middle height, or of dwarfed stature. In some the ground-color of the flowers is yellow, in others it is white, the yellow disappearing, with the exception of a large mark in the throat. On these ground-colors the red pigment is seen lying in streaks of pure carmine, with white intervals where the yellow fails, but combined with yellow to make a fiery red, and with yellow intervals when that color is present. This yellow color is quite constant and does not vary in any marked degree, notwithstanding the fact that it seems to make narrower and broader stripes, according to the parts of the corolla left free by the red pigment. But it is easily seen that this appearance is only a fallacious one.

The variety of snapdragon chosen was of medium height and with the yellow ground-color, and is known by horticulturists as *A. majus luteum rubro-striatum*. As the yellow tinge showed itself to be invariable, I may limit my description to the red stripes.

Some flowers of this race are striped, others are not. On a hasty survey there seem to be three types, pure yellow, pure red, and stripes with all their intermediate links of narrower and broader, fewer and more numerous streaks. But on a close inspection one does not succeed in finding pure yellow racemes. Little lines of red may be found on nearly every flower. They are the extreme type on this side of the range of variability. From them an almost endless range of patterns passes over to the broadest stripes and even to whole sections of a pure red. But then, between these and the wholly red flowers we observe a gap, which may be narrower by the choice of numerous broad striped individuals, but which is never wholly filled up. Hence we see that the red flowers are a separate type within the striped variety.

This red type springs yearly from the striped form, and yearly reverts to it. This is what in the usual descriptions of this snapdragon, is called its sporting. The breadth of the streaks is considered to be an ordinary case of variability, but the red flowers appear suddenly, without the expected links. Therefore they are to be considered as sports. Similarly the red forms may suddenly produce striped ones, and this too is to be taken as a sport, according to the usual conception of the word.

Such sports may occur in different ways. Either by seeds, or by buds, or even within the single spikes. Both opposite reversions, from striped to red and from red to stripes, occur by seed, even by the strictest exclusion of cross-fertilization. As far as my experiments go, they are the rule, and parent-plants that do not give such reversions, at least in some of their offspring, are very rare, if not wholly wanting. Bud-variations and variations within the spike I have as yet only observed on the striped individuals, and never on the red ones, though I am confident that they might appear in larger series of experiments. Both cases are more common on individuals with broad stripes than on plants bearing only the narrower red lines, as might be expected, but even on the almost purely yellow individuals they may be seen from time to time. Bud-variations produce branches with spikes of uniform red flowers. Every bud of the plant seems to have equal chances to be transformed in this way. Some striped racemes bear a few red flowers, which ordinarily are inserted on one side of the spike only. As they often cover a sharply defined section of the raceme, this circumstance has given rise to the term of sectional variability to cover such cases. Sometimes the section is demarcated on the axis of the flower-spike by a brownish or reddish color, sharply contrasting with the green hue of the remaining parts.

Sectional variation may be looked at as a

special type of bud-variation, and from this point of view we may simplify our inquiry and limit ourselves to the inheritance of three types, the striped plants, the red plants and the red asexual variants of the striped individuals. In each case the heredity should be observed not only for one, but at least for two successive generations.

Leaving these introductory remarks I now come at once to the genealogical tree, as it may be deduced from my experiments:

Year.			
1896		95% Str.	84% Red
1895		Striped Indiv.	Red Indiv.
1895	98% Str.	71% Red.	
1894	Striped branches.	Red branches.	
1894		98% Str.	76% Red.
1893		90% Striped Indiv.	10% Red Indiv.
1892		Striped Individual.	

This experiment was begun in the year 1892 with one individual out of a large lot of striped plants grown from seeds which I had purchased from a firm in Erfurt. The capsules were gathered separately from this individual and about 40 flowering plants were obtained from the seeds in the following year. Most of them had neatly striped flowers, some displayed broader stripes and spare flowers were seen with one-half wholly red. Four individuals were found with only uniform red flowers. These were isolated and artificially pollinated, and the same was done with some of the best striped individuals. The seeds from every parent were sown separately, so as to allow the determination of the proportion of uniform red individuals in the progeny.

Neither group was constant in its offspring. But as might be expected, the type of the parent plant prevailed in both groups, and more strongly so in the instances with the striped, than with the red ones. Or, in other words seed-reversions were more numerous among the already reverted reds than among the striped type itself. I counted 2% reversion in the latter case, but 24% from the red parents.

Among the striped plants from the striped parents, I found some that produced bud-variations. I succeeded in isolating these red flowering branches in paper bags and in pollinating them with their own pollen, and subjected the striped spikes of the same individuals to a similar treatment. Three individuals gave a sufficient harvest from both types, and these six lots of seeds were sown separately. The striped flowers repeated their character in 98% of their offspring, the red twigs in only 71%, the remaining individuals sporting into the opposite group.

In the following year I continued the experiment with the seeds of the offspring of the red bud-variations. The striped individuals gave 95%, but in the red ones only 84% of the progeny remained true to the parent type.

From these figures it is manifest that the red and striped types differ from one another not only in their visible attributes, but also in the degree of their heredity. The striped individuals repeat their peculiarity in 90 – 98% of their progeny, 2 – 10% sporting into the uniform red color. On the other hand the red individuals are constant in 71 – 84% of their offspring, while 16 – 29% go over to the striped type. Or, briefly, both types are inherited to a high degree, but the striped type is more strictly inherited than the red one.

Moreover the figures show that the degree of inheritance is not contingent upon the question as to how the sport may have arisen. Bud-sports show the same degree of inheritance as seed-sports. Sexual and asexual variability therefore seem to be one and the same process in this instance. But the deeper meaning of this and other special features of our genealogical tree are still awaiting further investigation. It seems that much important evidence might come from an extension of this line of work. Perhaps it might even throw some light on the intimate nature of the bud-variations of ever-sporting varieties in general. Sectional variations remain to be tested as to the degree of inheritance exhibited, and the different occurrences as to the breadth of the streaks require similar treatment.

In ordinary horticultural practice it is desirable to give some guarantee as to what may be expected to come from the seeds of brightly striped flowers. Neither the pure red type, nor the nearly yellow racemes are the object of the culture, as both of them may be had pure from their own separate varieties. In order to insure proper striping, both extremes are usually rejected and should be rooted out as soon as the flowering period begins. Similarly the broad-striped ones should be rejected, as they give a too large amount of uniform red flowers. Clearly, but not broadly striped individuals always yield the most reliable seed.

Summing up once more the results of our pedigree-experiment, we may assert that the striped variety of the snapdragon is wholly permanent, including the two opposite types of uniform color and of stripes. It must have been so since it first originated from the invariable uniform varieties, about the middle of the last century, in the nursery of Messrs. Vilmorin, and probably it will remain so as long as popular taste supports its cultivation. It has never been observed to trangress its limits or to sport into varieties without reversions or sports. It fluctuates from one extreme to the other yearly, always recurring in the following year, or even in the same summer by single buds. Highly variable within its limits, it is absolutely constant or permanent, when considered as a definite group.

Similar cases occur not rarely among cultivated plants. In the wild state they seem to be wholly wanting. Neither are they met with as occasional anomalies nor as distinct varieties. On the contrary, many garden-flowers that are colored in the species, and besides this have a white or yellow variety, have also striped sorts. The oldest instance is probably the marvel of Peru, *Mirabilis Jalappa*, which already had more than one striped variety at the time of its introduction from Peru into the European gardens, about the beginning of the seventeenth century. Stocks, liver-leaf (*Hepatica*), dame's violet (*Hesperis*), Sweet William *(Dianthus barbatus)*, and periwinkles (*Vinca minor*) seem to be in the same condition, as their striped varieties were already quoted by the writers of the same century. Tulips, hyacinths, *Cyclamen, Azalea, Camellia,* and even such types of garden-plants as the meadow crane's-bill (*Geranium pratense*) have striped varieties. It is always the red or blue color which occurs in stripes, the underlying ground being white or yellow, according to the presence or absence of the yellow in the original color-mixture.

All these varieties are known to be permanent, coming true during long series of successive generations. But very little is known concerning the more minute details of their hereditary qualities. They come from seed, when this is taken from striped individuals, and thence revert from time to time to the corresponding monochromatic type. But whether they would do so when self-fertilized, and whether the reversionary individuals are always bound to return towards the center of the group or towards the opposite limit, remains to be investigated. Presumably there is nowhere a real transgression of the limits, and never or only very rarely and at long intervals of time a true production of another race with other hereditary qualities.

In order to satisfy myself on these points, I made some pedigree-cultures with the striped forms of dame's violet *(Hesperis matronalis)* and of *Clarkia pulchella*. Both of them are ever-sporting varieties. The experiments were conducted during five generations with the violet, and during four with the striped *Clarkia*, including the progeny of the striped and of the monochromatic red offspring of a primitive striped plant. I need not give the figures here for the numerical relations between the different types of each group, and shall limit myself to the statement that they behaved in exactly the same manner as the snapdragon.

It is worth while to dwell a moment on the capacity of the individuals with red flowers to reproduce the striped type among their offspring. For it is manifest that this latter quality must have lain dormant in them during their whole life. Darwin has already pointed out that when a character of a grandparent, which is wanting in the progeny, reappears in the second generation, this quality must always be assumed to have been present though latent in the intermediate generation. To the many instances given by him of such alternative inheritance, the monochromatic reversionists of the striped varieties are to be added as a new type. It is moreover, a very suggestive type, since the latency is manifestly of quite another character than for instance in the case of Mendelian hybrids, and probably more allied to those instances, where secondary sexual marks, which are as a rule only evolved by one sex, are transferred to the offspring through the other.

Stripes are by no means limited to flowers. They may affect the whole foliage, or the fruits and the seeds, and even the roots. But all such cases occur much more rarely than the striped flowers. An interesting instance of striped roots is afforded by radishes. White and red varieties of different shapes are cultivated. Besides them sometimes a curious motley sort may be seen in the markets, which is white with red spots, which are few and narrow in some samples, and more numerous and broader in others. But what is very peculiar and striking is the circumstance, that these stripes do not extend in a longitudinal, but in a transverse direction. Obviously this must be the effect of the very notable growth in thickness. Assuming that the colored regions were small in the beginning, they must have been drawn out during the process of thickening of the root, and changed into transverse lines. Rarely a streak may have had its greatest extension in a transverse direction from the beginning, in which case it would only be broadened and not definitely changed in its direction.

This variety being a very fine one, and more agreeable to the eye than the uniform colors, is being more largely cultivated in some countries. It has one great drawback: it never comes wholly true from seed. It may be grown in full isolation, and carefully selected, all red or nearly monochromatic samples being rooted out long before blooming, but nevertheless the seed will always produce some red roots. The most careful selection, pursued through a number of years, has not been sufficient to get rid of this regular occurrence of reversionary individuals. Seed-growers receive many complaints from their clients on this account, but they are not able to remove the difficulty. This experience is in full agreement with the experimental evidence given by the snapdragon, and it would certainly be very interesting to make a complete pedigree-culture with the radishes to test definitely their compliance with the rules observed for striped flowers.

Horticulturists in such cases are in the habit of limiting themselves to the sale of so-called mixed seeds. From these no client expects purity, and the normal and hereditary diversity of types is here in some sense concealed under the impurities included in the mixture from lack of selection. Such cases invite scrutiny, and would, no doubt, with the methods of isolation, artificial pollination, and the sowing of the seeds separately from each parent, yield results of great scientific value. Any one who has a garden, and sufficient perseverance to make pure cultures during a series of years might make important contributions to scientific knowledge in this way.

Choice might be made from among a wide range of different types. A variety of corn called "Harlequin" shows stripes on its kernels, and one ear may offer nearly white and nearly red seeds and all the possible intermediate steps between them. From these seeds the next generation will repeat the motley ears, but some specimens will produce ears of uniform kernels of a dark purple, showing thus the ordinary way of reversion. Some varieties of beans have spotted seeds, and among a lot of them one may be sure to find some purely red ones. It remains to be investigated what will be their offspring, and whether they are due to partial or to individual variation.

The cockscomb *(Celosia cristata)* has varieties of nearly all colors from white and yellow to red and orange, and besides them some striped varieties occur in our gardens, with the stripes going from the lower parts of the stem up to the very crest of the comb. They are on sale as constant varieties, but nothing has as yet been recorded concerning their peculiar behavior in the inheritance of the stripes.

Striped grapes, apples and other fruits might be mentioned in this connection.

Before leaving the striped varieties, attention is called to an interesting deduction, which probably gives an explanation of one of the most widely known instances of ever-sporting garden plants. Striped races always include two types. Both of them are fertile, and each of them reproduces in its offspring both its own and the alternate type. It is like a game of ball, in which the opposing parties always return the ball. But now suppose that only one of the types were fertile and the other for some reason wholly sterile, and assume the reversionary, or primitive monochromatic individuals to be fertile, and the derivative striped specimens to bloom without seed. If this were the case, knowledge concerning the hereditary qualities would be greatly limited. In fact the whole pedigree would be reduced to a monochromatic strain, which would in each generation sport in some individuals into the striped variety. But, being sterile, they would not be able to propagate themselves.

Such seems to be the case with the double flowered stocks. Their double flowers produce neither stamens nor pistils, and as each individual is either double or single in all its flowers, the doubles are wholly destitute of seed.

Nevertheless, they are only reproduced by seed from single flowers, being an annual or biennial species.

Stocks are a large family, and include a wonderful variety of colors, ranging from white and yellow to purple and red, and with some variations toward blue. They exhibit also diversity in the habit of growth. Some are annuals, including the ten-week and pyramidal forms; others are intermediates and are suitable for pot-culture; and the biennial sorts include the well-known " Brompton " and "Queen" varieties. Some are large and others are small or dwarf. For their brightness, durability and fragrance, they are deservedly popular. There are even some striped varieties. Horticulturists and amateurs generally know that seed can be obtained from single stocks only, and that the double flowers never produce any. It is not difficult to choose single plants that will produce a large percentage of double blossoms in the following generation. But only a percentage, for the experiments of the most skilled growers have never enabled them to save seed, which would result entirely in double flowering plants. Each generation in its turn is a motley assembly of singles and doubles.

Before looking closer into the hereditary peculiarities of this old and interesting ever-sporting variety, it may be as well to give a short description of the plants with double flowers. Generally speaking there are two principal types of doubles. One is by the conversion of stamens into petals, and the other is an anomaly, known under the name of petalomany.

The change of stamens into petals is a gradual modification. All intermediate steps are easily to be found. In some flowers all stamens may be enlarged, in others only part of them. Often the broadened filaments bear one or two fertile anthers. The fertility is no doubt diminished, but not wholly destroyed. Individual specimens may occur, which cannot produce any seed, but then others of the same lot may be as fertile as can be desired. As a whole, such double varieties are regularly propagated by seed.

Petalomany is the tendency of the axis of some flowers never to make any stamens or pistils, not even in altered or rudimentary form. Instead of these, they simply continue producing petals, going on with this production without any other limit than the supply of available food. Numerous petals fill the entire space within the outer rays, and in the heart of the flower innumerable young ones are developed half-way, not obtaining food enough to attain full size. Absolute sterility is the natural consequence of this state of things.

Hence it is impossible to have races of petalomanous types. If the abnormality happens to show itself in a species, which normally propagates itself in an asexual way, the type may become a vegetative variety, and be multiplied by bulbs, buds or cuttings, etc. Some cultivated anemones and crowfoots *(Ranunculus)* are of this character, and even the marsh-marigold *(Caltha palustris)* has a petalomanous variety. I once found in a meadow such a form of the meadow-buttercup *(Ranunculus acris)*, and succeeded in keeping it in my garden for several years, but it did not make seeds and finally died. Camellias are known to have both types of double flowers. The petalomanous type is highly regular in structure, so much so as to be too uniform in all its parts to be pleasing, while the conversion of stamens into petals in the alternative varieties gives to these flowers a more lively diversity of structure. Lilies have a variety called *Lilium candidum flore pleno*, in which the flowers seem to be converted into a long spike of bright, white narrow bracts, crowded on an axis which never seems to cease their production.

It is manifestly impossible to decide how all such sterile double flowers have originated.

Perhaps each of them originally had a congruent single-flowered form, from which it was produced by seed in the same way as the double stocks now are yearly. If this assumption is right, the corresponding fertile line is now lost; it has perhaps died out, or been masked. But it is not absolutely impossible that such strains might one day be discovered for one or another of these now sterile varieties.

Returning to the stocks we are led to the conception that some varieties are absolutely single, while others consist of both single-flowered and double-flowered individuals. The single varieties are in respect to this character true to the original wild type. They never give seed which results in doubles, providing all intercrossing is excluded. The other varieties are ever-sporting, in the sense of this term previously assumed, but with the restriction that the sports are exclusively one-sided, and never return, owing to their absolute sterility.

The oldest double varieties of stocks have attained an age of a century and more. During all this time they have had a continuous pedigree of fertile and single-flowered individuals, throwing off in each generation a definite number of doubles. This ratio is not at all dependent on chance or accident, nor is it even variable to a remarkable degree. Quite on the contrary it is always the same, or nearly the same, and it is to be considered as an inherent quality of the race. If left to themselves, the single individuals always produce singles and doubles in the same quantity; if cultivated after some special method, the proportion may be slightly changed, bringing the proportion of doubles up to 60% or even more.

Ordinarily the single and double members of such a race are quite equal in the remainder of their attributes, especially in the color of their flowers. But this is not always the case. The colors of such a race may repeat for themselves the peculiarities of the ever-sporting characters. It often happens that one color is more or less strictly allied to the doubles, and another to the singles. This sometimes makes it difficult to keep the various colors true. There are certain sorts, which invariably exhibit a difference in color between the single and the double flowers. The sulphur-yellow varieties may be adduced as illustrative examples, because in them the single flowers always come white. Hence in saving seed, it is impossible so to select the plant, that an occasional white does not also appear among the double flowers, agreeing in this deviation with the general rule of the ever-sporting varieties.

I commend all the above instances to those

who wish to make pedigree-cultures. The cooperation of many is needed to bring about any notable advancement, since the best way to secure isolation is to restrict one's self to the culture of one strain, so as to avoid the intermixture of others. So many facts remain doubtful and open to investigation, that almost any lot of purchased seed may become the starting point for interesting researches. Among these the sulphur-yellow varieties should be considered in the first place.

In respect to the great questions of heredity, the stocks offer many points of interest. Some of these features I will now try to describe, in order to show what still remains to be done, and in what manner the stocks may clear the way for the study of the ever-sporting varieties.

The first point, is the question, which seeds become double-flowered and which single-flowered plants? Beyond all doubt, the determination has taken place before the ripening of the seed. But though the color of the seed is often indicative of the color of the flowers, as in some red or purple varieties, and though in balsams and some other instances the most "highly doubled" flowers are to be obtained from the biggest and plumpest seeds, no such rule seems to exist respecting the double stocks. Now if one half of the seeds gives doubles, and the other half singles, the question arises, where are the singles and the doubles to be found on the parent-plant?

The answer is partly given by the following experiment. Starting from the general rule of the great influence of nutrition on variability, it may be assumed that those seeds will give most doubles, that are best fed. Now it is manifest that the stem and larger branches are in a better condition than the smaller twigs, and that likewise the first fruits have better chances than the ones formed later. Even in the same pod the uppermost seeds will be in a comparatively disadvantageous position. This conception leads to an experiment which is the basis of a practical method much used in France in order to get a higher percentage of seeds of double-flowering plants.

This method consists in cutting off, in the first place the upper parts of all the larger spikes, in the second place, the upper third part of each pod, and lastly all the small and weak twigs. In doing so the percentage is claimed to go up to 67 – 70%, and in some instances even higher. This operation is to be performed as soon as the required number of flowers have ceased blossoming. All the nutrient materials, destined for the seeds, are now forced to flow into these relatively few embryos, and it is clear that they will be far better nourished than if **no** operation were made.

In order to control this experiment some breeders have made the operation on the fruits when ripe, instead of on the young pods, and have saved the seeds from the upper parts separately. This seed, produced in abundance, was found to be very poor in double flowers, containing only some 20 – 30%. On the contrary the percentage of doubles in the seed of the lower parts was somewhat augmented, and the average of both would have given the normal proportion of 50%.

Opposed to the French method is the German practice of cultivating stocks, as I have seen it used on a very large scale at Erfurt and at other places. The stocks are grown in pots on small scaffolds, and not put on or into the earth. The obvious aim of this practice is to keep the earth in the pots dry, and accordingly they are only scantily watered. In consequence they cannot develop as fully as they would have done when planted directly in the beds, and they produce only small racemes and no weak twigs, eliminating thereby without further operation the weaker seeds as by the French method. The effect is increased by planting from 6 – 10 separate plants in each pot.

It would be very interesting to make comparative trials of both methods, in order to discover the true relation between the practice and the results reached. Both should also be compared with cultures on open plots, which are said to give only 50% of doubles. This last method of culture is practiced wherever it is desired to produce great quantities of seeds at a low cost. Such trials would no doubt give an insight into the relations of hereditary characters to the distribution of the food within the plant.

A second point is the proportional increase of the double-flowering seeds with age. If seed is kept for two or three years, the greater part of the grains will gradually die, and among the remainder there is found on sowing, a higher percentage of double ones. Hence we may infer that the single-flowered seeds are shorter-lived than the doubles, and this obviously points to a greater weakness of the first. It is quite evident that there is some common cause for these facts and for the above cited experience, that the first and best pods give more doubles. Much, however, remains to be investigated before a satisfactory answer can be made to these questions.

A third point is the curious practice, called by the French " ésimpler," and which consists in pulling out the singles when very young. It seems to be done at an age when the flower-buds are not yet visible, or at least are not far enough developed to show the real distinctive marks. Children may be employed to choose and destroy the singles. There are some slight differences in the fullness and roundness of the buds and the pubescence of the young leaves. Moreover the buds of the doubles are said to be sweeter to the taste than those of the singles. But as yet I have not been able to ascertain, whether any scientific investigation of this process has ever been made, though according to some communications made to me by the late Mr. Cornu, the practice seems to be very general in the environs of Paris. In summer large fields may be seen, bearing exclusively double flowers, owing to the weeding out of the singles long before flowering.

Bud-variation is the last point to be taken up. It seems to be very rare with stocks, but some instances have been recorded in literature. Darwin mentions a double stock with a branch bearing single flowers, and other cases are known to have occurred. But in no instance does the seed of such a bud-variant seem to have been saved. Occasionally other reversions also occur. From time to time specimens appear with more luxurious growth and with divergent instead of erect pods. They are called, in Erfurt, " generals " on account of their stiff and erect appearance, and they are marked by more divergent horns crowning the pods. They are said to produce only a relatively small number of doubles from their seeds, and even this small number might be due to fertilization with pollen of their neighbors. I saw some of these reversionary types, when inspecting the nurseries of Erfurt, but as they are, as a rule, thrown out before ripening their seed, nothing is exactly known about their real hereditary qualities.

Much remains to be cleared up, but it seems that one of the best means to find a way through the bewildering maze of the phenomena of inheritance, is to make groups of related forms and to draw conclusions from a comparison of the members of such groups. Such comparisons must obviously give rise to questions, which in their turn will directly lead to experimental investigation.

Lecture XII

FIVE-LEAVED CLOVER

Every one knows the " four-leaved " clover. It is occasionally found on lawns, in pastures and by the roadsides. Specimens with five leaflets may be found now and then in the same place, or on the same plant, but these are rarer. I have often seen isolated plants with quaternate leaves, but only rarely have I observed individuals with more than one such leaf.

The two cases are essentially dissimilar. They may appear to differ but little morphologically, but from the point of view of heredity they are quite different. Isolated quaternate leaves are of but little interest, while the occurrence of many on the same individual indicates a distinct variety. In making experiments upon this point it is necessary to transplant the divergent individuals to a garden in order to furnish them proper cultural conditions and to keep them under constant observation. When a plant bearing a quaternate leaf is thus transplanted however, it rarely repeats the anomaly. But when plants with two or more quaternate leaves on the same individual are chosen it indicates that it belongs to a definite race, which under suitable conditions may prove to become very rich in the anomalies in question.

Obviously it is not always easy to decide definitely whether a given individual belongs to such a race or not. Many trials may be necessary to secure the special race. I had the good fortune to find two plants of clover, bearing one quinate and several quaternate leaves, on an excursion in the neighborhood of Loosdrecht in Holland. After transplanting them into my garden, I cultivated them during three years and observed a slowly increasing number of anomalous leaves. This number in one summer amounted to 46 quaternate and 16 quinate leaves, and it was evident that I had secured an instance of the rare " five-leaved " race which I am about to describe.

Before doing so it seems desirable to look somewhat closer into the morphological features of the problem. Pinnate and palmate leaves often vary in the number of their parts. This variability is generally of the nature of a common fluctuation, the deviations grouping themselves around an average type in the ordinary way. Ash leaves bear five pairs, and the mountain-ash (*Sorbus Aucuparia*) has six pairs of leaflets in addition to the terminal one. But this number varies slightly, the weaker leaves having less, the stronger more pairs than the average. Such however, is not the case with ternate leaves, which seem to be quite constant. Four leaflets occur so very rarely that one seems justified in regarding them rather as an anomaly than as a fluctuation. And this is confirmed by the almost universal absence of two-bladed clover-leaves.

Considering the deviation as an anomaly, we may look into its nature. Such an inquiry shows that the supernumerary leaflets owe their origin to a splitting of one or more of the normal ones. This splitting is not terminal, as is often the case with other species, and as it may be seen sometimes in the clover. It is for the most part lateral. One of the lateral nerves grows out becoming a median nerve of the new leaflet. Intermediate steps are not wanting, though rare, and they show a gradual separation of some lateral part of a leaflet, until this division reaches the base and divides the leaflet into two almost equal parts. If this splitting occurs in one leaflet we get the " four-leaved " clover, if it occurs in two there will be five leaflets. And if, besides this, the terminal leaflet produces a derivative on one or both of its sides, we obtain a crown of six or seven leaflets on one stalk. Such were often met with in the race I had under cultivation, but as a rule it did not exceed this limit.

The same phenomenon of a lateral doubling of leaflets may of course be met with in other instances. The common laburnum has a variety which often produces quaternate and quinate leaves, and in strawberries I have also seen instances of this abnormality. It occurs also in pinnate leaves, and complete sets of all the intermediate links may often be found on the false or bastard-acacia *(Robinia Pseud-Acacia)*.

Opposed to this increase of the number of leaflets, and still more rare and more curious is the occurrence of " single-leaved " varieties among trees and herbs with pinnate or ternate leaves. Only very few instances have been described, and are cultivated in gardens. The ashes and the bastard-acacia may be quoted among trees, and the " one-leaved " strawberry among herbs. Here it seems that several leaflets have been combined into one, since this one is, as a rule, much larger than the terminal leaflet of an ordinary leaf of the same species. These monophyllous varieties are interesting also on account of their continuous but often incomplete reversion to the normal type.

Pinnate and palmate leaves are no doubt derivative types. They must have originated from the ordinary simple leaf. The monophylly may therefore be considered as a reversion to a more primitive state and the monophyllous varieties may be called atavistic.

On the other hand we have seen that these atavistic varieties may revert to their nearest progenitors, and this leads to the curious conception of positive and negative atavism. For if the change of compound leaves into single ones is a retrograde or negative step, the conversion of single or ternate leaves into pinnate and palmate ones must evidently be considered in this case as positive atavism.

This discussion seems to throw some light on the increase of leaflets in the clover. The pea-family, or the group of papilionaceous plants, has pinnate leaves ordinarily, which, according to our premises, must be considered as a derivative type. In the clovers and their allies this type reverts halfway to the single form, producing only three leaflets on each stalk. If now the clover increases its number of leaflets, this may be considered as a reversion to its nearest progenitors, the papilionaceous plants with pinnate leaves. Hence a halfway returning and therefore positive atavism. And as I have already mentioned in a former lecture, pinnate leaves are also sometimes produced by my new race of clover.

Returning to the original plants of this race, it is evidently impossible to decide whether they were really the beginning of a new strain, and had originated themselves by some sudden change from the common type, or whether they belonged to an old variety, which had propagated itself perhaps during centuries, unobserved by man. But the same difficulty generally arises when new varieties are discovered. Even the behavior of the plants themselves or of their progeny does not afford any means of deciding the question. The simplest way of stating the matter therefore, is to say that I accidentally found two individuals of the "five-leaved" race. By transplanting them into my garden, I have isolated them and kept them free from cross-fertilization with the ordinary type. Moreover, I have brought them under such conditions as are necessary for the full development of their characters. And last but not least, I have tried to improve this character as far as possible by a very rigid and careful selection.

The result of all this effort has been a rapid improvement of my strain. I saved the seed of the original plants in 1889 and cultivated the second generation in the following year. It showed some increase of the anomaly, but not to a very remarkable degree. In the flowering period I selected four plants with the largest number of quaternate and quinate leaves and destroyed all the others. I counted in the average 25 anomalous organs on each of them. From their seed I raised the third generation of my culture in the year 1891.

This generation included some 300 plants, on which above 8000 leaves were counted. More than 1000 were quaternate or quinate, the ternate leaves being still in the majority. But the experiment clearly showed that "four-leaved" clovers may be produced in any desired quantity, provided that the seed of the variety is available. In the summer only three, four and five leaflets on one stalk were seen, but towards the fall, and after the selection of the best individuals, this number increased and came up to six and seven in some rare instances.

The selection in this year was by no means easy. Nearly all the individuals produced at least some quaternate leaves, and thereby showed the variety to be quite pure. I counted the abnormal organs on a large group of the best plants, and selected 20 excellent specimens from them, with more than one-third of all their leaves changed in the desired manner.

Having brought my race up to this point, I

was able to introduce a new and far more easy mark, afforded by the seedlings, for my selections. This mark has since remained constant, and has brought about a rapid continuance of the improvement, without necessitating such large cultures.

This seedling in the various species of clover usually begins with a first leaf above the cotyledons of a different structure from those that follow. It has only one blade instead of three. But in my variety the increase of the number of the leaflets may extend to these primary organs, and make them binate or even ternate. Now it is obvious that an individual, which begins with a divided primary leaf, will have a greater tendency to produce a large number of supernumerary leaflets than a plant which commences in the ordinary way. Or in other words, the primary leaves afford a sure criterion for the selection, and this selection may be made in the seed-pans. In consequence, no young individual with an undivided primary leaf was planted out. Choosing the 20 or 30 best specimens in the seed-pan, no further selection was required, and the whole lot could be left to cross-fertilization by insects.

The observation of this distinguishing mark in the young seedlings has led to the discovery of another quality as a starting-point for further selection. According to the general rule of pedigree-culture, the seeds of each individual plant are always saved and sowed separately. This is done even with such species as the clover, which are infertile when self-pollinated, and which are incapable of artificial pollination on the required scale, since each flower produces only one seed. My clover was always left free to be pollinated by insects. Obviously this must have led to a diminution of the differentiating characters of the individual plants. But this does not go far enough to obliterate the differences, and the selection made among the seedlings will always throw out at least a large part of those that have suffered from the cross.

Leaving this discussion, we may inquire closer into the nature of the new criterion afforded by the seedlings. Two methods present themselves. First, the choice of the best seedlings. In the second place it becomes possible to compare the parent-plants by counting the number of deviating seedlings. This leads to the establishment of a percentage for every single parent, and gives data for comparisons. Two or three hundreds of seeds from a parent may easily be grown in one pan, and in this way a sufficiently high degree of accuracy may be reached. Only those parents that give the highest percentage are chosen, and among their progeny only the seedlings with trifoliolate primary leaves are planted out. The whole procedure of the selection is by this means confined to the glasshouse during the spring, and the beds need not be large, nor do they require any special care during the summer.

By this method I brought my strain within two years up to an average of nearly 90 % of the seedlings with a divided primary leaf. Around this average the real numbers fluctuated between the maximum of 99% and the minimum of 70% or thereabouts. This condition was reached by the sixth generation in the year 1894, and has since proved to be the limit, the group of figures remaining practically the same during all the succeeding generations.

Such selected plants are very rich in leaves with four, five and six blades. Excluding the small leaves at the tops of the branches, and those on the numerous weaker side-branches, these three groups include the large majority of all the stronger leaves. In summer the range is wider, and besides many trifoliolate leaves the curiously shaped seven-bladed ones are not at all rare. In the fall and in the winter the range of variability is narrowed, and at first sight the plants often seem to bear only quinquefoliolate leaves.

I have cultivated a new generation of this race nearly every year since 1894, using always the strictest selection. This has led to a uniform type, but has not been adequate to produce any further improvement. Obviously the extreme limit, under the conditions of climate and soil, has been reached. This extreme type is always dependent upon repeated selection. No constant variety, in the older sense, has been obtained, nor was any indication afforded that such a type might ever be produced. On the contrary, it is manifest that the new form belongs to the group of ever-sporting varieties. It is never quite free from the old atavistic type of the trifoliolate leaves, and invariably, when external conditions become less favorable, this atavistic form is apt to gain dominion over the more refined varietal character. Reversions always occur, both partial and individual.

Some instances of these reversions may now be given. They are not of such a striking character as those of the snapdragon. Intermediate steps are always occurring, both in the leaves themselves, and in the percentages of deviating seedlings of the several parent plants.

On normal plants of my variety the quinquefoliolate leaves usually compose the majority, when there are no weak lateral branches, or when they are left out of consideration. Next to these come the fours and the sixes, while the trifoliolate and seven-bladed types are nearly equal in number. But out of a lot of plants, grown from seed of the same parent, it is often possible to choose some in which one extreme prevails, and others with a preponderating number of leaves with the other extreme number of leaflets. If seed from these extremes are saved separately, one strain, that with numerous seven-bladed leaves will remain true to the type, but the other will diverge more or less, producing leaves with a varying number of subdivisions.

Very few generations of such opposite selection are required to reduce the race to an utterly poor one. In three years I was able to nearly obliterate the type of my variety. I chose the seedlings with an undivided primary leaf, cultivated them and counted their offspring separately after the sowing. I found some parents with only 2 – 3% of seedlings with divided primary leaves. And by a repeated selection in this retrograde direction I succeeded in getting a great number of plants, which during the whole summer made only very few leaves with more than three blades. But an absolute reversion could no more be reached in this direction than in the normal one. Any sowing without selection would be liable to reduce the strain to an average condition.

The production of varietal and of atavistic leaves is dependent to a high degree on external conditions. It agrees with the general rule, that favorable circumstances strengthen the varietal peculiarities, while unfavorable conditions increase the number of the parts with the atavistic attribute. These influences may be seen to have their effect on the single individuals, as well as on the generations growing from their seed. I cannot cite here all the experimental material, but a single illustrative example may be given. I divided a strong individual into two parts, planted one in rich soil and the other in poor sand, and had both pollinated by bees with the pollen of some normal individuals of my variety growing between them. The seeds of both were saved and sown separately, and the two lots of offspring cultivated close to each other under the same external conditions. In the beginning no difference was seen, but as soon as the young plants had unfolded three or four leaves, the progeny of the better nourished half of the parent-plant showed a manifest advance. This difference increased rapidly and was easily seen in the beds, even before the flowering period.

This experience probably gives an explanation why the quinquefoliolate variety is so seldom met with in the wild state. For even if it did occur more often, the plants would hardly find circumstances favorable enough for the full development of their varietal character. They must often be so poor in anomalous leaves as to be overlooked, or to be taken for instances of the commonly occurring quadrifoliolate leaves and therefore as not indicating the true variety.

In the beginning of my discussion I have asserted the existence of two different races of "four-leaved" clovers, a poor one and a rich one, and have insisted on a sharp distinction between them. This distinction partly depends on experiments with clover, but in great part on tests with other plants. The previously mentioned circumstance, that clover cannot be pollinated on a sufficiently large scale otherwise than by insects, prevents trials in more than one direction at the same time and in the same garden. For this reason I have chosen another species of clover to be able to give proof or disproof of the assertion quoted.

This species is the Italian, or crimson clover, which is sometimes also called scarlet clover (*Trifolium incarnatum*). It is commonly used in Europe as a crop on less fertile soils than are required by the red clover. It is annual and erect and more or less hairy, and has stouter leaves than other kinds of clover. It has oblong or cylindrical heads with bright crimson flowers, and may be considered as one of the most showy types. As an annual it has some manifest advantages over the perennial species, especially in giving its harvest of hay at other seasons of the year.

I found some stray quaternate leaves of this plant some years ago, and tried to win from them, through culture and selection, a race that would be as rich in these anomalies as the red clover. But the utmost care and the most rigid selection, and all the attention I could afford, failed to produce any result. It is now ten years since I commenced this experiment, and more than once I have been willing to give it up. Last year (1903) I cultivated some hundreds of selected plants, but though they yielded a few more instances of the desired anomaly than in the beginning, no trace of a truly rich race could be discovered. The experimental evidence of this failure shows at least that stray "four-leaves" may occur, which do not indicate the existence of a true "four-" or "five-leaved" variety.

This conception seems destined to become of great value in the appreciation of anomalies, as they are usually found, either in the wild state or in gardens. And before describing the details of my unsuccessful pedigree-culture, it may be as well to give some more instances of what occurs in nature.

Stray anomalies are of course rare, but not so rare that they might not be found in large numbers when perseveringly sought for. Pitcher-like leaves may be found on many trees and shrubs and herbs, but ordinarily one or only two of them are seen in the course of many years on the same plant, or in the same strain. In some few instances they occur annually or nearly so, as in some individuals of the European lime-tree (*Tilia parvifolia*) and of the common magnolia (*Magnolia obovata*). Many of our older cultivated plants are very rich in anomalies of all kinds, and *Cyclamen, Fuchsia, Pelargonium* and some others are notorious sources of teratologic phenomena. Deviations in flowers may often be seen, consisting of changes in the normal number of the several organs, or alterations in their shape and color. Leaves may have two tips, instead of one, the mid-vein being split near the apex, and the fissure extending more or less towards the base. Rays of the umbels of umbelliferous plants may grow together and become united in groups of two or more, and in the same way the fruits of the composites may be united into groups. Many other instances could easily be given.

If we select some of these anomalies for breeding-experiments, our results will not agree throughout, but will tend to group themselves under two heads. In some cases the isolation of the deviating individuals will at once show the existence of a distinct variety, which is capable of producing the anomaly in any desired number of instances, only dependent on a favorable treatment and a judicious selection. In other cases no treatment and no selection are adequate to give a similar result, and the anomaly remains refractory despite all our endeavors to breed it. The cockscomb and the peloric fox-glove are widely known instances of permanent anomalies, and others will be dealt with in future lectures. On the other hand I have often tried in vain to win an anomalous race from an accidental deviation, or to isolate a teratologic variety out of more common aberrations. Two illustrative examples may be quoted. In our next lecture we shall deal with a curious phenomenon in poppies, consisting in the change of the stamens into pistils and giving rise to a bright crown of secondary capsules around the central one. Similar anomalies may be occasionally met with in other species of the same genus. But they are rare, and may show the conversion of only a single stamen in the described manner. I observed this anomaly in a poppy called *Papaver commutatum,* and subjected it during several years to a rigid selection of the richest individuals. No amelioration was to be gained and the culture had to be given up. In the same way I found on the bulbous buttercup (*Ranunculus bulbosus*) a strain varying largely in the number of the petals, amounting often to 6–8, and in some flowers even yet to higher figures. During five succeeding years I cultivated five generations, often in large numbers, selecting always those which had the highest number of petals, throwing out the remainder and saving the seed only from the very best plants. I got a strain of selected plants with an average number of nine petals in every flower, and found among 4000 flowers four having 20 petals or more, coming up even to 31 in one instance. But such rare instances had no influence whatever on the selection, since they were not indicative of individual qualities, but occurred quite accidentally on flowers of plants having only the average number of petals. Now double flowers are widely known to occur in other species of the buttercups, both in the cultivated varieties and in some wild forms. For this reason it might be expected that through a continuous selection of the individuals with the largest numbers a tendency to become double would be evolved. Such, however, was not the case. No propensity to vary in any definite direction could be observed. Quite on the contrary, an average condition was quickly reached, and then remained constant, strongly counteracting all selection.

Such experiences clearly show that the same anomaly may occur in different species, and no doubt in strains of the same species from different localities, according to at least two different standards. The one is to be called the poor, and the other the rich variety. The first always produces relatively few instances of the deviation, the last is apt to give as many of them as desired. The first is only half-way a variety, and therefore would deserve the name of a half-race; the second is not yet a full constant variety, but always fluctuates to and fro between the varietal and the specific mark, ever-sporting in both directions. It holds a middle position between a half-race and a variety, and therefore might be called a "middle-race." But the term ever-sporting variety seems more adequate to convey a right idea of the nature of this curious type of inheritance.

From this discussion it will be seen that the behavior of the crimson clover is not to be considered as an exception, but as a widely occurring type of phenomenon, occurring perhaps in all sorts of teratologic deviations, and in wide ranges of species and genera. Hence it may be considered worth while to give some more details of this extended experiment.

Ten years ago (1894 – 5) I bought and sowed about a pound of seed of the crimson clover. Among many thousands of normal seedlings I found two with three and one with four cotyledons. Trusting to the empirical rules of correlation, I transplanted these three individuals in order to isolate them in the flowering period. One of them produced during the ensuing summer one four-bladed and one five-bladed leaf. The seeds were saved separately and sown the following spring and the expected result could soon be seen. Among some 250 individual plants I counted 22 with one or two deviations, and 10 with from three to nine four- or five-bladed leaves. Proportions nearly similar have been observed repeatedly. Better nourished individuals have produced more deviating leaves on one plant, partly owing to the larger number of stems and branches, and poor or average specimens have mostly been without any aberration or with only one or two abnormal leaves. No further improvement could be attained. Quadrifoliolate leaves were always rare, never attaining a number that would put its stamp on a whole bed. I have endeavored to get some six- and seven-bladed crimson clover leaves, but in vain; selection, culture of many hundreds of individuals, manure, and the best possible treatment has not been adequate to produce them. Of course I am quite convinced that a repetition of my experiment on a far larger scale would yield the desired types, but then only in such rare instances that they would have no influence whatever on the average, or on the improvement of the race. The eighth generation in the year 1903 has not been noticeably better than the second and third generations after the first selection.

In comparing this statement with the results gained in the experiment with the red clover, the difference is at once striking. In one case a rich variety was isolated, and, by better treatment and sharp methods of selection, was brought up in a few years to its highest pitch of development. In the other case a very weak race was shown to exist, and no amount of work and perseverance was adequate to improve it to any noticeable degree.

I wish to point out that the decision of what is to be expected from deviating specimens may become manifest within one or two generations. Even the generation grown from the seeds of the first observed aberrant individuals, if gathered after sufficient isolation during the period of blossoming, may show which type of inheritance is present, whether it is an unpromising half-race, or a richly endowed sporting variety. I have kept such strains repeatedly after the first isolation, and a special case, that of cotyledoneous aberrations, will be dealt with later. The first generation always gave a final decision, provided that a suitable method of cultivation for the species under observation was found at the beginning. This however, is a condition, which it is not at all easy to comply with, when new sorts are introduced into a garden. Especially so when they had been collected in the wild state. Often one or two years, sometimes more, are necessary to find the proper method of sowing, manuring, transplanting and other cultural methods satisfactory to the plants. Many wild species require more care and more manure in gardens than the finest garden flowers. And a large number are known to be dependent on very particular conditions of soil.

One of the most curious features of anomalies, which has been learned from accumulated instances, is the fact that they obey definite laws as to their occurrence on the different parts of the plant. Obviously such laws are not apparent as long as each plant produces only one or two, or, at most, a few instances of the same deviation. On the contrary, any existing regularity must betray itself, as soon as a larger number of instances is produced. A rule of periodicity becomes most clearly manifest in such cases.

This rule is shown by no other race in a more undoubted and evident manner than by the " five-leaved " clover. Evidently the several degrees of deviation, going from three to seven leaflets, may be regarded as responses to different degrees of variation, and their distribution over the stems and branches, or over the whole plant, may be considered as the manifestation of the ever-changing internal tendency to vary.

Considered from this point of view, my plants always showed a definite periodicity in this distribution, which is the same for the whole plant. Each of them, and each of the larger branches, begin with atavistic leaves or with slight deviations. These are succeeded by greater deviations, but only the strongest axes show as many as seven leaflets on a stalk. This ordinarily does not occur before the height of development is reached, and often only towards its close. Then the deviation diminishes rapidly, returning often to atavistic leaves at the summit of the stem or branch. I give the numbers of the leaves of a branch, in their order from the base to the top. They were as follows:

3. 4. 5. 6. 7. 5. 5. 4.

But this is a selected case, and such regular examples of the expected periodicity are rarely found. Often one or more of the various steps are lacking, or even leaves with smaller numbers may be interspersed among those with larger numbers of leaflets. But while the regularity of the periodicity is in some degree diminished by such occurrences, yet the rule always holds good, when taken broadly. It may be expressed by stating that the bases and apices have on the average fewer leaflets on each leaf than the middle parts of the stem and branches, and that the number of leaflets gradually increases from the base toward a maximum, which is reached in organs on the middle or upper part of the axis, and then diminishes from this toward the apex.

This periodicity is not limited to the stems and branches, considered singly, but also holds good in a comparison made between the branches of a single stem, in regard to their relative places on that stem. So it is also for the whole plant. The first stems, produced by the subterranean axis, ordinarily show only a low maximum deviation: the next succeeding being more divergent and the last ones returning to less differentiated forms.

It is evident that on a given stem the group of deviating leaves will be extended upward and downward, with the increase of the number of these organs. This shows that a stem, or even a plant, promises a higher degree of differentiation if it commences with its aberration earlier. Hence it becomes possible to discern the most promising individuals in early youth, and this conclusion leads to a very easy and reliable method of selection, which may be expressed simply as follows: the seedlings which commence earliest with the production of four- and five-foliolate leaves are the best and should be selected for the continuance of the race. And it is easily seen that this rule agrees with that given above, and which was followed in my pedigree-culture.

Furthermore it is seen that there is a complete agreement between the law of periodicity and the responses of the deviations to nourishment and other conditions of life. Weak plants only produce low degrees of deviation, the stronger the individual becomes, the higher it reaches in the scale of differentiation, and the more often it develops leaves with five or more blades. Whether weakness or strength are derived from outer causes, or from the internal succession of the periods of life, is evidently of no consequence, and in this way the law of periodicity may be regarded as a special instance of the more general law of response to external conditions.

The validity of this law of periodicity is of course not limited to our " five-leaved " clover. Quite on the contrary it is universal in eversporting varieties. Moreover it may be ascertained and studied in connection with the most widely different morphologic abnormalities, and therefore affords easily accessible material for statistical inquiry. I will now give some further instances, but wish to insist first upon the necessity of an inquiry on a far larger scale, as the evidence as yet is very scanty.

The great celandine *(Chelidonium majus)* has a very curious double variety. Its flowers are simpler and much more variable than in ordinary garden-varieties. The process of doubling consists mainly in a change of stamens into petals. This change is dependent on the season. On each stem the earliest flowers are single. These are succeeded by blossoms with one or two converted stamens, and towards the summer this number increases gradually, attaining 10 – 11 and in some instances even more altered filaments. Each year the same succession may be seen repeating itself on the stems of the old roots. Double tuberous begonias are ordinarily absolutely sterile throughout the summer, but towards autumn the new flowers become less and less altered, producing some normal stamens and pistils among the majority of metamorphosed organs. From these flowers the seeds are saved. Sometimes similar flowers occur at the beginning of the flowering-period. Double garden-camomiles (*Chrysanthemum inodorum plenissimum*) and many other double varieties of garden-plants among the great family of the composites are very sensitive to external agencies, and their flower-heads are fuller the more favorable the external conditions. Towards the autumn many of them produce fewer and fewer converted heads and often only these are fertile and yield seeds.

Ascidia afford another instance of this periodicity, though ordinarily they are by far too rare to show any regularity in their distribution. However, it is easy to observe that on lime-trees they prefer the lower parts of each twig, while on magnolias the terminal leaves of the branches are often pitcher-bearing. Ascidia of the white clover have been found in numbers, in my own experiment-garden, but always in the springtime. The thick-leaved saxifrage (*Saxifraga crassifolia*) is often very productive of ascidia, especially in the latter part of the season, and as these organs may be developed to very different degrees, they afford fine material for the study of the law of periodicity. On a garden-cytisus (*Cytisus candicans attleyanus*) I once had the good fortune to observe a branch with ascidia, which ordinarily are very rare in this species. It had produced seven ascidia in all, each formed by the conversion of one leaflet on the trifoliolate leaves. The first six leaves were destitute of this malformation and were quite normal. Then followed a group of five leaves, constituting the maximum of the period. The first bore one small pitcher-like blade, the second and third, each one highly modified organ, the fourth, two ascidia, and the last, one leaflet with slightly connate margins. The whole upper part of the branch was normal, with the exception of the seventeenth leaf, which showed a slight change in the same direction. All in all, the tendency to produce ascidia increased from the beginning to the tenth leaf, and decreased from this upward.

The European Venus' looking-glass was observed in my garden to produce some quaternate and some quinate flowers on the same specimens. The quinate were placed at the end of the branches, those with four petals and sepals lower down. The peloric fox-glove shows the highest degree of metamorphy in the terminal flowers of the stem itself, the weaker branches having but little tendency towards the formation of the anomaly. The European pine or *Pinus sylvestris* ordinarily has two needles in each sheath, but trifoliolate sheaths occur on the stems and stronger branches, where they prefer, as a rule, the upper parts of the single annual shoots. *Camellia japonica* is often striped in the fall and during the winter, but when flowering in the spring it returns to the monochromatic type.

Peloric flowers are terminal in some cases, but occur in the lower parts of the flower-spikes in others. Some varieties of gladiolus commence on each spike with more or less double flowers, which, higher up, are replaced by single ones. A wide range of bulbs and perennial garden-plants develop their varietal characters only partly when grown from seed and flowering for the first time. The annual garden-forget-me-not of the Azores (*Myosotis azorica*) has a variety with curiously enlarged flowers, often producing 20 or more corolla-segments in one flower. But this number gradually diminishes as the season advances. It would be quite superfluous to give further proof of the general validity of the law of periodicity in ever-sporting varieties.

Lecture XIII

PISTILLODY IN POPPIES

One of the most curious anomalies that may be met with in ornamental garden-plants is the conversion of stamens into pistils. It is neither common nor rare, but in most cases the change is so slight comparatively that it is ordinarily overlooked. In the opium-poppy, on the contrary, it is very showy, and heightens the ornamental effect of the young fruits after the fading of the flowers. Here the central capsule is surrounded by a large crown of metamorphosed stamens.

This peculiarity has attracted the attention both of horticulturists and of botanists. As a rule not all the stamens are changed in this way but only those of the innermost rows. The outer stamens remain normal and fertile, and the flowers, when pollinated with their own pollen, bear as rich a harvest of seeds as other opium-poppies. The change affects both the filament and the anther, the former of which is dilated into a sheath. Within this sheath perfect and more or less numerous ovules may be produced. The anthers become rudimentary and in their place broad leafy flaps are developed, which protrude laterally from the tip and constitute the stigmas. Ordinarily these altered organs are sterile, but in some instances a very small quantity of seed is produced, and when testing their viability I succeeded in raising a few plants from them.

The same anomaly occurs in other plants. The common wall-flower (*Cheiranthus Cheiri*) and the houseleek (*Sempervivum tectorum*) are the best known instances. Both have repeatedly been described by various investigators. In compiling the literature of this subject it is very interesting to observe the two contrasting views respecting the nature of this anomaly. Some writers, and among them Masters in his " Vegetable Teratology " consider the deviations to be merely accidental. According to them some species are more subject to this anomaly than others, and the houseleek is said to be very prone to this change. Goeppert, Hofmeister and others occasionally found the pistilloid poppies in fields or gardens, and sowed their seeds in order to ascertain whether the accidental peculiarity was inheritable or not. On the other hand De Candolle in his " Prodromus " mentions the pistilloid wall-flowers as a distinct variety, under the name of *Cheiranthus Cheiri gynantherus,* and the analogous form of the opium-poppy is not at all an accidental anomaly, but an old true horticultural variety, which can be bought everywhere under the names of *Papaver somniferum monstruosum* or *polycephalum.* Since it is an annual plant, only the seeds are for sale, and this at once gives a sufficient proof of its heredity. In all cases, where it was met with accidentally by botanists, it is to be assumed that stray seeds had been casually mixed with those of other varieties, or that the habit had been transmitted by a spontaneous cross.

Wherever opportunity led to experiments on heredity, distinct races were found to be in possession of this quality, while others were not. It is of no use to cultivate large numbers of wall-flowers in the hope of one day seeing the anomaly arise; the only means is to secure the strain from those who have got it. With poppies the various varieties are so often intercrossed by bees, that the appearance of an accidental change may sometimes be produced, and in the houseleek the pistilloid variety seems to be the ordinary one, the normal strain being very rare or perhaps wholly wanting.

Our three illustrative examples are good and permanent races, producing their peculiar qualities regularly and abundantly. In this respect they are however very variable and dependent on external circumstances. Such a regularity is not met with in other instances. Often pedigree-experiments lead to poor races, betraying their tendency to deviate only from time to time and in rare cases. Such instances constitute what we have called in a former lecture, "half-races," and their occurrence indicates that the casual observation of an anomaly is not in itself adequate to give an opinion as to the chance of repetition in sowing experiments. A large number of species seem to belong to this case, and their names may be found in the above mentioned work by Masters and elsewhere. But no effort has yet been made to separate thoroughly the pistilloid half-races from the corresponding ever-sporting varieties. Some plants are recorded as being more liable to this peculiarity than others.

Stamens are sometimes replaced by open carpels with naked ovules arising from their edges and even from their whole inner surfaces. This may be seen in distinct strains of the cultivated bulbous *Begonia,* and more rarely in primroses. Here the apex of the carpellary leaf is sometimes drawn out into a long style, terminated by a flattened spatulate stigma.

The pistillody of the stamens is frequently

combined with another deviation in the poppies. This is the growing together of some of the altered stamens so as to constitute smaller or larger connate groups. Often two are united, sometimes three, four or more. Flowers with numerous altered stamens are seldom wholly free from this most undesirable secondary anomaly. I call it undesirable with respect to experiments on the variability of the character. For it may easily be seen that while it is feasible to count the stamens even when converted into pistils, it is not possible when groups of them are more or less intimately united into single bodies. This combination makes all enumeration difficult and inaccurate and often wholly unreliable. In such cases the observation is limited to a computation of the degree of the change, rather than to a strict numerical inquiry. Happily the responses to the experimental influences are so marked and distinct that even this method of describing them has proved to be wholly sufficient.

In extreme instances I have seen all the changed stamens of a flower of the opium-poppy united into a single body, so as to form a close sheath all around the central ovary. Lesser sheaths, surrounding one-half or one-third of the capsule are of course less rarely met with.

Leaving this description of the outer appearance of our anomaly, we may now consider it from the double point of view of inheritance and variability.

The fact of inheritance is shown by the experience of many authors, and by the circumstance already quoted, that the variety has been propagated from seed for more than half a century, and may be obtained from various seed-merchants. In respect to the variability, the variety belongs to the ever-sporting group, constituting a type which is more closely related to the "five-leaved" clover than to the striped flowers or even the double stocks.

It fluctuates around an average type with half filled crowns, going as far as possible in both directions, but never transgressing either limit. It is even doubtful whether the presumable limits are, under ordinary circumstances, ever reached. Obviously one extreme would be the conversion of all the stamens, and the other the absolute deficiency of any marked tendency to such a change. Both may occur, and will probably be met with from time to time. But they must be extremely rare, since in my own extensive experiments, which were strictly controlled, I never was able to find a single instance of either of them. Some of the outer stamens have always remained unchanged, yielding enough pollen for the artificial pollination of the central ovary, and on the other hand some rudiments of hardened filaments were always left, even if they were reduced to small protuberances on the thalamus of the flower.

Between these extremes all grades occur. From single, partially or wholly changed stamens upwards to 150 and over, all steps may be seen. It is a true fluctuating variability. There is an average of between 50 and 100, constituting a nearly filled crown around the central capsule. Around this average the smaller deviations are most numerous and the larger ones more rare. The inspection of any bed of the variety suffices to show that, taken broadly, the ordinary laws of fluctuating variability are applicable. No counting of the single individuals is required to dispel all doubts on this point.

Moreover all intermediate steps respecting the conversion of the single stamens may nearly always be seen. Rarely all are changed into normal secondary ovaries with a stigma and with a cavity filled with ovules. Often the stigma is incomplete or even almost wanting, in other instances the ovules are lacking or the cavity itself is only partially developed. Not rarely some stamens are reduced and converted into thin hard stalks, without any appearance of an ovary at their tip. But then the demarcation between them and the thalamus fails, so that they cannot be thrown off when the flower fades away, but remain as small stumps around the base of the more fully converted filaments. This fact would frequently render the enumeration of the altered organs quite unreliable.

For these reasons I have chosen a group of arbitrary stages in order to express the degree of deviation for a given lot of plants. The limits were chosen so as to be sufficiently trustworthy and easy to ascertain. In each group the members could be counted, and a series of figures was reached by this means which allowed of a further comparison of the competing sets of plants.

It should be stated that in such experiments and especially in the case of such a showy criterion as the pistilloid heads afford after the time of flowering is over, the inspection of the controlling beds at once indicates the result of the experiment. Even a hasty survey is in most cases sufficient to get a definite conclusion. Where this is not the case, the counting of the individuals of the various groups often does not add to the evidence, and the result remains uncertain. On the other hand, the impression made by the groups of plants on the experimenter and on his casual visitors, cannot well be conveyed to the readers of his account by other means than by figures. For this reason the result of the experiments is expressed in this way.

I made six groups. The first includes the cases where the whole circle is reduced to small rudiments. The second shows 1 – 10 secondary capsules. The two following constitute half a crown around the central fruit, the third going up to this limit, the fourth going from this limit to a nearly filled circle. Wholly filled circles of secondary capsules without gaps give the two last degrees, the fifth requiring only continuity of the circle, the sixth displaying a large and bright crown all around the central head. The fifth group ordinarily includes from 90 – 100 altered stamens, while the sixth has from 100 – 150 of these deviating parts.

In ordinary cultures the third and fourth group, with their interrupted crowns, predominate. Large crowns are rare and flowers which at first sight seem to be wholly normal, occur only under circumstances definitely known to be unfavorable to growth, and to the development of the anomaly.

Having reached by this means a very simple and easy method of stating the facts shown by equal lots under contrasting influences, we will now make use of it to inquire into the relation of this exceptionally high degree of variability to the inner and outer conditions of life.

As a rule, all experiments show the existence of such a relation. Unfavorable conditions reduce the numbers of altered stamens, favorable circumstances raise it to its highest point. This holds true for lots including hundreds of specimens, but also for the sundry heads of one bed, and often for one single plant.

We may compare the terminal flower with those of the lateral branches on a plant, and when no special influences disturb the experiment, the terminal head ordinarily bears the richest crown. If the first has more than 100 metamorphosed parts, the latter have often less than 50 on the same plant. In poor soil, terminal heads are often reduced to 10 – 20 monstrous organs, and in such cases I found the lateral flowers of the same plants ordinarily with less than 10 altered stamens. In some cases I allowed the branches of the third and fourth degree, in other words, the side twigs of the first branches of my selected plants to grow out and produce flowers in the fall. They were ordinarily weak, sometimes very small, having only 5 – 9 stigmas on their central fruit. Secondary capsules were not seen on such flowers, even when the experiment was repeated on a somewhat larger scale and during a series of years.

Among the same lot of plants individual differences almost always occur. They are partly due to inequalities already existing in the seeds, and partly to the diversity of the various parts of the same bed. Some of the plants become stout and have large terminal heads. Others remain very weak, with a slender stem, small leaves and undersized flowers. The height and thickness of the stem, the growth of the foliage and of the axillary buds are the most obvious measures of the individual strength of the plant. The development of the terminal flower and the size of its ovary manifestly depends largely on this individual strength, as may be seen at once by the inspection of any bed of opium-poppies. Now this size of the head can easily be measured, either by its height or circumference, or by its weight. Moreover we can arrange them into a series according to their size. If we do this with the polycephalous variety, the relation between individual strength and degree of metamorphosis at once becomes manifest. The largest heads have the brightest crowns, and the number of supernumerary carpels diminishes in nearly exact proportion to the size of the fruits. Fruits with less than 50 altered stamens weighed on an average 5 grams, those with 50 – 100 such organs 7 grams and those with a bright crown 10 grams, the appendices being removed before the weighing. Corresponding results have been reached by the comparison of the height of the capsules with their abnormal surroundings. The degree of development of the monstrosity is shown by this observation to be directly dependent on, and in a sense proportionate to the individual strength of the plant.

The differences between the specimens grown from a single lot of seeds, for instance from the seeds of one self-fertilized capsule are, as I have said, partly due to the divergences which are always present in a bed, even if the utmost care has been taken to make it as uniform as possible. These local differences are ordinarily underrated and overlooked, and it is often considered to be sufficient to cultivate small lots of plants under apparently similar conditions on neighboring beds, to be justified in imputing all the observed deviations of the plants to hereditary inequalities. This of course is true for large lots, whenever the averages only are compared. In smaller experiments the external conditions of the single individuals should always be considered carefully. Lots of one or two square meters suffice for such comparisons, but smaller lots are always subject to chances and possibilities, which should never be left out of consideration.

Therefore I will now point out some circumstances, which are ordinarily different on various parts of one and the same bed.

In the first place comes the inequality of the seeds themselves. Some of them will germinate earlier and others later. Those that display their cotyledons on a sunny day will be able to begin at once with the production of organic food. Others appear in bad weather, and will thus be retarded in their development. These effects are of a cumulative nature as the young plants must profit by every hour of sunshine, according to the size of the cotyledons. Any inequality between two young seedlings is apt to be increased by this cumulative effect.

The same holds good for the soil of the bed. It is simply impossible to mix the manure so equally that all individuals receive the same amount of it from the very beginning. I am in the habit of using manures in a dry and pulverized condition, of giving definite quantities to each square meter, and of taking the utmost care to get equal distribution and mixture with the soil, always being present myself during this most important operation. Nevertheless it is impossible to make the nourishment exactly equal for all the plants of even a small bed.

Any inequality from this cause will increase the difference in the size of the young leaves, augment the inequality of their production of organic matter and for this reason go on in an ever increasing rate.

Rain and spraying, or on the other hand dryness of the soil, have still greater consequences. The slightest unevenness of the surface will cause some spots to dry rapidly and others to retain moisture during hours and even sometimes during days.

Seeds, germinating in such little moist depressions grow regularly and rapidly, while those on the dryer elevations may be retarded for hours and days, before fully unfurling their seed-leaves. After heavy rains these differences may be observed to increase continually, and in some instances I found that plants were produced only on the wet spots, while the dry places remained perfectly bare. From this the wet spots seem to be the most favorable, but on the other hand, seeds may come to germinate there too numerously and so closely that the young plants will be crowded together and find neither space nor light enough, for a free and perfect development. The advantage may change to disadvantage in this way unless the superfluous individuals are weeded out in due time.

From all these and other reasons some plants will be favored by the external conditions from the beginning, while others will be retarded, and the effects will gradually increase until at last they become sufficient to account for a considerable amount of individual variability. There is no doubt that the difference in the strength of the plant and in the size of the capsules, going from 5 – 10 grams for a single fruit, are for the most part due to these unavoidable circumstances. I have tried all conceivable means to find remedies for these difficulties, but only by sowing my seeds in pans in a glass-house have I been able to reach more constant and equal conditions. But unfortunately such a method requires the planting out of the young seedlings in the beginning of the summer, and this operation is not without danger for opium-poppies, and especially not without important influence on the monstrosity of the pistilloid variety. Consequently my sowings of this plant have nearly always been made in the beds.

In order to show how great the influence of all these little things may become, we only have to make two sowings on neighboring beds and under conditions which have carefully been made as equal as possible. If we use for these controlling experiments seeds from one and the same capsule, it will soon become evident that no exact similarity between the two lots may be expected. Such differences as may be seen in these cases are therefore never to be considered of value when comparing two lots of seeds of different origin, or under varying conditions. No amount of accuracy in the estimation of the results of a trial, or in the counting out of the several degrees of the anomaly, is adequate to overcome the inaccuracy resulting from these differences.

It is certainly of great importance to have a correct conception in regard to the influence of the surrounding conditions on the growth of a plant and on the development of the attribute we are to deal with. No less important is the question of the sensibility of the plants to these factors. Obviously this sensibility must not be expected to remain the same during the entire life-period, and periods of stronger and of weaker responses may be discerned.

In the first place it is evident that external or inner influences are able to change the direction of the development of an organ only so long as this development is not yet fully finished. In the young flower-bud of the pistilloid poppy there must evidently be some moment in which it is definitely decided whether the young stamens will grow out normally or become metamorphosed into secondary pistils. From this moment no further change of external conditions is able to produce a corresponding change in the degree of the anomaly. The individual strength of the whole plant may still be affected in a more or less manifest degree, but the number of converted stamens of the flower has been definitely fixed. The sensitive period has terminated.

In order to determine the exact moment of this termination of the period of sensibility, I have followed the development of the flower-buds during the first weeks of the life of the young plants. The terminal flower may already be seen in young plants only seven weeks old, with a stem not exceeding 5 – 6 cm. in height and a flower-bud with a diameter of nearly 1mm., in which the stamens and secondary pistils are already discernible, but still in the condition of small rounded protuberances on the thalamus. Though it is not possible at that time to observe any difference between the future normal and converted stamens, it does not seem doubtful that the development is so far advanced, that in the inner tissues the decision has already definitely been taken. In the next few days this decision rapidly becomes visible, and the different parts of the normal stamens and the metamorphosed carpels soon become apparent. From this observation it can be inferred that the sensitive period of the anomaly is limited for the terminal flower-head, to the first few weeks of the life of the young plants. The secondary heads manifestly leave this period at a somewhat later stage.

In order to prove the accuracy of this conclusion I have tried to injure the anomalies after the expiration of the first six or seven weeks. I deprived them of their leaves, and damaged them in different ways. I succeeded in making them very weak and slender, without being able to diminish the number of the supernumerary carpels. The proportionality of the size of the central fruit and the development of the surrounding crown can often be modified or even destroyed by this means, and the apparent exceptions from this rule, which are often observed, may find their explanation in this way.

In the second place I have tried to change the development of the anomaly during the period of sensibility, and even in the last part of it. This experiment succeeded fully when carried out within the fifth or sixth week after the beginning of the germination. As means of injury I transplanted the young plants. To this end I sowed my seeds in pans in unmanured soil, planted them out in little pots with richly prepared earth, grew them in these during a few weeks and afterwards transferred them to the beds, taking care that the pots were removed, but the balls of earth not broken.

In consequence of this treatment the plants became very large and strong, with luxuriant foliage and relatively numerous large flowers and fruits. But almost without exception they were poor in anomalous stamens, at least so on the terminal heads. On a lot of some 70 plants more than 50 had less than half a crown of secondary capsules, while from the same packet of seed the control-plants gave in an equal number more than half of filled crowns on all plants with the exception of five weak specimens.

It is curious to compare such artificially injured plants with the ordinary cultures. Strong stems and heavy fruits, which otherwise are always indicative of showy crowns, now bear fruits wholly or nearly destitute of any anomalous change. The commonly prevailing rule seems to be reversed, showing thereby the possibility of abolishing the correlation between individual strength and anomaly by an artificial encroachment upon the normal conditions.

Aside from these considerations the experiments clearly give proof of the existence of a period of sensibility limited to the first weeks of the life of the plant for the terminal flower. This knowledge enables us to explain many apparent abnormalities, which may occur in the experiments.

We now may take a broader view of the period of sensibility. Evidently the response to external influences will be greater the younger the organ. Sensibility will gradually diminish, and the phenomena observed in the last part of this period may be considered as the last remainder of a reaction which previously must have been much stronger and much readier, providing that it would be possible to isolate them from, and contrast them with, the other responses of the same plant.

With the light thus cast upon the question, we may conclude that the sensitive period commences not only at the beginning of the germination, but must also be considered to include the life of the seed itself. From the moment of fertilization and the formation of the young embryo the development must be subjected to the influence of external agencies which determine the direction it will take and the degree of development it will finally be able to acquire. Probably the time of growth of the embryo and of the ripening of the seed correspond exactly to the period of highest sensibility. This period is only interrupted during the resting stage of the seed, to be repeated in germination. Afterwards the sensibility slowly and gradually decreases, to end with the definite decision of all further growth sometime before the outer form of the organ becomes visible under the microscope. The last period of life includes only an expansion of the tissues, which may still have some influence on their final size, but not on their form. This has been definitely arrested before the end of the sensitive period, and ordinarily before the commencement of that rapid development, which is usually designated by the name of growth, as contrasted with evolution.

Within the seed the evolution of the young plant manifestly depends upon the qualities and life-conditions of the parent-plant. The stronger this is, and the more favorable circumstances it is placed under, the more food will be available for the seed, and the healthier will be the development of the embryo. Only well-nourished plants give well-nourished seeds, and the qualities of each plant are for this reason at least, partly dependent on the properties of its parents and even of its grandparents.

From these considerations the inference is forced upon us that the apparently hereditary differences, which are observed to exist among the seeds of a species or a variety and even of a single strain or a single parent-plant, may for a large part, and perhaps wholly, be the result of the life-conditions of their parents and grandparents. Within the race all variability would in this way be reduced to the effects of external circumstances. Among these nourishment is no doubt the most momentous, and this to such a degree that older writers designated the external conditions by the term nourishment. According to Knight nutrition reigns supreme in the whole realm of variability, the kind of food and the method of nourishment coming into consideration only in a secondary way. The amount of useful nutrition is the all-important factor.

If this is so, and if nutrition decides the degree of deviation of any given character, the widest deviating individuals are the best nourished ones. The best nourished not only during the period of sensibility of the attribute under consideration, but also in the broadest sense of the word.

This discussion casts a curious light upon the whole question of selection. Not of course upon the choice of elementary species or varieties out of the original motley assembly which nature and old cultures offer us, but upon the selection of the best individuals for isolation and for the improvement of the race. These are, according to my views, only the best nourished ones. Their external conditions have been the most favorable, not only from the beginning of their own life in the field, but also during their embryonic stages, and even during the preparation of these latter in the life of their parents and perhaps even their grandparents. Selection then, would only be the choice of the best nourished individuals.

In connection with the foregoing arguments I have tried to separate the choicest of the poppies with the largest crown of pistilloid stamens, from the most vigorous individuals. As we have already seen, these two attributes are as a rule proportional to one another. Exceptions occur, but they may be explained by some later changes in the external circumstances, as I have also pointed out. As a rule, these exceptions are large fruits with comparatively too few converted stamens; they are exactly the contrary from what is required for a selection. Or plants, which from the beginning were robust, may have become crowded together by further growth, and for these reasons become weaker than their congeners, though retaining the full development of the staminodal crown, which was fixed during the sensitive period and before the crowding. I have searched my beds yearly for several years in vain to find individuals which might recommend themselves for selection without having the stamp of permanent, or at least temporarily better, nourishment. No starting-point for such an independent selection has ever been met with.

Summing up the consequences of this somewhat extended discussion, we may state it as a rule that a general proportion between the individual strength and the degree of development of the anomaly exists. And from this point of view it is easy to see that all external causes which are known to affect the one, must be expected to influence the other also.

It will therefore hardly be necessary to give a full description of all my experiments on the relations of the monstrosity to external conditions. A hasty survey will suffice.

This survey is not only intended to convey an idea of the relations of pistilloid poppies to their environment, but may serve as an example of the principle involved. According to my experience with a large range of other anomalies, the same rule prevails everywhere. And this rule is so simple that exact knowledge of one instance may be considered as sufficient to enable us to calculate from analogy what is to be expected from a given treatment of any other anomaly. Our appreciation of observed facts and the conditions to be chosen for intended cultures are largely dependent on such calculations. What I am now going to describe is to be considered therefore as an experimental basis for such expectations.

First of all comes the question how many individuals are to be grown in a given place. When sowing plants for experimental purposes it is always best to sow in rows, and to give as few seeds to each row as possible, so as to insure all necessary space to the young plants. On the other hand the seeds do not all germinate, and after sowing too thinly, gaps may appear in the rows. This would cause not only a loss of space, but an inequality between the plants in later life, as those nearest the gaps would have more space and more light, and a larger area for their roots than those growing in the unbroken rows. Hence the necessity of using large quantities of seed and of weeding out a majority of young plants on the spots where the greatest numbers germinate.

Crowded cultures as a rule, will give weak plants with thin stems, mostly unbranched and bearing only small capsules. According to the rule, these will produce imperfect crowns of secondary pistils. The result of any culture will thus be dependent to a high degree on the number of individuals per square meter. I have sown two similar and neighboring beds with the thoroughly mixed seeds of parent-plants of the same strain and culture, using as much as 2.5 cub. cm. per square meter. On one of the beds I left all the germinating plants untouched and nearly 500 of them flowered, but among them 360 were almost without pistillody, and only 10 had full crowns. In the other bed I weeded away more than half of the young plants, leaving only some 150 individuals and got 32 with a full crown, nearly 100 with half crowns and only 25 apparently without monstrosity.

These figures are very striking. From the same quantity of seed, in equal spaces, by similar exposure and treatment I got 10 fully developed instances in one and 32 in the other case. The weeding out of supernumerary individuals had not only increased the percentage of bright crowns, but also their absolute number per square meter. So the greatest number of anomalies upon a given space may be obtained by taking care that not too many plants are grown upon it: any increase of the number beyond a certain limit will diminish the probability of obtaining these structures. The most successful cultures may be made after the maximum number of individuals per unit of area has been determined. A control-experiment was made under the same conditions and with the same seed, but allowing much less for the same space. I sowed only 1 cu. cm. on my bed of 2 square meters, and thereby avoided nearly all weeding out. I got 120 plants, and among them 30 with full crowns of converted stamens, practically the same number as after the weeding out in the first experiment. This shows that smaller quantities of seed give an equal chance for a greater number of large crowns, and should therefore always be preferred, as it saves both seed and labor.

Weeding out is a somewhat dangerous operation in a comparative trial. Any one who has done it often, knows that there is a strong propensity to root out the weaker plants and to spare the stronger ones. Obviously this is the best way for ordinary purposes, but for comparisons evidently one should not discriminate. This rule is very difficult in practice, and for this reason one should never sow more than is absolutely required to meet all requirements.

Our second point is the manuring of the soil. This is always of the highest importance, both for normal and for anomalous attributes. The conversion of the stamens into pistils is in a large measure dependent upon the conditions of the soil. I made a trial with some 800 flowering plants, using one sample of seed, but sowing one-third on richly manured soil, one-third on an unprepared bed of my garden, and one-third on nearly pure sand. In all other respects the three groups were treated in the same way. Of the manured plants one-half gave full crowns, of the non-manured only one-fifth, and on the sandy soil a still smaller proportion. Other trials led to the same results. I have often made use of steamed and ground horn, which is a manure very rich in nitrogenous substances. One-eighth of a kilo per square meter is an ample amount. And its effect was to increase the number of full crowns to an exceptional degree.

In the controlling trial and under ordinary circumstances this figure reached some 50%, but with ground horn it came up as high as 90%. We may state this result by the very striking assertion that the number of large crowns in a given culture may be nearly doubled by rich manure.

All other external conditions act in a similar manner. The best treatment is required to attain the best result. A sunny exposure is one of the most essential requisites, and in some attempts to cultivate my poppies in the shade, I found the pistillody strongly reduced, not a single full crown being found in the whole lot. Often the weather may be hurtful, especially during the earlier stages of the plants. I protected my beds during several trials by covering them with glass for a few weeks, until the young plants reached the glass covering. I got a normal number of full crowns, some 55%, at a time when the weather was so bad as to reduce the number in the control experiments to 10%.

It would be quite superfluous to give more details or to describe additional experiments. Suffice to say, that the results all point in the same direction, and that pistillody of the poppies always clearly responds to the treatment, especially to external conditions during the first few weeks, that is, during the period of sensitiveness. The healthier and the stronger the plants the more fully they will develop their anomaly.

In conclusion something is to be said about the choice of the seed. Obviously it is possible to compare seeds of different origin by sowing and treating them in the same way, giving attention to all the points above mentioned. In doing so the first question will be, whether there is a difference between the seeds of strong plants with a bright crown around the head and those of weaker individuals with lesser development of the anomaly. It is evident that such a difference must be expected, since the nutrition of the seed takes place during the period of the greatest sensitiveness.

But the experiments will show whether this effect holds good against the influences which tend to change the direction of the development of the anomaly during the time of germination.

The result of my attempt has shown that the choice of the seeds has a manifest influence upon the ultimate development of the monstrosity, but that this influence is not strong enough to overwhelm all other factors.

The choice of the fullest or smallest crowns may be repeated during succeeding generations, and each time compared with a culture under average conditions. By this means we come to true selection-experiments, and these result in a notable and rapid change of the whole strain. By selecting the brightest crowns I have come up in three years from 40 to 90 and ultimately to 120 converted stamens in the best flower of my culture, and in selecting the smallest crowns I was able in three years to exclude nearly all good crowns, and to make cultures in which heads with less than half-filled crowns constituted the majority. But such selected strains always remain very sensitive to treatment, and by changing the conditions the effect may be wholly lost in a single year, or even turned in the contrary direction. In other words, the anomaly is more dependent on external conditions during the germinating period than on the choice of the seeds, providing these belong to the pistilloid variety and have not deteriorated by some crossing with other sorts.

At the beginning of this lecture I stated that

no selection is adequate to produce either a pure strain of brightly crowned flower-heads without atavism, or to conduce to an absolute and permanent loss of the anomaly. During a series of years I have tested my plants in both directions, but without the least effect. Limits are soon reached on both sides, and to transgress these seems quite impossible.

Taking these limits as the marks of the variety, and considering all fluctuations between them as responses to external influences working during the life of the individual or governing the ripening of the seeds, we get a clear picture of a permanent ever-sporting type. The limits are absolutely permanent during the whole existence of this already old variety. They never change. But they include so wide a range of variability that the extremes may be said to sport into one another, so much the more so as one of the extremes is to be considered morphologically as the type of the variation, while the other extreme can hardly be distinguished from the normal form of the species.

Lecture XIV

MONSTROSITIES

I have previously dealt with the question of the hereditary tendencies that cause monstrosities. These tendencies are not always identical for the same anomaly. Two different types may, generally, be distinguished. One of them constitutes a poor variety, the other a rich one. But this latter is abundant and the first one is poor in instances of exactly the same conformation. Therefore the difference only lies in the frequency of the anomaly, and not in its visible features. In discovering an instance of any anomaly it is therefore impossible to tell whether it belongs to a poor or to a rich race. This important question can only be answered by direct sowing-experiments to determine the degree of heredity.

Monstrosities are often considered as accidents, and rightfully so, at least as long as they are considered from a morphological point of view. Physiology of course excludes all accidentality. And in our present case it shows that some internal hereditary quality is present, though often latent, and that the observed anomalies are to be regarded as responses of this innate tendency to external conditions. Our two types differ in the frequency of these responses. Rare in the poor race, they are numerous in the rich variety. The external conditions being the same for both, the hereditary factor must be different. The tendency is weak in the one and strong in the other. In both cases, according to my experience, it may be weakened or strengthened by selection and by treatment. Often to a very remarkable degree, but not so far as to transgress the limits between the two races. Such transgression may apparently be met with from time to time, but then the next generation generally shows the fallacy of the conclusion, as it returns more or less directly to the type from which the strain had been derived.

Monstrosities should always be studied by physiologists from this point of view. Poor and rich strains of the same anomaly seem at first sight to be so nearly allied that it might be thought to be very easy to change the one into the other. Nevertheless such changes are not on record, and although I have made several attempts in this line, I never succeeded in passing the limit. I am quite convinced that sometime a method will be discovered of arbitrarily producing such conversions, and perhaps the easiest way to attain artificial mutations may lie concealed here. But as yet not the slightest indication of this possibility is to be found, save the fallacious conclusions drawn from too superficial observations.

Unfortunately the poor strains are not very interesting. Their chance of producing beautiful instances of the anomaly for which they are cultivated is too small. Exceptions to this rule are only afforded by those curious and rare anomalies, which command general attention, and of which, therefore, instances are always welcome. In such cases they are searched for with perseverance, and the fact of their rarity impresses itself strongly on our mind.

Twisted stems are selected as a first example. This monstrosity, called *biastrepsis,* consists of strongly marked torsions as are seen in many species with decussate leaves, though as a rule it is very rare. Two instances are the most generally known, those of the wild valerian (*Valeriana officinalis*) and those of cultivated and wild sorts of teasels (*Dipsacus fullonum, D. sylvestris,* and others). Both of these I have cultivated during upwards of fifteen years, but with contradictory results. The valerian is a perennial herb, multiplying itself yearly by slender rootstocks or runners producing at their tips new rosettes of leaves and in the center of these the flowering stem. My original plant has since been propagated in this manner, and during several years I preserved large beds with hundreds of stems, in others I was compelled to keep my culture within more restricted limits. This plant has produced twisted stems of the curious shape, with a nearly straight flag of leaves on one side, described by De Candolle and other observers, nearly every year. But only one or two instances of abnormal stems occurred in each year, and no treatment has been found that proved adequate to increase this number in any appreciable manner. I have sown the seeds of this plant repeatedly, either from normal or from twisted stems, but without better results. It was highly desirable to be able to offer instances of this rare and interesting peculiarity to other universities and museums, but no improvement of the race could be reached and I have been constrained to give it up. My twisted valerian is a poor race, and hardly anything can be done with it. Perhaps, in other countries the corresponding rich race may be hidden somewhere, but I have never had the good fortune of finding it.

This good fortune however, I did have with the wild teasel or *Dipsacus sylvestris*. Twisted stems of this and of allied species are often met with and have been described by several writers, but they were always considered as accidents and nobody had ever tried to cultivate them. In the summer of 1885 I saw among a lot of normal wild teasels, two nicely twisted stems in the botanical garden of Amsterdam. I at once proposed to ascertain whether they would yield a hereditary race and had all the normal individuals thrown away before the flowering time. My two plants flowered in this isolated condition and were richly pollinated by insects. Of course, at that time, I knew nothing of the dependency of monstrosities on external conditions, and made the mistake of sowing the seeds and cultivating the next generation in too great numbers on a small space. But nevertheless the anomaly was repeated, and the aberrant individuals were once more isolated before flowering. The third generation repeated the second, but produced sixty twisted stems on some 1600 individuals. The result was very striking and quite sufficient for all further researches, but the normal condition of the race was not reached. This was the case only after I had discovered the bad effects of growing too many plants in a limited space. In the fourth generation I restricted my whole culture to about 100 individuals, and by this simple means at once got up to 34% of twisted stems. This proportion has since remained practically the same. I have selected and isolated my plants during five succeeding generations, but without any further result, the percentage of twisted stems fluctuating between 30 and about 45 according to the size of the cultures and the favorableness or unfavorableness of the weather.

It is very interesting to note that all depends on the question whether one has the good fortune of finding a rich race or not, as this pedigree-culture shows. Afterwards everything depends on treatment and very little on selection. As soon as the treatment becomes adequate, the full strength of the race at once displays itself, but afterwards no selection is able to improve it to any appreciable amount. Of course, in the long run, the responses will be the same as those of the pistilloid poppies on the average, and some influence of selection will show itself on closer scrutiny.

Compared with the polycephalous poppies my race of twisted teasels is much richer in atavists. They are never absent, and always constitute a large part of each generation and each bed, comprising somewhat more than half of the individuals. Intermediate stages between them and the wholly twisted stems are not wanting, and a whole series of steps may easily be observed from sufficiently large cultures. But they are always relatively rare, and any lot of plants conveys the idea of a dimorphous race, the small twisted stems contrasting strongly with the tall straight ones.

A sharper contrast between good representatives of a race and their atavists is perhaps to be seen in no other instance. All the details contribute to the differentiation in appearance. The whole stature of the plants is affected by the varietal mark. The atavists are not, as in the case of the poppies, obviously allied with the type by a full range of intermediate steps, but quite distant from it by their rarity. There seems to be a gap in the same way as between the striped flowers of the snapdragon and their uniform red atavists, while with the poppies the atavists may be viewed as being only the extremes of a series of variations fluctuating around some average type.

From this reason it is as interesting to appreciate the hereditary position of the atavists of twisted varieties as it was for the red-flowered descendants of the striped flowers. In order to ascertain this relation it is only necessary to isolate some of them during the blooming-period. I made this experiment in the summer of 1900 with the eighth generation of my race, and contrived to isolate three groups of plants by the use of parchment bags, covering them alternately, so the flowers of only one group were accessible to insects at a time. I made three groups, because the atavists show two different types. Some specimens have decussate stems, others bear all their leaves in whorls of three, but in respect to the hereditary tendency of the twisting character this difference does not seem to be of any importance.

In this way I got three lots of seeds and sowed enough of them to have three groups of plants each containing about 150 – 200 well developed stems. Among these I counted the twisted individuals, and found nearly the same numbers for all three. The twisted parents gave as many as 41% twisted children, but the decussate atavists gave even somewhat more, viz., 44%, while the ternate specimens gave 37%. Obviously the divergencies between these figures are too slight to be dwelt upon, but the fact that the atavists are as true or nearly as true inheritors of the twisted race as the best selected individuals is clearly proved by this experience.

It is evident that here we have a double race, including two types, which may be combined in different degrees. These combinations determine a wide range of changes in the stature of the plants, and it seems hardly right to use the same term for such changes as for common variations. It is more a contention of opposite characters than a true phenomenon of simple variability. Or perhaps we might say that it is the effect of the cooperation of a very variable mark, the twisting, with a scarcely varying attribute of the normal structure of the stem. Between the two types an endless diversity prevails, but outwardly there are limits which are never transgressed. The double race is as permanent, and in this sense as constant, as any ordinary simple variety, both in external form, and in its intimate hereditary qualities.

I have succeeded in discovering some other rich races of twisted plants. One of them is the Sweet William (*Dianthus barbatus*), which yielded, after isolation, in the second generation, 25% of individuals with twisted stems, and as each individual produces often 10 and more stems, I had a harvest of more than half a thousand of instances of this curious, and ordinarily very rare anomaly. My other race is a twisted variety of *Viscaria oculata*, which is still in cultivation, as it has the very consistent quality of being an annual. It yielded last summer (1903) as high a percentage as 65 of twisted individuals, many of them repeating the monstrosity on several branches. After some occasional observations *Gypsophila pani-*

culata seems to promise similar results. On the other hand I have sowed in vain the seeds of twisted specimens of the soapwort and the cleavewort (*Saponaria officinalis* and *Galium Aparine*). These and some others seems to belong to the same group as the valerian and to constitute only poor or so-called half-races.

Next to the torsions come the fasciated stems. This is one of the most common of all malformations, and consists, in its ordinary form, of a flat ribbon-like expansion of the stems or branches. Below they are cylindrical, but they gradually lose this form and assume a flattened condition. Sometimes the rate of growth is unequal on different portions or on the opposite sides of the ribbon, and curvatures are produced and these often give to the fasciation a form that might be compared with a shepherd's crook. It is a common thing for fasciated branches and stems to divide at the summit into a number of subdivisions, and ordinarily this splitting occurs in the lower part, sometimes dividing the entire fasciated portion. In biennial species the rosette of the root-leaves of the first year may become changed by the monstrosity, the heart stretching in a transverse direction so as to become linear. In the next year this line becomes the base from which the stem grows. In such cases the fasciated stems are broadened and flattened from the very beginning, and often retain the incipient breadth throughout their further development. Species of primroses (*Primula japonica* and others), of buttercups (*Ranunculus bulbosus*), the rough hawksbeard (*Crepis biennis*), the *Aster Tripolium* and many others could be given as instances.

Some of these are so rare as to be considered as poor races, and in cultural trials do not produce the anomaly except in a very few instances. Heads of rye are found in a cleft condition from time to time, single at their base and double at the top, but this anomaly is only exceptionally repeated from seed. Flattened stems of *Rubia tinctorum* are not unfrequently met with on the fields, but they seem to have as little hereditary tendency as the split rye (*Secale Cereale*). Many other instances could be given. Both in the native localities and in pedigree-cultures such ribboned stems are only seen from time to time, in successive years, in annual and biennial as well as in perennial species. The purple pedicularis (*Pedicularis palustris*) in the wild state, and the sunflower among cultivated plants, may be cited instead of giving a long list of analogous instances.

On the other hand rich races of flattened stems are not entirely lacking. They easily betray themselves by the frequency of the anomaly, and therefore may be found, and tried in the garden. Under adequate cultivation they are here as rich in aberrant individuals as the twisted races quoted above, producing in good years from 30 – 40% and often more instances. I have cultivated such rich races of the dandelion (*Taraxacum officinale*), of *Thrincia hirta,* of the dame's violet (*Hesperis matronalis*), of the hawkweed (*Picris hieracioides*), of the rough hawksbeard (*Crepis biennis*), and others.

Respecting the hereditary tendencies these rich varieties with flattened stems may be put in the same category with the twisted races. Two points however, seem to be of especial interest and to deserve a separate treatment.

The common cockscomb or *Celosia cristata,* one of the oldest and most widely cultivated fasciated varieties may be used to illustrate the first point. In beds it is often to be seen in quite uniform lots of large and beautiful crests, but this uniformity is only secured by careful culture and selection of the best individuals. In experimental trials such selection must be avoided, and in doing so a wide range of variability at once shows itself. Tall, branched stems with fan-shaped tops arise, constituting a series of steps towards complete atavism. This last however, is not to be reached easily. It often requires several successive generations grown from seed collected from the most atavistic specimens. And even such selected strains are always reverting to the crested type. There is no transgression, no springing over into a purely atavistic form, such as may be supposed to have once been the ancestor of the present cockscomb. The variety includes crests and atavists, and may be perpetuated from both. Obviously every gardener would select the seeds of the brightest crests, but with care the full crests may be recovered, even from the worst reversionists in two or three generations. It is a double race of quite the same constitution as the twisted teasels.

My second point is a direct proof of this assertion, but made with a fasciated variety of a wild species. I took for my experiment the rough hawksbeard. In the summer of 1895 I isolated some atavists of the fifth generation of my race, which, by ordinary selection, gave in the average from 20 – 40% of fasciated stems. My isolated atavists bore abundant fruit, and from these I had the next year a set of some 350 plants, out of which about 20% had broadened and linear rosettes. This proportion corresponds with the degree of inheritance which is shown in many years by the largest and strongest fasciated stems. It strengthens our conclusion as to the innermost constitution of the double races or ever-sporting varieties.

Twisted stems and fasciations are very striking monstrosities. But they are not very good for further investigation. They require too much space and too much care. The calculation of a single percentage requires the counting of some hundreds of individuals, taking many square meters for their cultivation, and this, as my best races are biennial, during two years. For this reason the countings must always be very limited, and selection is restrained to the most perfect specimens.

Now the question arises, whether this mark is the best upon which to found selection. This seems to be quite doubtful. In the experiments on the heredity of the atavists, we have seen that they are, at least often, in no manner inferior to even the best inheritors of the race. This suggests the idea that it is not at all certain that the visible characters of a given individual are a trustworthy measure of its value as to the transmission of the same character to the offspring. In other words, we are confronted with the existence of two widely different groups of characters in estimating the hereditary tendency. One is the visible quality of the individuals and the other is the direct observation of the degree in which the attribute is transmitted. These are by no means parallel, and seem in some sense to be nearly independent of each other. The fact that the worst atavists may have the highest percentage of varietal units seems to leave no room for another explanation.

Developing this line of thought, we gradually arrive at the conclusion that the visible attribute of a varying individual is perhaps the most untrustworthy and the most unreliable character for selection, even if it seems in many cases practically to be the only available one. The direct determination of the degree of heredity itself is obviously preferable by far. This degree is expressed by the proportion of its inheritors among the offspring, and this figure therefore should be elevated to the highest rank, as a measure of the hereditary qualities. Henceforward we will designate it by the name of *hereditary percentage*.

In scientific experiments this figure must be determined for every plant of a pedigree-culture singly, and the selection should be founded exclusively or at least mainly on it. It is easily seen that this method requires large numbers of individuals to be grown and counted. Some two or three hundred progeny of one plant are needed to give the decisive figure for this one individual, and selection requires the comparison of at least fifty or more individuals. This brings the total amount of specimens to be counted up to some tens of thousands. In practice, where important interests depend upon the experiments, such numbers are usually employed and often exceeded, but for the culture of monstrosities, other methods are to be sought in order to avoid these difficulties.

The idea suggests itself here that the younger the plants are, when showing their distinguishing marks, the more of them may be grown on a small space. Hence the best way is to choose such attributes, as may already be seen in the young seedlings, in the very first few weeks of their lives. Fortunately the seed-leaves themselves afford such distinctive marks, and by this means the plants may be counted in the pans, requiring no culture at all in the garden. Only the selected individuals need be grown to ripen their seeds, and the whole selection may be made in the spring, in the glasshouse. Instead of being very troublesome, the determination of the hereditary percentages becomes a definite reduction of the size of the experiments. Moreover it may easily be effected by any one who cares for experimental studies, but has not the means required for cultures on a larger scale. And lastly, there are a number of questions about heredity, periodicity, dependency on nourishment and other life-conditions, and even about hybridizing, which may be answered by this new method.

Seed-leaves show many deviations from the ordinary shape, especially in dicotyledonous plants. A very common aberration is the multiplication of their number, and three seed-leaves in a whorl are not rarely met with. The whorl may even consist of four, and in rare cases of five or more cotyledons. Cleft cotyledons are also to be met with, and the fissure may extend varying distances from the tips. Often all these deviations may be seen among the seedlings of one lot, and then it is obvious that together they constitute a scale of cleavages, the ternate and quaternate whorls being only cases where the cleaving has reached its greatest development. All in all it is manifest that here we are met by one type of monstrosity, but that this type allows of a wide range of fluctuating variability. For brevity's sake all these cleft and ternate, double cleft and quaternate cotyledons and even the higher grades are combined under one common name and indicated as tricotyls.

A second aberration of young seed-plants is exactly opposite to this. It consists of the union of the two seed-leaves into a single organ. This ordinarily betrays its origin by having two separate apices, but not always. Such seedlings are called syncotyledonous or syncotyls. Other monstrosities have been observed from time to time, but need not be mentioned here.

It is evident that the determination of the hereditary percentage is very easy in tricotylous or syncotylous cultures. The parent-plants must be carefully isolated while blooming. Many species pollinate themselves in the absence of bees; from these the insects are to be excluded. Others have the stamens and stigmas widely separated and have to be pollinated artificially. Still others do not lend themselves to such operations, but have to be left free to the visits of bees and of humble-bees, this being the only means of securing seed from every plant. At the time of the harvest the seeds should be gathered separately from each plant, and this precaution should also be observed in studies of the hereditary percentage at large, and in all scientific pedigree-cultures. Every lot of seeds is to be sown in a separate pan, and care must be taken to sow such quantities that three to four hundred seedlings will arise from each. As soon as they display their cotyledons, they are counted, and the number is the criterion of the parent-plant. Only parent-plants with the highest percentages are selected, and out of their seedlings some fifty or a hundred of the best ones are chosen to furnish the seeds for the next generation.

This description of the method shows that the selection is a double one. The first feature is the hereditary percentage. But then not all the seedlings of the selected parents can be planted out, and a choice has to be made. This second selection may favor the finest tricotyls, or the strongest individuals, or rely on some other character, but is unavoidable.

We now come to the description of the cultures. Starting points are the stray tricotyls which are occasionally found in ordinary sowings. In order to increase the chance of finding them, thousands of seeds of the same species must be inspected, and the range of species must be widened as much as possible.

Material for beginning such experiments is very easily obtained, and almost any large sample of seeds will be found suitable. Some tricotyls may be found among every thousand seedlings in many species, while in others ten or a hundred times as many plants must be examined to secure them, but species with absolutely pure dicotylous seeds are very rare.

The second phase of the experiment however, is not so promising. Some species are rich, and others are poor in this anomaly. This difference often indicates what may be expected from further culture. Stray tricotyls point to poor or half-races, while more frequent deviations suggest rich or double-races. In both cases however, the trial must be made, and this requires the isolation of the aberrant individuals and the determination of their hereditary percentage.

In some instances the degree of their inheritance is only a very small one. The isolated tricotyls yield 1 or 2% of inheritors, in some cases even less, or upwards to 3 or 4%. If the experiment is repeated, no amelioration is observed, and this result remains the same during a series of successive generations. In the case of *Polygonum Convolvulus,* the black bindweed, I have tried as many as six generations without ever obtaining more than 3%. With other species I have limited myself to four successive years with the same negative result, as with spinage, the Moldavian dragon-head (*Dracocephalum moldavicum*), and two species of corn catch-fly (*Silene conica* and *S. conoidea*).

Such poor races hardly afford a desirable material for further inquiries. Happily the rich races, though rare, may be discovered also from time to time. They seem to be more common among cultivated plants and horticultural as well as agricultural species may be used. Hemp and mercury (*Mercurialis annua*) among the first, snapdragon, poppies, *Phacelia, Helichrysum,* and *Clarkia* among garden-flowers may be given as instances of species containing the rich tricotylous double races.

It is very interesting to note how strong the difference is between such cases and those which only yield poor races. The rich type at once betrays itself. No repeated selection is required. The stray tricotyls themselves, that are sought out from among the original samples, give hereditary percentages of a much higher type after isolation than those quoted above. They come up to 10 – 20% and in some cases even to 40%. As may be expected, individual differences occur, and it must even be supposed that some of the original tricotyls may not be pure, but hybrids between tricotylous and dicotylous parents. These are at once eliminated by selection, and if only the tricotyls which have the highest percentages are chosen for the continuance of the new race, the second generation comes up with equal numbers of dicotyls and tricotyls among the seedlings. The figures have been observed to range from 51 – 58% in the majority of the cases, and average 55%, rarely diverging somewhat more from this average.

Here we have the true type of an ever-sporting variety. Every year it produces in the

same way heirs and atavists. Every plant, if
fertilized with its own pollen, gives rise to
both types. The parent itself may be tricotylous or dicotylous, or show any amount of
multiplication and cleavage in its seed-leaves,
but it always gives the entire range among its
progeny of the variation. One may even select
the atavists, pollinate them purely and repeat
this in a succeeding generation without any
chance of changing the result. On an average
the atavists may give lower hereditary figures,
but the difference will be only slight.

Such tricotylous double races offer highly
interesting material for inquiries into questions
of heredity, as they have such a wide range of
variability. There is little danger in asserting
that they go upwards to nearly 100%, and downwards to 0%, diverging symmetrically on both
sides of their average (50 – 55%). These limits
they obviously cannot transgress, and are not
even able to reach them. Samples of seed consisting only of tricotyls are very rare, and when
they are met with the presumption is that they
are too few to betray the rare aberrants they
might otherwise contain. Experimental evidence can only be reached by the culture of a
succeeding generation, and this always discloses
the hidden qualities, showing that the double

type was only temporarily lost, but bound to return as soon as new trials are made.

This wide range of variability between definite limits is coupled with a high degree of sensibility and adequateness to the most diverging experiments. Our tricotylous double races are perhaps more sensitive to selection than any other variety, and equally dependent on outer circumstances. Here, however, I will limit myself to a discussion of the former point.

In the second generation after the isolation of stray tricotylous seedlings the average condition of the race is usually reached, but only by some of the strongest individuals, and if we continue the race, sowing or planting only from their offspring, the next generation will show the ordinary type of variability, going upwards in some and downwards in other instances. With the *Phacelia* and the mercury and some others I had the good luck in this one generation to reach as high as nearly 90% of tricotylous seedlings, a figure indicating that the normal dicotylous type had already become rare in the race. In other cases 80% or nearly 80% was easily attained. Any further divergence from the average would have required very much larger sowings, the effect of selection between a limited number of parents being only to retain the high degree once reached; so for instance with the mercury, I had three succeeding generations of selection after reaching the average of 55%, but their extremes gave no increasing advance, remaining at 86, 92 and 91%.

If we compare these results with the effects of selection in twisted and fasciated races, we observe a marked contrast. Here they reached their height at 30 – 40%, and no number of generations had the power of making any further improvement. The tricotyls come up in two generations to a proportion of about 54%, which shows itself to correspond to the average type. And as soon as this is reached, only one generation is required to obtain a very considerable improvement, going up to 80 or even 90%.

It is evident that the cause of this difference does not lie in the nature of the monstrosity, but is due to the criterion upon which the selection is made. Selection of the apparently best individuals is one method, and it gives admirable results. Selection on the ground of the hereditary percentages is another method and gives results which are far more advantageous than the former.

In the lecture on the pistillody of the poppies we limited ourselves to the selection of the finest individuals and showed that there is always a manifest correlation between the individual strength of the plant and the degree of development of its anomaly. The same holds good with other monstrosities, and badly nourished specimens of rich races with twisted or fasciated stems always tend to reversion. This reversion, however, is not necessarily correlated with the hereditary percentage and therefore does not always indicate a lessening of the degree of inheritance. This shows that even in those cases an improvement may be expected, if only the means can be found to subject the twisted and the fasciated races to the same sharp test as the tricotylous varieties.

Much remains to be done, and the principle of the selection of parents according to the average constitution of their progeny seems to be one of the most promising in the whole realm of variability.

Besides tricotylous, the syncotylous seedlings may be used in the same way. They are more rarely met with, and in most instances seem to belong only to the unpromising half-races. The black bindweed (*Polygonum Convolvulus*), the jointed charlock (*Raphanus Raphanistrum*), the glaucous evening-primrose (*Oenothera glauca*) and many other plants seem to contain such half-races. On the other hand I found a plant of *Centranthus macrosiphon* yielding as much as 55% of syncotylous children and thereby evidently betraying the nature of a rich or double race. Likewise the mercury was rich in such deviations. But the best of all was the Russian sunflower, and this was chosen for closer experiments.

In the year of 1888 I had the good luck to isolate some syncotylous seedlings and of finding among them one with 19% of inheritors among its seeds. The following generation at once surpassed the ordinary average and came up in three individuals to 76, 81 and even 89%. My race was at once isolated and ameliorated by selection. I have tried to improve it further and selected the parents with the highest percentages during seven more generations; but without any remarkable result. I got figures of 90% and above, coming even in one instance up to the apparent purity of 100%. These, however, always remained extremes, the averages fluctuating yearly between 80–90% or thereabouts, and the other extremes going nearly every year downwards to 50%, the value which would be attained, if no selection were made.

Contra-selection is as easily made as normal selection. According to our present principle it means the choice of the parents with the smallest hereditary percentage. One might easily imagine that by this means the dicotylous seedlings could be rendered pure. This, however, is not at all the case. It is easy to return from so highly selected figures as for instance 95% to the average about of 50%, as regression to mediocrity is always an easy matter. But to transgress this average on the lower side seems to be as difficult as it is on the upper side. I continued the experiment during four succeeding generations, but was not able to go lower than about 10%, and could not even exclude the high figures from my strain. Parents with 65 – 75% of syncotylous seedlings returned in each generation, notwithstanding the most careful contra-selection. The attribute is inherent in the race, and is not to be eliminated by so simple a means as selection, nor even by a selection on the ground of hereditary percentages.

We have dealt with torsions and fasciations and with seedling variations at some length, in order to point out the phases needing investigation according to recent views. It would be quite superfluous to consider other anomalies in a similar manner, as they all obey the same laws. A hasty survey may suffice to show what prospects they offer to the student of nature.

First of all come the variegated leaves. They are perhaps the most variable of all variations. They are evidently dependent on external circumstances, and by adequate nutrition the leaves may even become absolutely white or yellowish, with only scarcely perceptible traces of green along the veins. Some are very old cultivated varieties, as the wintercress, or *Barbarea vulgaris*. They continuously sport into green, or return from this normal color, both by seeds and by buds. Sports of this kind are very often seen on shrubs or low trees, and they may remain there and develop during a long series of years. Bud-sports of variegated holly, elms, chestnuts, beeches and others might be cited. One-sided variegation on leaves or twigs with the opposite side wholly green are by no means rare. It is very curious to note that variegation is perhaps the most universally known anomaly, while its hereditary tendencies are least known.

Cristate and plumose ferns are another instance. Half races or rare accidental cleavages seem to be as common with ferns as cultivated double races, which are very rich in beautiful crests. But much depends on cultivation. It seems that the spores of crested leaves are more apt to reproduce the variety than those of normal leaves, or even of normal parts of the same leaves. But the experiments on which this assertion is made are old and should be repeated. Other cases of cleft leaves should also be tested. Ascidia are far more common than is usually believed. Rare instances point to poor races, but the magnolias and lime-trees are often so productive of ascidia as to suggest the idea of ever-sporting varieties. I have seen many hundred ascidia on one lime-tree, and far above a hundred on the magnolia. They differ widely in size and shape, including in some cases two leaves instead of one, or are composed of only half a leaf or of even still a smaller part of the summit. Rich ascidia-bearing varieties seem to offer notable opportunities for scientific pedigree-cultures.

Union of the neighboring fruits and flowers on flower-heads, of the rays of the umbellifers or of the successive flowers of the racemes of cabbages and allied genera, seem to be rare. The same holds good for the adhesion of foliar to axial organs, of branches to stems and other cases of union. Many of these cases return regularly in each generation, or may at least be seen from time to time in the same strains. Proliferation of the inflorescence is very common and changes in the position of staminate and pistillate flowers are not rare. We find starting points for new investigations in almost any teratological structure. Half-races and double-races are to be distinguished and isolated in all cases, and their hereditary qualities, the periodicity of the recurrence of the anomaly, the dependency on external circumstances and many other questions have to be answered.

Here is a wide field for garden experiments easily made, which might ultimately yield much valuable information on many questions of heredity of universal interest.

Lecture XV

DOUBLE ADAPTATIONS

The chief object of all experimentation is to obtain explanations of natural phenomena. Experiments are a repetition of things occurring in nature with the conditions so guarded and so closely followed that it is possible to make a clear analysis of facts and their causes, it being rightfully assumed that the laws are the same in both cases.

Experiments on heredity and the experience of the breeder find their analogy in the succession of generations in the wild state. The stability of elementary species and of retrograde varieties is quite the same under both conditions. Progression and retrogression are narrowly linked everywhere, and the same laws govern the abundance of forms in cultivated and in wild plants.

Elementary species and retrograde varieties are easily recognizable. Ever-sporting varieties on the contrary are far less obvious, and in many cases their hereditary relations have had to be studied anew. A clear analogy between them and corresponding types of wild plants has yet to be pointed out. There can be no doubt that such analogy exists; the conception that they should be limited to cultivated plants is not probable. Striped flowers and variegated leaves, changes of stamens into carpels or into petals may be extremely rare in the wild state, but the " five-leaved " clover and a large number of monstrosities cannot be said to be typical of the cultivated condition. These, however, are of rare occurrence, and do not play any important part in the economy of nature.

In order to attain a better solution of the problem we must take a broader view of the facts. The wide range of variability of ever-sporting varieties is due to the presence of two antagonistic characters which cannot be evolved at the same time and in the same organ, because they exclude one another. Whenever one is active, the other must be latent. But latency is not absolute inactivity and may often only operate to encumber the evolution of the antagonistic character, and to produce large numbers of lesser grades of its development. The antagonism however, is not such in the exact meaning of the word; it is rather a mutual exclusion, because one of the opponents simply takes the place of the other when absent, or supplements it to the extent that it may be only imperfectly developed. This completion ordinarily occurs in all possible degrees and thus causes the wide range of the variability. Nevertheless it may be wanting, and in the case of the double stocks only the two extremes are present.

It is rather difficult to get a clear conception of the substitution, and it seems necessary to designate the peculiar relationship between the two characters forming such a pair by a simple name. They might be termed alternating, if only it were clearly understood that the alternation may be complete, or incomplete in all degrees. Complete alternation would result in the extremes, the incomplete condition in the intermediate states. In some cases as with the stocks, the first prevails, while in other cases, as with the poppies, the very extremes are only rarely met with.

Taking such an alternation as a real character of the ever-sporting varieties, a wide range of analogous cases is at once revealed among the normal qualities of wild plants. Alternation is here almost universal. It is the capacity of young organs to develop in two diverging directions. The definitive choice must be made in extreme youth, or often at a relatively late period of development. Once made, this choice is final, and a further change does not occur in the normal course of things.

The most curious and most suggestive instance of such an alternation is the case of the water-persicaria or *Polygonum amphibium*. It is known to occur in two forms, one aquatic and the other terrestrial. These are recorded in systematic works as varieties, and are described under the names of *P. amphibium* var. *natans* Moench, and *P. amphibium* var. *terrestre* Leers or *P. amphibium* var. *terrestris* Moench. Such authorities as Koch in his German flora, and Grenier and Godron in their French flora agree in the conception of the two forms as varieties.

Notwithstanding this, the two varieties may often be observed to sport into one another. They are only branches of the same plant, grown under different conditions. The aquatic form has floating or submerged stems with oblong or elliptic leaves, which are glabrous and have long petioles. The terrestrial plants are erect, nearly simple, more or less hispid throughout, with lanceolate leaves and short petioles, often nearly sessile. The aquatic form flowers regularly, producing its peduncle at right angles from the floating stems, but the terrestrial specimens are ordinarily seen without flower-spikes, which are but rarely met with, at least as far as my own experience goes. In-

termediate forms are very rare, perhaps wholly
wanting, though in swamps the terrestrial
plants may often vary widely in the direction of
the floating type.

That both types sport into each other has
long been recognized in field-observations, and
has been the ground for the specific name of
amphibium, though in this respect herbarium-
material seems usually to be scant. The matter has recently been subjected to critical and
experimental studies by the Belgian botanist
Massart, who has shown that by transplanting
the forms into the alternate conditions, the
change may always be brought about artificially. If floating plants are established on
the shore they make ascending hairy stems, and
if the terrestrial shoots are submerged, their
buds grow into long and slack, aquatic stems.
Even in such experiments, intermediates are
rare, both types agreeing completely with the
corresponding models in the wild state.

Among all the previously described cases of
horticultural plants and monstrosities there is
no clearer case of an ever-sporting variety than
this one of the water-persicaria. The var.
terrestris sports into the var. *natans*, and
as often as the changing life conditions may
require it. It is true that ordinary sports occur without our discerning the cause and with-

out any relation to adaptation. This however is partly due to our lack of knowledge, and partly to the general rule that in nature only such sports as are useful are spared by natural selection, and what is useful we ordinarily term adaptive.

Another side of the question remains to be considered. The word variety, as is now becoming generally recognized, has no special meaning whatever. But here it is assumed in the clearly defined sense of a systematic variety, which includes all subdivisions of species. Such subdivisions may be, from a biological point of view, elementary species and also be eversporting varieties. They may be retrograde varieties, and the two alternating types may be described as separate varieties.

It is readily granted that many writers would not willingly accept this conclusion. But it is simply impossible to avoid it. The two forms of the water-persicaria must remain varieties, though they are only types of the different branches of a single plant.

If not, hundreds and perhaps thousands of analogous cases are at once exposed to doubt, and the whole conception of systematic varieties would have to be thrown over. Biologists of course would have no objection to this, but the student of the flora of any given country or region requires the systematic subdivisions and should always use his utmost efforts to keep them as they are. There is no intrinsic difficulty in the statement that different parts of the same plant should constitute different varieties.

In some cases different branches of the same plant have been described as species. So for instance with the climbing forms of figs. Under the name of *Ficus repens* a fine little plant is quite commonly cultivated as a climber in flower baskets. It is never seen bearing figs. On the other hand a shrub of our hothouses called *Ficus stipulata,* is cultivated in pots and makes a small tree which produces quite large, though non-edible figs. Now these two species are simply branches of the same plant. If the *repens* is allowed to climb up high along the walls of the hothouses, it will at last produce *stipulata*-branches with the corresponding fruits. *Ficus radicans* is another climbing form, corresponding to the shrub *Ficus ulmifolia* of our glasshouses. And quite the same thing occurs with ivy, the climbing stems of which never flower, but always first produce erect and free branches with rhombic leaves. These branches have often been used as cuttings and yield little erect and richly flowering shrubs, which are known in horticulture under the varietal name of *Hedera Helix arborea.*

Manifestly this classification is as nearly right as that of the two varieties of the water-persicaria. Going one step further, we meet with the very interesting case of alpine plants. The vegetation of the higher regions of mountains is commonly called alpine, and the plants show a large number of common features, differentiating them from the flora of lower stations. The mountain plants have small and dense foliage, with large and brightly-colored flowers. The corresponding forms of the lowlands have longer and weaker stems, bearing their leaves at greater distances, the leaves themselves being more numerous. The alpine forms, if perennial, have thick, strongly developed and densely branched rootstocks with heavy roots, in which a large amount of food-material is stored up during the short summer, and is available during the long winter months of the year.

Some species are peculiar to such high altitudes, while many forms from the lowlands have no corresponding type on the mountains. But a large number of species are common to both regions, and here the difference of course is most striking. *Lotus corniculatus* and *Calamintha Acinos, Calluna vulgaris* and *Campa-*

nula rotundifolia may be quoted as instances, and every botanist who has visited alpine regions may add other examples. Even the edelweiss of the Swiss Alps, *Gnaphalium Leontopodium*, loses its alpine characters, if cultivated in lowland gardens. Between such lowland and alpine forms intermediates regularly occur. They may be met with whenever the range of the species extends from the plains upward to the limit of eternal snow.

In this case the systematists formerly enumerated the alpine plants as *forma alpestris,* but whenever the intermediate is lacking the term *varietas alpestris* was often made use of.

It is simply impossible to decide concerning the real relation between the alpine and lowland types without experiments. About the middle of the last century it was quite a common thing to collect plants not only for herbarium-material, but also for the purpose of planting them in gardens and thus to observe their behavior under new conditions. This was done with the acknowledged purpose of investigating the systematic significance of observed divergencies. Whenever these held good in the garden they were considered to be reliable, but if they disappeared they were regarded as the results of climatic conditions, or of the influence of soil or nourishment. Between these two alternatives, many writers have tried to decide, by transplanting their specimens after some time in the garden, into arid or sandy soil, in order to see whether they would resume their alpine character.

Among the systematists who tested plants in this way, Nägeli especially, directed his attention to the hawkweeds or *Hieracium*. On the Swiss Alps they are very small and exhibit all the characters of the pure alpine type. Thousands of single plants were cultivated by him in the botanical garden of Munich, partly from seed and partly from introduced rootstocks. Here they at once assumed the tall stature of lowland forms. The identical individual, which formerly bore small rosettes of basal leaves, with short and unbranched flower-stalks, became richly leaved and often produced quite a profusion of flower-heads on branched stems. If then they were transplanted to arid sand, though remaining in the same garden and also under the same climatic conditions they resumed their alpine characters. This proved nutrition to be the cause of the change and not the climate.

The latest and most exact researches on this subject are due to Bonnier, who has gone into all the details of the morphologic as well as of the physiologic side of the problem.

His purpose was the study of partial variability under the influence of climate and soil. In every experiment he started from a single individual, divided it into two parts and planted one half on a mountain and the other half on the plain. The garden cultures were made chiefly at Paris and Fontainebleau, the alpine cultures partly in the Alps, partly in the Pyrenees. From time to time the halved plants were compared with each other, and the cultures lasted, as a rule, during the lifetime of the individual, often covering many years.

The common European frostweed or *Helianthemum vulgare* will serve to illustrate his results. A large plant growing in the Pyrenees in an altitude of 2400 meters was divided. One half was replanted on the same spot, and the other near Cadéac, at the base of the mountain range (740 M.). In order to exclude the effect of a change of soil, a quantity of the earth from the original locality was brought into the garden and the plant put therein. Further control-experiments were made at Paris. As soon as the two halved individuals commenced to grow and produced new shoots, the influence of the different climates made itself felt. On the mountain, the underground portions remained strong and dense, the leaves and internodes small and hairy, the flowering stems nearly

procumbent, the flowers being large and of a
deep yellow. At Cadéac and at Paris the whole
plant changed at once, the shoots becoming
elongated and loose, with broad and flattened,
rather smooth leaves and numerous pale-hued
flowers. The anatomical structure exhibited corresponding differences, the intercellular spaces
being small in the alpine plant and large in the
one grown in the lowlands, the wood-tissues
strong in the first and weak in the second case.

The milfoil (*Achillea Millefolium*) served
as a second example, and the experiments were
carried on in the same localities. The long and
thick rootstocks of the alpine plant bearing
short stems only with a few dense corymbs
contrasted markedly with the slender stems,
loose foliage and rich groups of flowerheads of
the lowland plant. The same differences in inner and outer structures were observed in numerous instances, showing that the alpine type
in these cases is dependent on the climate, and
that the capacity for assuming the antagonistic
characters is present in every individual of the
species. The external conditions decide which
of them becomes active and which remains inactive, and the case seems to be exactly parallel to that of the water-persicaria.

In the experiments of Bonnier the influence
of the soil was, as a rule, excluded by trans-

planting part of the original earth with the transplanted half of the plant. From this he concluded that the observed changes were due to the inequality of the climate. This involved three main factors, light, moisture and temperature. On the mountains the light is more intense, the air drier and cooler. Control-experiments were made on the mountains, depriving the plants of part of the light. In various ways they were more or less shaded, and as a rule responded to this treatment in the same way as to transplantation to the plain below. Bonnier concluded that, though more than one factor takes part in inciting the morphologic changes, light is to be considered as the chief agency. The response is to be considered as a useful one, as the whole structure of the alpine varieties is fitted to produce a large amount of organic material in a short time, which enables the plants to thrive during the short summers and long winters of their elevated stations.

In connection with these studies on the influences of alpine climates, Bonnier has investigated the internal structure of arctic plants, and made a series of experiments on growth in continuous electric light. The arctic climate is cold, but wet, and the structure of the leaves is correspondingly loose, though the plants become as small as on the Alps. Continuous electric light had very curious effects; the plants became etiolated, as if growing in darkness, with the exception that they assumed a deep green tinge. They showed more analogy with the arctic than with the alpine type.

The influence of the soil often produces changes similar to that of climate. This was shown by the above cited experiments of Nägeli with the hawkweeds, and may easily be controlled in other cases. The ground-honeysuckle or *Lotus corniculatus* grows in Holland partly on the dry and sandy soil of the dunes, and occasionally in meadows. It is small and dense in the first case, with orange and often very darkly colored petals, while it is loose and green in the meadows, with yellower flowers. Numerous analogous cases might be given. On mountain slopes in South Africa, and especially in Natal, a species of composite is found, which has been introduced into culture and is used as a hanging plant. It is called *Othonna crassifolia* and has fleshy, nearly cylindrical leaves, and exactly mimics some of the crassulaceous species. On dry soil the leaves become shorter and thicker and assume a reddish tinge, the stems remain short and woody and bear their leaves in dense rosettes. On moist and rich garden-soil this aspect becomes changed at once, the stems grow longer and of a deeper green. Intermediates occur, but notwithstanding this the two extremes constitute clearly antagonistic types.

The flora of the deserts is known to exhibit a similar divergent type. Or rather two types, one adapted to paucity of water, and the other to a storage of fluid at one season in order to make use of it at other times, as is the case with the cactuses. Limiting ourselves to the alternate group, we observe a rich and dense branching, small and compact leaves and extraordinarily long roots. Here the analogy with the alpine varieties is manifest, and the dryness of the soil evidently affects the plants in a similar way, as do the conditions of life in alpine regions. The question at once comes up as to whether here too we have only instances of partial variability, and whether many of the typical desert-species would lose their peculiar character by cultivation under ordinary conditions. The varieties of *Monardella macrantha,* described by Hall, from the San Jacinto Mountain, Cal., are suggestive of such an intimate analogy with the cases studied by Bonnier, that it seems probable that they might yield similar results, if tested by the same method.

Leaving now the description of these special

cases, we may resume our theoretical discussion of the subject, and try to get a clearer insight into the analogy of ever-sporting varieties and the wild species quoted. All of them may be characterized by the general term of dimorphism. Two types are always present, though not in the same individual or in the same organ. They exclude one another, and during their juvenile stage a decision is taken in one direction or in the other. Now, according to the theory of natural selection, wild species can only retain useful or at least innocuous qualities, since all mutations in a wrong direction must perish sooner or later. Cultivated species on the other hand are known to be largely endowed with qualities, which would be detrimental in the wild condition. Monstrosities are equally injurious and could not hold their own if left to themselves.

These same principles may be applied to ever-sporting or antagonistic pairs of characters. According to the theory of mutations such pairs may be either useful or useless. But only the useful will stand further test, and if they find suitable conditions will become specific or varietal characters. On this conclusion it becomes at once clear, why natural dimorphism is, as a rule, a very useful quality, while the cultivated dimorphous varieties strike us as something unnatural. The relation between cause and effect, is in truth other than it might seem to be at first view, but nevertheless it exists, and is of the highest importance.

From this same conclusion we may further deduce some explanation of the hereditary races characterized by monstrosities. It is quite evident that the twisted teasels are inadequate for the struggle with their tall congeners, or with the surrounding plants. Hence the conclusion that a pure and exclusively twisted race would soon die out. The fact that such races are not in existence finds its explanation in this circumstance, and therefore it does not prove the impossibility or even the improbability that some time a pure twisted race might arise. If chance should put such an accidental race in the hands of an experimenter, it could be protected and preserved, and having no straight atavistic branches, but being twisted in all its organs, might yield the most curious conceivable monstrosity, surpassing even the celebrated dwarf twisted shrubs of Japanese horticulturists.

Such varieties however, do not exist at present. The ordinary twisted races on the other hand, are found in the wild state and have only to be isolated and cultivated to yield large numbers of twisted individuals. In nature they are able to maintain themselves during long centuries, quite as well as normal species and varieties. But they owe this quality entirely to their dimorphous character. A twisted race of teasels might consist of successive generations of tall atavistic individuals, and produce yearly some twisted specimens, which might be destroyed every time before ripening their seeds. Reasoning from the evidence available, and from analogous cases, the variety would, even under such extreme circumstances, be able to last as long as any other good variety or elementary species. And it seems to me that this explanation makes clear how it is possible that varieties, which are potentially rich in their peculiar monstrosity, are discovered from time to time among plants when tested by experimental methods.

Granting these conclusions, monstrosities on the one side, and dimorphous wild species on the other, constitute the most striking examples of the inheritance of latent characters.

The bearing of the phenomena of dimorphism upon the principles of evolution formulated by Lamarck, and modified by his followers to constitute Neo-Lamarckianism, remains to be considered. Lamarck assumed that the external conditions directly affected the organisms in such a way as to make them better adapted to life, under prevailing circumstances. Nägeli gave to this conception the name "Theory of direct causation" (Theorie der directen Bewirkung), and it has received the approval of Von Wettstein, Strasburger and other German investigators. According to this conception a plant, when migrating from lowlands into the mountains would slowly be changed and gradually assume alpine habits. Once acquired this habit would become fixed and attain the rank of specific characters. In testing this theory by field-observations and culture-experiments, the defenders of the Nägelian principle could easily produce evidence upon the first point. The change of lowland-plants into alpine varieties can be brought about in numerous cases, and corresponding changes under the influence of soil, or climate, or life-conditions are on record for the most various characters and qualities.

The second point, however, is as difficult to prove as the first is of easy treatment. If after hundreds and thousands of years of exposure to alpine or other extreme conditions a fixed change is proved to have taken place, the question remains unanswered, whether the change has been a gradual or a sudden one. Darwin pointed out that long periods of life afford a chance for a sudden change in the desired direction, as well as for the slow accumulation of slight deviations. Any mutations in a wrong direction would at once be destroyed, but an accidental change in a useful way would be preserved, and multiply itself. If in the course of centuries this occurred, they would be nearly sure to become established, however rare at the outset. Hence the positive assertion is scarcely capable of direct proof.

On the other hand the negative assertion must be granted full significance. If the alpine climate has done no more than produce a transitory change, it is clear that thousands of years do not, necessarily, cause constant and specific alterations. This requirement is one of the indispensable supports of the Lamarckian theory. The matter is capable of disproof however, and such disproof seems to be afforded by the direct evidence of the present condition of the alpine varieties at large, and by many other similar cases.

Among these the observations of Holtermann on some desert-plants of Ceylon are of the highest value. Moreover they touch questions which are of wide importance for the study of the biology of American deserts. For this reason I may be allowed to introduce them here at some length.

The desert of Kaits, in Northern Ceylon, nourishes on its dry and torrid sands some species, represented by a large number of individuals, together with some rarer plants. The commonest forms are *Erigeron astcroides, Vernonia cinerea, Laurea pinnatifida, Vicoa auriculata, Heylandia latebrosa* and *Chrysopogon montanus*. In direct contrast with the ordinary desert-types they have a thin epidermis, with exposed stomata, features that ordinarily were characteristic of species of moister regions. They are annuals, growing rapidly, blooming and ripening their seeds before the height of the dry season. Evidently they are to be considered as the remainder of the flora of a previous period, when the soil had not yet become arid. They might be called relics. Of course they are small and dwarf-like, when compared with allied forms.

These curious little desert-plants disprove the Nägelian views in two important points. First, they show that extreme conditions do not necessarily change the organisms subjected to them, in a desirable direction. During the many centuries that these plants must have existed in the desert in annual generations, no single feature in the anatomical structure has become changed. Hence the conclusion that small leaves, abundant rootstocks and short stems, a dense foliage, a strongly cuticularized epidermis, few and narrow air-cavities in the tissues and all the long range of characteristics of typical desert-plants are not a simple result of the influence of climate and soil. There is no direct influence in this sense.

The second point, in which Nägeli's idea is broken down by Holtermann's observations, results from the behavior of the plants of the Kaits desert when grown or sown on garden-soil. When treated in this way they at once lose the only peculiarity which might be considered as a consequence of the desert-life of their ancestors, their dwarf stature. They behave exactly like the alpine plants in Bonnier's experiments, and with even more striking differences. In the desert they attain a height of a few centimeters, but in the garden they attain half a meter and more in height. Nothing in the way of stability has resulted from the action of the dry soil, not even in such a minor point as the height of the stems.

From these facts and discussions we may conclude that double adaptation is not induced by external influences, at least not in any way in which it might be of use to the plant. It may arise by some unknown cause, or may not be incited at all. In the first case the plant becomes capable of living under the alternating circumstances, and if growing near the limits of such regions it will overlap and get into the new area. All other species, which did not acquire the double habit, are of course excluded, with such curious exceptions as those of Kaits. The typical vegetation under such extreme conditions however, finds explanation quite as well by the one as by the other view.

Leaving these obvious cases of double adaptation, there still remains one point to be considered. It is the dwarf stature of so many desert and alpine plants. Are these dwarfs only the extremes of the normal fluctuating variability, or is their stature to be regarded as the expression of some peculiar adaptive but latent quality? It is as yet difficult to decide this question, because statistical studies of this form of variability are still wanting. The capacity of ripening the seed on individuals of dwarf stature however, is not at all a universal accompaniment of a variable height. Hence it cannot be considered as a necessary consequence of it. On the other hand the dwarf varieties of numerous garden-plants, as for instance: of larkspurs, snapdragon, opium-poppies and others are quite stable and thence are obviously due to peculiar characteristics. Such characteristics, if combined with tall stature into a pair of antagonists, would yield a double adaptation, and on such a base a hypothetical explanation could no doubt be rested.

Instead of discussing this problem from the theoretical side, I prefer to compare those species which are capable of assuming a dwarf stature under less uncommon conditions than those of alpine and desert-plants. Many weeds of our gardens and many wild species have this capacity. They become very tall, with large leaves, richly branched stems and numerous flowers in moist and rich soil. On bad soil, or if germinating too late, when the season is drier, they remain very small, producing only a few leaves and often limiting themselves to one flower-head. This is often seen with thorn-apples and amaranths, and even with oats and rye, and is notoriously the case with buckwheat. Gauchéry has observed that the extremes differ often as much from one another as 1:10. In the case of the Canadian horse-weed or *Erigeron canadensis,* which is widely naturalized in Europe, the tallest specimens are often twenty-five times as tall as the smallest, the difference increasing to greater extremes, if besides the main stem, the length of the numerous branches of the tall plants are taken into consideration. Other instances studied by the French investigator are *Erythraea pulchella* and *Calamintha Acinos.*

Dimorphism is of universal occurrence in the whole vegetable kingdom. In some cases it is typical, and may easily be discerned from extreme flutuating variability. In others the contrast is not at all obvious, and a closer investigation is needed to decide between the two possibilities. Sometimes the adaptive quality is evident, in other cases it is not. A large number of plants bear two kinds of leaves linked with one another by intermediate forms. Often the first leaves of a shoot, or those of accidentally strong shoots, exhibit deviating shapes, and the usefulness of such occurrences seems to be quite doubtful. The elongation of stems and linear leaves, and the reduction of lateral organs in darkness, is manifestly an adaptation. Many plants have stolons with double adaptations which enable them to retain their character of underground stems with bracts or to exchange it for the characteristics of erect stems with green leaves according to the outer circumstances. In some shrubs and trees the capacity of a number of buds to produce either flowers or shoots with leaves seems to be in the same condition. The capacity of producing spines is also a double adaptation, active on dry and arid soil and latent in a moist climate or under cultivation, as with the wild and cultivated apple, and in the experiments of Lothelier with *Berberis, Lycium* and other species, which lose their spines in damp air.

In some conifers the evolution of horizontal branches may be modified by simply turning the buds upside down. Or the lateral branches can be induced to become erect stems by cutting off the normal summit of a tree. Numerous organs and functions lie dormant until aroused by external agencies, and many other cases could be cited, showing the wide occurrence of double adaptation.

There are, however, two points, which should not be passed over without some mention. One of them is the influence of sun and shade on leaves, and the other the atavistic forms, often exhibited during the juvenile period.

The leaves of many plants, and especially those of some shrubs and trees, have the capacity of adapting themselves either to intense or to diffuse light. On the circumference of the crown of a tree the light is stronger and the leaves are small and thick, with a dense tissue. In the inner parts of the crown the light is weak and the leaves are broader in order to get as much of it as possible. They become larger but thinner, consisting often of a small number of cell layers. The definitive formation is made in extreme youth, often even during the previous summer, at the time of the very first evolution of the young organs within the buds. *Iris,* and *Lactuca Scariola* or the prickly lettuce, and many other plants afford similar instances. As the definitive decision must be made in these cases long before the direct influence of the conditions which would make the change useful is felt, it is hardly conceivable how they could be ascribed to this cause.

It is universally known that many plants show deviating features when very young, and that these often remind us of the characters of their probable ancestors. Many plants that must have been derived from their nearest systematic relatives, chiefly by reductions, are constantly betraying this relation by a repetition of the ancestral marks during their youth.

There can be hardly a doubt that the general law of natural selection prevails in such cases as it does in others. Or stated otherwise, it is very probable, that in most cases the atavistic characters have been retained during youth because of their temporary usefulness. Unfortunately, our knowledge of utility of qualities is as yet very incomplete. Here we must assume that what is ordinarily spared by natural selection is to be considered as useful, until direct experimental investigations have been made.

So it is for instance with the submerged leaves of water-plants. As a rule they are linear, or if compound, are reduced to densely branching filiform threads. Hence we may conclude that this structure is of some use to them. Now two European and some corresponding American species of water-parsnip, the *Sium latifolium* and *Berula angustifolia* with their allies, are umbellifers, which bear pinnate instead of bi- or tri-pinnate leaves. But the young plants and even the young shoots when developing from the rootstocks under water comply with the above rule, producing very compound, finely and pectinately dissected leaves. From a systematic point of view these leaves indicate the origin of the water-parsnips from ordinary umbellifers, which generally have bi- and tri-pinnate leaves.

Similar cases of double adaptation, dependent on external conditions at different periods of the evolution of the plant are very numerous. They are most marked among leguminous plants, as shown by the trifoliolate leaves of the thorn-broom and allies, which in the adult state have green twigs destitute of leaves.

As an additional instance of dimorphism and probable double adaptation to unrecognized external conditions I might point to the genus *Acacia*. As we have seen in a previous lecture some of the numerous species of this genus bear bi-pinnate leaves, while others have only flattened leaf-stalks. According to the prevailing systematic conceptions, the last must have been derived from the first by the loss of the blades and the corresponding increase of size and superficial extension of the stalk. In proof of this view they exhibit, as we have described, the ancestral characters in the young plantlets, and this production of bi-pinnate leaves has probably been retained at the period of the corresponding negative mutations, because of some distinct, though still unknown use.

Summarizing the results of this discussion, we may state that useful dimorphism, or double adaptation, is a substitution of characters quite analogous to the useless dimorphism of cultivated ever-sporting varieties and the stray occurrence of hereditary monstrosities. The same laws and conditions prevail in both cases.

E. MUTATIONS

Lecture XVI

THE ORIGIN OF THE PELORIC TOAD-FLAX

I have tried to show previously that species, in the ordinary sense of the word, consist of distinct groups of units. In systematic works these groups are all designated by the name of varieties, but it is usually granted that the units of the system are not always of the same value. Hence we have distinguished between elementary species and varieties proper. The first are combined into species whose common original type is now lost or unknown, and from their characters is derived an hypothetical image of what the common ancestor is supposed to have been. The varieties proper are derived in most cases from still existing types, and therefore are subjoined to them. A closer investigation has shown that this derivation is ordinarily produced by the loss of some definite attribute, or by the re-acquisition of an apparently lost character. The elementary species, on the other hand, must have arisen by the production of new qualities, each new acquisition constituting the origin of a new elementary form.

Moreover we have seen, that such improvements and such losses constitute sharp limits between the single unit-forms. Every type, of course, varies around an average, and the extremes of one form may sometimes reach or even overlap those of the nearest allies, but the offspring of the extremes always return to the type. The transgression is only temporary and a real transition of one form to another does not come within ordinary features of fluctuating variability. Even in the cases of eversporting varieties, where two opposite types are united within one race, and where the succeeding individuals are continually swinging from one extreme to the other, passing through a wide range of intermediate steps, the limits of the variety are as sharply defined and as free from real transgression as in any other form.

In a complete systematic enumeration of the real units of nature, the elementary species and varieties are thus observed to be discontinous and separated by definite gaps. Every unit may have its youth, may lead a long life in the adult state and may finally die. But through the whole period of its existence it remains the same, at the end as sharply defined from its nearest allies as in the beginning. Should some of the units die out, the gaps between the neighboring ones will become wider, as must often have been the case. Such segregations, however important and useful for systematic distinctions, are evidently only of secondary value, when considering the real nature of the units themselves.

We may now take up the other side of the problem. The question arises as to how species and varieties have originated. According to the Darwinian theory they have been produced from one another, the more highly differentiated ones from the simpler, in a graduated series from the most simple forms to the most complicated and most highly organized existing types. This evolution of course must have been regular and continuous, diverging from time to time into new directions, and linking all organisms together into one common pedigree. All lacunae in our present system are explained by Darwin as due to the extinction of the forms, which previously filled them.

Since Lamarck first propounded the conception of a common origin for all living beings, much has been done to clear up our ideas as to the real nature of this process. The broader aspect of the subject, including the general pedigree of the animal and vegetable kingdom, may be said to have been outlined by Darwin and his followers, but this phase of the subject lies beyond the limits of our present discussion.

The other phase of the problem is concerned with the manner in which the single elementary species and varieties have sprung from one another. There is no reason to suppose that the world is reaching the end of its development, and so we are to infer that the production of new species and varieties is still going on. In reality, new forms are observed to originate from time to time, both wild and in cultivation, and such facts do not leave any doubt as to their origin from other allied types, and according to natural and general laws.

In the wild state however, and even with cultivated plants of the field and garden, the conditions, though allowing of the immediate observation of the origination of new forms, are by no means favorable for a closer inquiry into the real nature of the process. Therefore I shall postpone the discussion of the facts till another lecture, as their bearing will be more easily understood after having dealt with more complete cases.

These can only be obtained by direct experimentation. Comparative studies, of course, are valuable for the elucidation of general problems and broad features of the whole pedigree, but the narrower and more practical question as to the genetic relation of the single forms to one another must be studied in another way, by direct experiment. The exact methods of the laboratory must be used, and in this case the garden is the laboratory. The cultures must be guarded with the strictest care and every precaution taken to exclude opportunities for error. The parents and grandparents and their offspring must be kept pure and under control, and all facts bearing upon the birth or origin of the new types should be carefully recorded.

Two great difficulties have of late stood in the way of such experimental investigation. One of them is of a theoretical, the other of a practical nature. One is the general belief in the supposed slowness of the process, the other is the choice of adequate material for experimental purposes. Darwin's hypothesis of natural selection as the means by which new types arise, is now being generally interpreted as stating the slow transformation of ordinary fluctuating divergencies from the average type into specific differences. But in doing so it is overlooked that Quetelet's law of fluctuating variability was not yet discovered at the time, when Darwin propounded his theory. So there is no real and intimate connection between these two great conceptions. Darwin frequently pointed out that a long period of time might be needed for slow improvements, and was also a condition for the occurrence of rare sports. In any case those writers have been in error, according to my opinion, who have refrained from experimental work on the origin of species, on account of this narrow interpretation of Darwin's views. The choice of the material is quite another question, and obviously all depends upon this choice. Promising instances must be sought for, but as a rule the best way is to test as many plants as possible. Many of them may show nothing of interest, but some might lead to the desired end.

For to-day's lecture I have chosen an instance, in which the grounds upon which the choice was based are very evident. It is the origin of the peloric toad-flax (*Linaria vulgaris peloria*).

The ground for this choice lies simply in the fact that the peloric toad-flax is known to have originated from the ordinary type at different times and in different countries, under more or less divergent conditions. It had arisen from time to time, and hence I presumed that there was a chance to see it arise again. If this should happen under experimental circumstances the desired evidence might easily be gathered. Or, to put it in other words, we must try to arrange things so as to be present at the time when nature produces another of these rare changes.

There was still another reason for choosing this plant for observational work. The step from the ordinary toad-flax to the peloric form is short, and it appears as if it might be produced by slow conversion. The ordinary species produces from time to time stray peloric flowers. These occur at the base of the raceme, or rarely in the midst of it. In other species they are often seen at the summit. Terminal pelories are usually regular, having five equal spurs. Lateral pelories are generally of zygomorphic structure, though of course in a less degree than the normal bilabiate flowers, but they have unequal spurs, the middle one being of the ordinary length, the two neighboring being shorter, and those standing next to the opposite side of the flower being the shortest of all. This curious remainder of the original symmetrical structure of the flower seems to have been overlooked hitherto by the investigators of peloric toad-flaxes.

The peloric variety of this plant is characterized by its producing only peloric flowers. No single bilabiate or one-spurred flower remains.

I once had a lot of nearly a hundred specimens of this fine variety, and it was a most curious and beautiful sight to observe the many thousands of nearly regular flowers blooming at the same time. Some degree of variability was of course present, even in a large measure. The number of the spurs varied between four and six, transgressing these limits in some instances, but never so far as to produce really one-spurred flowers. Comparing this variety with the ordinary type, two ways of passing over from the one to the other might be imagined. One would entail a slow increase of the number of the peloric flowers on each plant, combined with a decrease of the number of the normal ones, the other a sudden leap from one extreme to the other without any intermediate steps. The latter might easily be overlooked in field observations and their failure may not have the value of direct proof. They could never be overlooked, on the other hand, in experimental culture.

The first record of the peloric toad-flax is that of Zioberg, a student of Linnaeus, who found it in the neighborhood of Upsala. This curious discovery was described by Rudberg in his dissertation in the year 1744. Soon afterwards other localities were discovered by Link near Göttingen in Germany about 1791 and afterwards in the vicinity of Berlin, as stated by Ratzeburg, 1825. Many other localities have since been indicated for it in Europe, and in my own country some have been noted of late, as for instance near Zandvoort in 1874 and near Oldenzaal in 1896. In both these last named cases the peloric form arose spontaneously in places which had often been visited by botanists before the recorded appearance, and therefore, without any doubt, they must have been produced directly and independently by the ordinary species which grows in the locality. The same holds good for other occurrences of it.

In many instances the variety has been recorded to disappear after a certain lapse of time, the original specimens dying out and no new ones being produced. *Linaria* is a perennial herb, multiplying itself easily by buds growing on the roots, but even with this means of propagation its duration seems to have definite limits.

There is one other important point arguing strongly for the independent appearance of the peloric form in its several localities. It is the difficulty of fertilization and the high degree of sterility, even if artificially pollinated. Bees and humble-bees are unable to crawl into the narrow tubular flowers, and to bring the fertilizing pollen to the stigma. Ripe capsules with seeds have never been seen in the wild state. The only writer who succeeded in sowing seeds of the peloric variety was Wildenow and he got only very few seedlings. But even in artificial pollination the result is the same, the anthers seeming to be seriously affected by the change. I tried both self-fertilization and cross-pollination, and only with utmost care did I succeed in saving barely a hundred seeds. In order to obtain them I was compelled to operate on more than a thousand flowers on about a dozen peloric plants.

The variety being wholly barren in nature, the assumption that the plants in the different recorded localities might have a common origin is at once excluded. There must have been at least nearly as many mutations as localities. This strengthens the hope of seeing such a mutation happen in one's own garden. It should also be remembered that peloric flowers are known to have originated in quite a number of different species of *Linaria,* and also with many of the allied species within the range of the *Labiatiflorae.*

I will now give the description of my own experiment. Of course this did not give the expected result in the first year. On the contrary, it was only after eight years' work that I had the good fortune of observing the mutation.

But as the whole life-history of the preceding generations had been carefully observed and recorded, the exact interpretation of the fact was readily made.

My culture commenced in the year 1886. I chose some plants of the normal type with one or two peloric flowers besides the bilabiate majority which I found on a locality in the neighborhood of Hilversum in Holland. I planted the roots in my garden and from them had the first flowering generation in the following summer. From their seeds I grew the second generation in three following years. They flowered profusely and produced in 1889 only one, and in 1890 only two peloric structures. I saved the seeds in 1889 and had in 1890-1891 the third generation. These plants likewise flowered only in the second year, and gave among some thousands of symmetrical blossoms, only one five-spurred flower. I pollinated this flower myself, and it produced abundant fruit with enough seeds for the entire culture in 1892, and they only were sown.

Until this year my generations required two years each, owing to the perennial habit of the plants. In this way the prospects of the culture began to decrease, and I proposed to try to heighten my chances by having a new generation yearly. With this intention I sowed the selected seeds in a pan in the glasshouse of my laboratory and planted them out as soon as the young stems had reached a length of some few centimeters. Each seedling was put in a separate pot, in heavily manured soil. The pots were kept under glass until the beginning of June, and the young plants produced during this period a number of secondary stems from the curious hypocotylous buds which are so characteristic of the species. These stems grew rapidly and as soon as they were strong enough, the plants were put into the beds. They all, at least nearly all, some twenty specimens, flowered in the following month.

I observed only one peloric flower among the large number present. I took the plant bearing this flower and one more for the culture of the following year, and destroyed all others. These two plants grew on the same spot, and were allowed to fertilize each other by the agency of the bees, but were kept isolated from any other congener. They flowered abundantly, but produced only one-spurred bilabiate flowers during the whole summer. They matured more than 10 cu. cm. of seeds.

It is from this pair of plants that my peloric race has sprung. And as they are the ancestors of the first closely observed case of peloric mutation, it seems worth while to give some details regarding their fertilization.

Isolated plants of *Linaria vulgaris* do not produce seed, even if freely pollinated by bees. Pollen from other plants is required. This requirement is not at all restricted to the genus *Linaria,* as many instances are known to occur in different families. It is generally assumed that the pollen of any other individual of the same species is capable of producing fertilization, although it is to be said that a critical examination has been made in but few instances.

This, however, is not the case, at least not in the present instance. I have pollinated a number of plants, grown from seed of the same strain and combined them in pairs, and excluded the visits of insects, and pollen other than that of the plant itself and that of the specimen with which it was paired. The result was that some pairs were fertile and others barren. Counting these two groups of pairs, I found them nearly equal in number, indicating thereby that for any given individual the pollen of half of the others is potent, but that of the other half impotent. From these facts we may conclude the presence of a curious case of dimorphy, analogous to that proposed for the primroses, but without visible differentiating marks in the flowers. At least such opposite characters have as yet not been ascertained in the case of our toad-flax.

In order to save seed from isolated plants it is necessary, for this reason, to have at least two individuals, and these must belong to the two physiologically different types. Now in the year 1892, as in other years, my plants, though separated at the outset by distances of about 20 cm. from each other, threw out roots of far greater length, growing in such a way as to abolish the strict isolation of the individuals. Any plot may produce several stems from such roots, and it is manifestly impossible to decide whether they all belong to one original plant or to the mixed roots of several individuals. No other strains were grown on the same bed with my plants however, and so I considered all the stems of the little group as belonging to one plant. But their perfect fertility showed, according to the experience described, that there must have been at least two specimens mingled together.

Returning now to the seeds of this pair of plants, I had, of course, not the least occasion to ascribe to it any higher value than the harvest of former years. The consequence was that I had no reason to make large sowings, and grew only enough young plants to have about 50 in bloom in the summer of 1894. Among these, stray peloric flowers were observed in somewhat larger number than in the previous generations, 11 plants bearing one or two, or even three such abnormalities. This however, could not be considered as a real advance, since such plants may occur in varying, though ordinarily small numbers in every generation.

Besides them a single plant was seen to bear only peloric flowers; it produced racemes on several stems and their branches. All were peloric without exception. I kept it through the winter, taking care to preserve a complete isolation of its roots. The other plants were wholly destroyed. Such annihilation must include both the stems and roots and the latter of course requires considerable labor. The following year, however, gave proof of the success of the operation, since my plant bloomed luxuriously for the second time and remained true to the type of the first year, producing peloric flowers exclusively.

Here we have the first experimental mutation of a normal into a peloric race. Two facts were clear and simple. The ancestry was known for over a period of four generations, living under the ordinary care and conditions of an experimental garden, isolated from other toad-flaxes, but freely fertilized by bees or at times by myself. This ancestry was quite constant as to the peloric peculiarity, remaining true to the wild type as it occurs everywhere in my country, and showing in no respect any tendency to the production of a new variety.

The mutation took place at once. It was a sudden leap from the normal plants with very rare peloric flowers to a type exclusively peloric. No intermediate steps were observed. The parents themselves had borne thousands of flowers during two summers, and these were inspected nearly every day, in the hope of finding some pelories and of saving their seed separately. Only one such flower was seen. If there had been more, say a few in every hundred flowers, it might be allowable to consider them as previous stages, showing a preparation of the impending change. But nothing of this kind was observed. There was simply no visible preparation for the sudden leap.

This leap, on the other hand, was full and complete. No reminiscence of the former condition remained. Not a single flower on the mutated plant reverted to the previous type. All were thoroughly affected by the new attribute, and showed the abnormally augmented number of spurs, the tubular structure of the corolla and the round and narrow entrance of its throat. The whole plant departed absolutely from the old type of its progenitors.

Three ways were open to continue my experiment. The first was indicated by the abundant harvest from the parent-plants of the mutation. It seemed possible to compare the numerical proportion of the mutated seeds with those of normal plants. In order to ascertain this proportion I sowed the greatest part of my 10 cu. cm. of seed and planted some 2000 young plants in little pots with well-manured soil. I got some 1750 flowering plants and observed among them 16 wholly peloric individuals. The numerical proportion of the mutation was therefore in this instance to be calculated equal to about 1% of the whole crop.

This figure is of some importance. For it shows that the chance of finding mutations requires the cultivation of large groups of individuals. One plant in each hundred may mutate, and cultures of less than a hundred specimens must therefore be entirely dependent on chance for the appearance of new forms, even if such should accidentally have been produced and lay dormant in the seed. In other cases mutations may be more numerous, or on the contrary, more rare. But the chance of mutative changes in larger numbers is manifestly much reduced by this experiment, and they may be expected to form a very small proportion of the culture.

The second question which arose from the above result was this. Could the mutation be repeated? Was it to be ascribed to some latent cause which might be operative more than once? Was there some hidden tendency to mutation, which, ordinarily weak, was strengthened in my cultures by some unknown influence? Was the observed mutation to be explained by a common cause with the other cases recorded by field-observations? To answer this question I had only to continue my experiment, excluding the mutated individuals from any intercrossing with their brethren. To this end I saved the seeds from duly isolated groups in different years and sowed them at different times. For various causes I was not prepared to have large cultures from these seeds, but notwithstanding this, the mutation repeated itself. In one instance I obtained two, in another, one peloric plant with exclusively many-spurred flowers. As is easily understood, these were related as "nieces" to the first observed mutants. They originated in quite the same way, by a sudden leap, without any preparation and without any intermediate steps.

Mutation is proved by this experience to be of an iterative nature. It is the expression of some concealed condition, or as it is generally called, of some hidden tendency. The real nature of this state of the hereditary qualities is as yet wholly unknown. It would not be safe to formulate further conclusions before the evidence offered by the evening-primroses is considered.

Thirdly, the question arises, whether the mutation is complete, not only as to the morphologic character, but also as to the hereditary constitution of the mutated individuals. But here unfortunately the high degree of sterility of the peloric plants, as previously noted, makes the experimental evidence a thing of great difficulty. During the course of several years I isolated and planted together the peloric individuals already mentioned, all in all some twenty plants. Each individual was nearly absolutely sterile when treated with its own pollen, and the aid of insects was of no avail. I intercrossed my plants artificially, and pollinated more than a thousand flowers. Not a single one gave a normal fruit, but some small and nearly rudimentary capsules were produced, bearing a few seeds. From these I had 119 flowering plants, out of which 106 were peloric and 13 one-spurred. The great majority, some 90%, were thus shown to be true to their new type. Whether the 10% reverting ones were truly atavists, or whether they were only vicinists, caused by stray pollen grains from another culture, cannot of course be decided with sufficient certitude.

Here I might refer to the observations concerning the invisible dimorphous state of the flowers of the normal toad-flax. Individuals of the same type, when fertilized with each other, are nearly, but not absolutely, sterile. The yield of seeds of my peloric plants agrees fairly well with the harvest which I have obtained from some of the nearly sterile pairs of individuals in my former trial. Hence the suggestion is forced upon us that perhaps, owing to some unknown cause, all the peloric individuals of my experiment belonged to one and the same type, and were sterile for this reason only. If this is true, then it is to be presumed that all previous investigators have met the same condition, each having at hand only one of the two required types. And this discussion has the further advantage of showing the way, in which perhaps a full and constant race of peloric toad-flaxes may be obtained. Two individuals of different type are required to start from. They seem as yet never to have arisen from one group of mutations. But if it were possible to combine the products of two mutations obtained in different countries and under different conditions, there would be a chance that they might belong to the supposed opposite types, and thus be fertile with one another.

My peloric plants are still available, and the occurrence of this form elsewhere would give material for a successful experiment. The probability thereof is enhanced by the experience that my peloric plants bear large capsules and a rich harvest of seeds when fertilized from plants of the normal one-spurred race, while they remain nearly wholly barren by artificial fertilization with others. I suppose that they are infertile with the normal toad-flaxes of their own sexual disposition, but fertile with those of the opposite constitution. At all events the fact that they may bear abundant seed when properly pollinated is an indication of successful experiments on the possibility of gaining a hereditary race with exclusively peloric flowers. And such a race would be a distinct gain for sundry physiologic inquiries, and perhaps not wholly destitute of value from an horticultural point of view.

Returning now to the often recorded occurrence of peloric toad-flaxes in the wild state and recalling our discussion about the improbability of a dispersion from one locality to another by seed, and the probability of independent origin for most of these cases, we are confronted with the conception that a latent tendency to mutation must be universally present in the whole species. Another observation, although it is of a negative character, gains in importance from this point of view. I refer to the total lack of intermediate steps between normal and peloric individuals. If such links had ordinarily been produced previous to the purely peloric state they would no doubt have been observed from time to time. This is so much the more probable as *Linaria* is a perennial herb, and the ancestors of a mutation might still be in a flowering condition together with their divergent offspring. But no such intermediates are on record. The peloric toad-flaxes are, as a rule, found surrounded by the normal type, but without intergrading forms. This discontinuity has already been insisted upon by Hofmeister and others, even at the time when the theory of descent was most under discussion, and any link would surely have been produced as a proof of a slow and continuous change. But no such proof has been found, and the conclusion seems admissible that the mutation of toad-flaxes ordinarily, if not universally, takes place by a sudden step. Our experiment may simply be considered as a thoroughly controlled instance of an often recurring phenomenon. It teaches us how, in the main, the peloric mutations must be assumed to proceed.

This conception may still be broadened. We may include in it all similar occurrences, in allied and other species. There is hardly a limit to the possibilities which are opened up by this experience. But it will be well to refrain from hazardous theorizing, and consider only those cases which may be regarded as exact repetitions of the same phenomenon and of which our culture is one of the most recent instances on record. We will limit ourselves to the probable origin of peloric variations at large, of which little is known, but some evidence may be derived from the recorded facts. Only one case can be said to be directly analogous to our observations.

This refers to the peloric race of the common snapdragon, or *Antirrhinum majus* of our gardens. It is known to produce peloric races from time to time in the same way as does the toadflax. But the snapdragon is self-fertile and so is its peloric variety. Some cases are relatively old, and some of them have been recorded and in part observed by Darwin. Whence they have sprung and in what manner they were produced, seems never to have been noted. Others are of later origin, and among these one or two varieties have been accidentally produced in the nursery of Mr. Chr. Lorenz in Erfurt, and are now for sale, the seeds being guaranteed to yield a large proportion of peloric individuals. The peloric form in this case appeared at once, but was not isolated, and was left free to visiting insects, which of course crossed it with the surrounding varieties. Without doubt the existence of two color-varieties of the peloric type, one of a very dark red, indicating the " Black prince " variety as the pollen-parent, and the other with a white tube of the corolla, recalling the form known as " Delila," is due to these crossings. I had last year (1903) a large lot of plants, partly normal and partly peloric, but evidently of hybrid origin, from seeds from this nursery, showing moreover all intermediate steps between nearly wholly peloric individuals and apparently normal ones. I have saved the seeds of the isolated types and before seeing the flowers of their offspring, nothing can be said about the purity and constancy of the type, when freed from hybrid admixtures. The peloric snapdragon has five small unequal spurs at the base of its long tube, and in this respect agrees with the peloric toad-flax.

Other pelories are terminal and quite regular, and occur in some species of *Linaria,* where I observed them in *Linaria dalmatica.* The terminal flowers of many branches were large and beautifully peloric, bearing five long and equal spurs. About their origin and inheritance nothing is known.

A most curious terminal pelory is that of the common foxglove or *Digitalis purpurea*. As we have seen in a previous lecture, it is an old variety. It was described and figured for the first time by Vrolik of Amsterdam, and the original specimens of his plates are still to be seen in the collections of the botanic garden of that university. Since his time it has been propagated by seed as a commercial variety, and may be easily obtained. The terminal flower of the central stem and those of the branches only are affected, all other flowers being wholly normal. Almost always it is accompanied by other deviations, among which a marked increase of the number of the parts of the corolla and other whorls is the most striking. Likewise supernumerary petals on the outer side of the corolla, and a production of a bud in the center of the capsule may be often met with. This bud as a rule grows out after the fading away of the flower, bursting through the green carpels of the unripe fruit, and producing ordinarily a secondary raceme of flowers. This raceme is a weak but exact repetition of the first, bearing symmetrical foxgloves all along and terminating in a peloric structure.

On the branches these anomalies are more or less reduced, according to the strength of the branch, and conforming to the rule of periodicity, given in our lecture on the " five-leaved " clover. Through all this diminution the peloric type remains unchanged and therefore becomes so much the purer, the weaker the branches on which it stands.

I am not sure whether such peloric flowers have ever been purely pollinated and their seed saved separately, but I have often observed that the race comes pure from the seed of the zygomorphic flowers. It is as yet doubtful whether it is a half race or a double race, and whether it might be purified and strengthened by artificial selection. Perhaps the determination of the hereditary percentage described when dealing with the tricotyls might give the clue to the acquisition of a higher specialized race. The variety is old and widely disseminated, but must be subjected to quite a number of additional experiments before it can be said to be sufficiently understood.

The most widespread peloric variety is that of gloxinia. It has erect instead of drooping flowers; and with the changed position the structure is also changed. Like other pelories it has five equal stamens instead of four unequal ones, and a corolla with five equal segments instead of an upper and a lower lip. It shows the peloric condition in all of its flowers and is often combined with a small increase of the number of the parts of the whorls. It is for sale under the name of *erecta,* and may be had in a wide range of color-types. It seems to be quite constant from seed.

Many other instances of peloric flowers are on record. Indian cress or *Tropaeolum majus* loses the spur in some double varieties and with it most of its symmetrical structure; it seems to be considered justly as a peloric malformation. Other species produce such anomalies only from time to time and nothing is known about their hereditary tendency. One of the most curious instances is the terminal flower of the raceme of the common laburnum, which loses its whole papilionaceous character and becomes as regularly quinate as a common buttercup.

Some families are more liable to pelorism than others. Obviously all the groups, the flowers of which are not symmetrical, are to be excluded. But then we find that labiates and their allies among the dicotyledonous plants, and orchids among the monocotyledonous ones are especially subjected to this alteration. In both groups many genera and a long list of species could be quoted as proof. The family of the labiates seems to be essentially rich in terminal pelories, as for instance in the wild sage or *Salvia* and the dead-nettle or *Lamium*. Here the pelories have long and straight corolla-tubes, which are terminated by a whorl of four or five segments. Such forms often occur in the wild state and seem to have a geographic distribution as narrowly circumscribed as in the case of many small species. Those of the labiates chiefly belong to southern Europe and are unknown at least in some parts of the other countries. On the contrary terminal pelories of *Scrophularia nodosa* are met with from time to time in Holland. Such facts clearly point to a common origin, and as only the terminal flowers are affected by the malformation, the fertility of the whole plant is evidently not seriously infringed upon.

Before leaving the labiates, we may cite a curious instance of pelorism in the toad-flax, which is quite different from the ordinary peloric variety. This latter may be considered from a morphologic standpoint to be owing to a five-fold repetition of the middle part of the underlip. This conception would at once explain the occurrence of five spurs and of the orange border all around the corolla-tube. We might readily imagine that any other of the five parts of the corolla could be repeated five-fold, in which case there would be no spur, and no orange hue on the upper corolla-ring. Such forms really occur, though they seem to be more rare than the five-spurred pelories. Very little is known about their frequency and hereditary qualities.

Orchids include a large number of peloric monstrosities and moreover a wild pelory which is systematically described not only as a separate species but even as a new genus. It bears the name of *Uropedium lindenii*, and is so closely related to *Cypripedium caudatum* that many authors take it for the peloric variety of this plant. It occurs in the wild state in some parts of Mexico, where the *Cypripedium* also grows. Its claims to be a separate genus are lessened by the somewhat monstrous condition of the sexual organs, which are described as quite abnormal. But here also, intermediates are lacking, and this fact points to a sudden origin.

Many cases of pelorism afford promising material for further studies of experimental mutations. The peloric toad-flax is only the prototype of what may be expected in other cases. No opportunity should be lost to increase the as yet too scanty evidence on this point.

Lecture XVII

THE PRODUCTION OF DOUBLE FLOWERS

Mutations occur as often among cultivated plants as among those in the wild state. Garden flowers are known to vary markedly. Much of their variability, however, is due to hybridism, and the combination of characters previously separate has a value for the breeder nearly equal the production of really new qualities. Nevertheless there is no doubt that some new characters appear from time to time.

In a previous lecture we have seen that varietal characters have many features in common. One of them is their frequent recurrence both in the same and in other, often very distantly related, species. This recurrence is an important factor in the choice of the material for an experimental investigation of the nature of mutations.

Some varieties are reputed to occur more often and more readily than others. White-colored varieties, though so very common, seem for the most part to be of ancient date, but only few have a known origin, however. Without any doubt many of them have been found in a wild state and were introduced into culture. On the other hand double flowers are exceedingly rare in the wild state, and even a slight indication of a tendency towards doubling, the stray petaloid stamens, are only rarely observed growing wild. In cultivation, however, double flowers are of frequent occurrence; hence the conclusion that they have been produced in gardens and nurseries more frequently than perhaps any other type of variety.

In the beginning of my experimental work I cherished the hope of being able to produce a white variety. My experiments, however, have not been successful, and so I have given them up temporarily. Much better chances for a new double variety seemed to exist, and my endeavors in this direction have finally been crowned with success.

For this reason I propose to deal now with the production of double flowers, to inquire what is on record about them in horticultural literature, and to give a full description of the origin thereof in an instance which it was my good fortune to observe in my garden.

Of course the historical part is only a hasty survey of the question and will only give such evidence as may enable us to get an idea of the chances of success for the experimental worker.

In the second half of the seventeenth century (1671), my countryman, Abraham Munting, published a large book on garden plants with many beautiful figures. It is called "Waare Oeffeninge der Planten," or "True Exercises With Plants." The descriptions pertain to ordinary typical species in greater part, but garden-varieties receive special attention. Among these a long list of double flowers are to be seen. Double varieties of poppies, liverleaf (*Hepatica*), wallflowers (*Cheiranthus*), violets, *Caltha*, *Althaea*, *Colchicum*, and periwinkles (*Vinca*), and a great many other common flowers were already in cultivation at that time.

Other double forms have been since added. Many have been introduced from Japan, especially the Japanese marigold, *Chrysanthemum indicum*. Others have been derived from Mexico, as for instance the double zinnias. The single dahlias only seem to have been originally known to the inhabitants of Mexico. They were introduced into Spain at about 1789, and the first double ones were produced in Louvain, Belgium, in 1814. The method of their origin has not been described, and probably escaped the originators themselves. But in historical records we find the curious statement that it took place after three years' work. This indicates a distinct plan, and the possibility of carrying it to a practical conclusion within a few years' time.

Something more is known about other cases. Garden anemones, *Anemone coronaria,* are said to have become double in the first half of the last century in an English nursery. The owner, Williamson, observing in his beds a flower with a single broadened stamen, saved its seeds separately, and in the next generations procured beautifully filled flowers. These he afterwards had crossed by bees with a number of colored varieties, and in this way succeeded in producing many new double types of anemone.

The first double petunia is known to have suddenly and accidentally arisen from ordinary seed in a private garden at Lyons about 1855. From this one plant all double races and varieties have been derived by natural and partly by artificial crosses. Carrière, who reported this fact, added that likewise other species were known at that time to produce new double varieties rapidly. The double fuchsias originated about the same time (1854) and ten years later the range of double varieties of this plant had become so large that Carrière found it impossible to enumerate all of them.

Double carnations seem to be relatively old, double corn-flowers and double blue-bells being of a later period. A long list could easily be made, to show that during the whole history of horticulture double varieties have arisen from time to time. As far as we can judge, such appearances have been isolated and sudden. Sometimes they sprang into existence in the full display of their beauty, but most commonly they showed themselves for the first time, exhibiting only spare supernumerary petals. Whenever such sports were worked up, a few years sufficed to reach the entire development of the new varietal attribute.

From this superficial survey of historical facts, the inference is forced upon us that the chance of producing a new double variety is good enough to justify the attempt. It has frequently succeeded for practical purposes, why should it not succeed as well for purely scientific investigation? At all events the type recommends itself to the student of nature, both on account of its frequency, and of the apparent insignificance of the first step, combined with the possibility of rapidly working up from this small beginning of one superfluous petal towards the highest degree of duplication.

Compared with the tedious experimental production of the peloric toad-flax, the attempt to produce a double flower has a distinct attraction. The peloric toad-flax is nothing new; the experiment was only a repetition of what presumably takes place often within the same species. To attempt to produce a double variety we may choose any species, and of course should select one which as yet has not been known to produce double flowers. By doing so we will, if we succeed, produce something new. Of course, it does not matter whether the new variety has an horticultural interest or not, and it seems preferable to choose a wild or little cultivated species, to be quite sure that the variety in question is not already in existence. Finally the prospect of success seems to be enhanced if a species is chosen, the nearest allies of which are known to have produced double flowers.

For these reasons and others I chose for my experiment the corn-marigold, or *Chrysanthemum segetum.* It is also called the golden cornflower. In the wheat and rye fields of central Europe it associates with the blue-bottle or blue corn-flower. It is sometimes cultivated and the seeds are offered for sale by many nurserymen. It has a cultivated variety, called *grandiflorum,* which is esteemed for its brilliancy and long succession of golden bloom. This variety has larger flower-heads, surrounded with a fuller border of ray-florets the species belongs to a genus many species of which have produced double varieties. One of them is the Japanese marigold, others are the *carinatum* and the *imbricatum* species. Nearly allied are quite a number of garden-plants with double flower-heads. among which are the double camomiles.

My attention was first drawn to the structure of the heads and especially to the number of the ray-florets of the corn-marigold. The species appertains to that group of composites which have a head of small tubular florets surrounded by a broad border of rays. These rays, when counted, are observed to occur in definite numbers, which are connected with each other by a formula, known as " the series " of Braun and Schimper. In this formula, which commences with 1 and 2, each number is equal to the sum of the two foregoing figures. Thus 5, 8 and 13 are very frequent occurrences, and the following number, 21, is a most general one for apparently full rays, such as in daisies, camomiles, *Arnica* and many other wild and cultivated species.

These numbers are not at all constant. They are only the averages, around which the real numbers fluctuate. There may even be an overlapping of the extremes, since the fluctuation around 13 may even go beyond 8 and 21, and so on. But such extremes are only found in stray flowers, occurring on the same individuals with the lesser degrees of deviation.

Now the marigold averages 13, and the *grandiflorum* 21 rays. The wild species is pure in this respect, but the garden-variety is not. The seeds which are offered for sale usually contain a mixture of both forms and their hybrids. So I had to isolate the pure types from this mixture and to ascertain their constancy and mutual independency. To this end I isolated from the mixture first the 13-rayed, and afterwards the 21-rayed types. As the marigolds are not sufficiently self-fertile, and are not easily pollinated artificially, it seemed impossible to carry on these two experiments at the same time and in the same garden. I devoted the first three years to the lower form, isolated some individuals with 12 – 13 rays out of the mixture of 1892 and counted the ray-florets on the terminal head of every plant of the ensuing generation next year. I cultivated and counted in this way above 150 individuals and found an average of exactly 13 with comparatively few individuals displaying 14 or only 12 rays, and with the remainder of the plants grouped symmetrically around this average. I continued the experiment for still another year and found the same group of figures. I was then satisfied as to the purity of the isolated strain. Next year I sowed a new mixture in order to isolate the reputed pure *grandiflorum* type. During the beginning of the flowering period I ruthlessly threw away all plants displaying less than 21 rays in the first or terminal head. But this selection was not to be considered as complete, because the 13-rayed race may eventually transgress its boundary and come over to the 21 and more. This made a second selection necessary. On the selected plants all the secondary heads were inspected and their ray-florets counted. Some individuals showed an average of about 13 and were destroyed. Others gave doubtful figures and were likewise eliminated, and only 6 out of a lot of nearly 300 flowering plants reached an average of 21 for all of the flowers.

Our summer is a short one, compared with the long and beautiful summer of California, and it was too late to cut off the faded and the open flowers, and await new ones, which might be purely fertilized after the destruction of all minor plants. So I had to gather the seed from flowers, which might have been partially fertilized by the wrong pollen. This however, is not so great a drawback in selection experiments as might be supposed at first sight. The selection of the following year is sure to eliminate the offspring of such impure parentage.

A far more important principle is that of the hereditary percentage, already discussed in our lecture on the selection of monstrosities. In our present case it had to be applied only to the six selected plants of 1895. To this end the seeds of each of them were sown separately, the ray-florets of the terminal heads of each of the new generation were counted, and curves and averages were made up for the six groups. Five of them gave proof of still being mixtures and were wholly rejected. The children of the sixth parent, however, formed a group of uniform constitution, all fluctuating around the desired average of 21. All in all the terminal heads of over 1500 plants have been subjected to the somewhat tedious work of counting their ray-florets. And this not in the laboratory, but in the garden, without cutting them off. Otherwise it would obviously have been impossible to recognize the best plants for preservation. I chose only two plants which in addition recommended themselves by the average number of rays on their secondary heads, sowed their seeds next year separately and compared the numerical constitution of their offspring. Both groups averaged 21 and were distributed very symmetrically around this mean. This result showed that no further selection could be of any avail, and that I had succeeded in purifying the 21-rayed *grandiflorum* variety.

It is from this *grandiflorum* that I have finally produced my double variety. In the year 1896 I selected from among the above quoted 1500 plants, 500 with terminal heads bearing 21 or more rays. On these I counted the rays of all the secondary heads about the middle of August (1896) and found that they had, as a rule, retrograded to lower figures. On many thousands of heads only two were found having 22 rays. All others had the average number of 21 or even less. I isolated the individual which bore these two heads, allowed them to be fertilized by insects with the pollen of some of the best plants of the same group, but destroyed the remainder.

This single exceptional plant has been the starting point of my double variety. It was not remarkable for its terminal head, which exhibited the average number of rays of the 21-rayed race. Nor was it distinguished by the average figure for all its heads. It was only selected because it was the one plant which had some secondary heads with one ray more than all the others. This indication was very slight, and could not have been detected save by the counting of the rays of thousands of heads.

But the rarity of the anomaly was exactly the indication wanted, and the same deviation would have had no signification whatever, had it occurred in a group fluctuating symmetrically around the average figure. On the other hand, the observed anomaly was only an indication, and no guarantee of future developments.

Here it should be remarked that the indication alluded to was not the appearance of the expected character of doubling in ever so slight a measure. It was only a guide to be followed in further work. The real character of double flower-heads among composites lies in the production of rays on the disk. No increase of the number of the outer rays can have the same significance. A hasty inspection of double flower-heads may convey the idea that all rays are arranged around a little central cluster of disk-florets, the remainder of the original disk. But a closer investigation will always reveal the fallacy of this conclusion. Hidden between the inner rays, and covered by them, lie the little tubular and fertile florets everywhere on the disk. They may not be easily seen, but if the supernumerary rays are pulled out, the disk may be seen to bear numerous small florets at intervals. But these intervals are not at all numerous, showing thereby that only a relatively small number of tubes has been converted into rays. This conversion is obviously the true mark of the doubling, and before traces of it are found, no assertion whatever can be given as to the issue of the pedigree-experiment.

Three more years were required before this first, but decisive trace was discovered. During these years I subjected my strain to the same sharp selection as has already been described. The chosen ancestor of the race had flowered in 1896, and the next year I sowed its seeds only. From this generation I chose the one plant with the largest number of rays in its terminal head, and repeated this in the following year.

The consequence was that the average number of rays increased rapidly, and with it the absolute maximum of the whole strain. The average came up from 21 to 34. Brighter and brighter crowns of the yellow rays improved my race, until it became difficult and very time-consuming to count all the large rays of the borders. The largest numbers determined in the succeeding generations increased by leaps from 21 to 34 in the first year, and thence to 48 and 66 in the two succeeding summers. Every year I was able to save enough seed from the very best plant and to use it only for the continuance of the race. Before the selected plants were allowed to open the flowers from which the seed was to be gathered, nearly the whole remaining culture was exterminated, excepting only some of the best examples, in order to have the required material for cross-pollination by insects. Each new generation was thereby as sharply selected as possible with regard to both parents.

All flower-heads were of course closely inspected. Not the slightest indication of real doubling was discovered, even in the summer of 1899 in the fourth generation of my selected race. But among the best the new character suddenly made its appearance. It was at the commencement of September (1899), too late to admit of the seeds ripening before winter. An inspection of the younger heads was made, which revealed three heads with some few rays in the midst of the disk on one plant, the result of the efforts of four years. Had the germ of the mutation lain hidden through all this time? Had it been present, though dormant in the original sample of seed? Or had an entirely new creation taken place during my continuous endeavors? Perhaps as their more or less immediate result? It is obviously impossible to answer these questions, before further and similar experiments shall have been performed, bringing to light other details that will enable us to reach a more definite conclusion.

The fact that the origination of such forms is accessible to direct investigation is proven quite independently of all further considerations. The new variety came into existence at once. The leap may have been made by the ancestor of the year 1895, or by the plant of 1899, which showed the first central rays, or the sport may have been gradually built up during those four years. In each case there was a leap, contrasting with the view which claims a very long succession of years for the development of every new character.

Having discovered this first trace of doubling, it was to be expected that the new variety would be at once as pure and as rich as other double composites usually are. Some effect of the crossing with the other seed-bearing individuals might still disturb this uniformity in the following year, but another year's work would eliminate even this source of impurity.

These two years have given the expected result. The average number of the rays, which had already arisen from 13 to 34 now at once came up to 47 and 55, the last figure being the sum of 21 and 34 and therefore the probable uttermost limit to be reached before absolute doubling. The maximum numbers came as high as 100 in 1900, and reached even 200 in 1901. Such heads are as completely double as are the brightest heads of the most beautiful double commercial varieties of composites. Even the best white camomiles (*Chrysanthemum inodorum*) and the gold-flowers or garden-marigolds (*Calendula officinalis*) do not come nearer to purity since they always have scores of little tubular florets between the rays on their disks.

Real atavists or real reversionists were seen no more after the first purification of the race. I have continued my culture and secured last summer (1903) as many and as completely doubled heads as previously. The race has at once become permanent and constant. It has of course a wide range of fluctuating variability, but the lower limit has been worked up to about 34 rays, a figure never reached by the *grandiflorum* parent, from which my new variety is thus sharply separated.

Unfortunately the best flowers and even the best individuals of my race are wholly barren. Selection has reached its practical limit. Seeds must be saved from less dense heads, and no way has been found of avoiding it. The rayflorets are sterile, even in the wild species, and when growing in somewhat large numbers on the disk, they conceal the fertile flowers from the visiting insects, and cause them also to be sterile. The same is the case with the best cultivated forms. Their showiest individuals are barren, and incapable of the reproduction of the race.

This last is therefore, of necessity, always continued by means of individuals whose deviation from the mean average is the least. But in many cases the varieties are so highly differentiated that selection has become quite superfluous for practical purposes. I have already discussed the question as to the actual moment, in which the change of the *grandiflorum* variety into the new *plenum* form must be assumed to have taken place. In this respect some stress is to be laid on the fact that the improvement through selection has been gradual and continuous, though very rapid from the first moment. But with the appearance of the first stray rays within the disk, this continuity suddenly changed. All the children of this original mutated plant showed the new character, the rays within the disk, without exception. Not on all the heads, nor even on the majority of the heads on some individuals, but on some heads all gave clear proof of the possession of the new attribute. This was present in all the representatives of the new race, and had never been seen in any of their parents and grandparents. Here there was evidently a sudden leap, at least in the external form of the plants. And it seems to me to be the most simple conception, that this visible leap directly corresponded to that inner change, which brought about the complete inheritability of the new peculiarity. It is very interesting to observe how completely my experience agrees with the results of the observations of breeders at large. No doubt a comparison is difficult, and the circumstances are not adequate to a close study.

Isolation and selection have been applied commonly only so far as was consistent with the requirements of practical horticulture, and of course a determination of the hereditary percentage was never made. The disregard of this feature made necessary a greater length of time and a larger number of generations to bring about the desired changes. Notwithstanding this, however, it has been seen that double varieties are produced suddenly. This may have occurred unexpectedly or after a few years' effort toward the end desired. Whether this sudden appearance is the consequence of a single internal differentiating step, or of the rapid succession of lesser changes, cannot yet be made out. The extreme variability of double flowers and the chance of their appearance with only slight indications of the previous petaloid alterations of a few stamens may often result in their origin being overlooked, while subsequent generations may come in for full notice. In the greater number of cases recorded it remains doubtful whether the work said to be done to obtain a new double variety was done before the appearance of these preliminary indications or afterward.

In the first case, it would correspond with our selection of large numbers of florets in the outer rays, in the second however, with the ordinary purification of new races from hybrid mixtures.

In scientific selection-experiments such crosses are of course avoided, and the process of purification is unnecessary, even as in the *Chrysanthemum* culture. The first generation succeeding the original plant with disk-rays was in this respect wholly uniform and true to the new type.

In practice the work does not start from such slight indications, and is done with no other purpose in view than to produce double flowers in species in which they did not already exist. Therefore it is of the highest importance to know the methods used and the chances of success. Unfortunately the evidence is very scanty on both points.

Lindley and other writers on horticultural theory and practice assert that a large amount of nourishment tends to produce double flowers, while a culture under normal conditions, even if the plants are very strong and healthy, has no such effect. But even here it remains doubtful whether it applies to the period before or after the internal mutation. On the other hand success is not at all to be relied upon, nor is the work to be regarded as easy. The instances of double flowers said to be obtainable at will, are too rare in comparison with the number of cases, where the first indication of them was found accidentally.

Leaving all these doubtful points, which will have to be cleared up by further scientific investigation, the high degree of variability requires further discussion. It may be considered from three different points of view according to the limit of the deviation from the average, to the dependency on external conditions and to periodicity. It seems best to take up the last two points first.

On a visit to a nursery at Erfurt I once inspected an experiment with a new double variety of the common blue-bottle or blue corn-flower. The plants were dependent on the weather to a high degree. Bad weather increased the number of poorly filled flower-heads, while warm and sunny days were productive of beautiful double flowers. The heads that are borne by strong branches have a greater tendency to become double than those of the weaker ones, and towards the autumn, when all those of the first group are faded away, and only a weak though large section of the heads is still flowering, the whole aspect of the variety gradually retrogrades. The same law of dependency and periodicity is prevalent everywhere. In my own cultures of the improved field-marigold I have observed it frequently. The number of the ray-florets may be considered as a direct response to nourishment, both when this is determined by external circumstances, and when it depends on the particular strength of the branch, which bears the head in question. It is a case exactly similar to that of the supernumerary carpels of the pistilloid poppy, and the deductions arrived at with that variety may be applied directly to double flowers.

This dependency upon nourishment is of high practical importance in combination with the usual effect of the doubling which makes the flowers sterile. It is a general rule that the most perfect flowers do not produce seed. At the height of the flowering period the external circumstances are the most favorable, and the flowering branches still constitute the stronger axes of the plants. Hence we may infer that sterility will prevail precisely in this period. Many varieties are known to yield only seeds from the very last flowers, as for instance some double begonias. Others bear only seed on their weaker lateral branches, as the double camomile, or become fertile only towards the fall, as is often the case with the above quoted Erfurt variety of the blue-bottle. As far as I have been able to ascertain, such seeds are quite adequate for the reproduction and perpetuation of the double varieties, but the question whether there are differences between the seeds of the more or less double flowers of the same plants still remains open. It is very probable, from a theoretical point of view, that such differences exist, but perhaps they are so slight, as to have practically no bearing on the question.

On the ground of their wide range of variability, the double varieties must be regarded as pertaining to the group of ever-sporting forms. On one side they fluctuate in the direction towards such petalomanous flowers as are borne by the stocks and others, which we have previously discussed. Here no trace of the fertile organs is left. But this extreme is never reached by petaloid double flowers. A gap remains which, often overlooked, always exists, and which sharply separates the two types. On the other hand the alteration of the stamens gradually relapses to perfectly single flowers. Here the analogy with the pistillody of the poppies and with the " five-leaved " clover is obvious.

This conception of the inner nature of double flowers explains the fact that the varietal mark is seldom seen to be complete throughout larger groups of individuals, providing these have not been already selected by this character. *Tagetes africana* is liable to produce some poorly filled specimens, and some double varieties of carnations are offered for sale with the note that the seed yields only 80% of doubles. With *Chrysanthemum coronarium* and blue-bottles this figure is often announced to be only about 50%. No doubt it is partly due to impurities, caused by vicinism, but it is obviously improbable that the effect of these impurities should be so large.

Some cases of partial reversion may be interpreted in the same way. Among the garden anemones, *Anemone coronaria,* there is a variety called the "Bride," on account of its pure white flowers. It is for sale with single and with double flowers, and these two forms are known to sport into one another, although they are multiplied in the vegetative way. Such cases are known to be of quite ordinary occurrence. Of course such sports must be considered as partial, and the same stem may bear both types of flowers. It even happens that some particular flower is partly double and partly single. Mr. Krelage, of Haarlem, had the kindness to send me such a curious flower. One half of it was completely double, while the other half was entirely single, bearing normal and fertile stamens in the ordinary number.

The same halfway doubling is recorded to occur among composites sometimes, and from the same source I possess in my collection a head of *Pyrethrum roseum,* bearing on half of its disk elongated corolla tubes, and on the other half the small disk-florets of the typical species.

It is a current belief, that varieties are improved by continued culture. I have never been able to ascertain the grounds on which this conviction rests. It may be referred either to the purity of the race or to the complete development of the varietal character. In the first case it is a question of hybrid mixtures from which many young varieties must be freed before being placed on the market. But as we have already seen in a former lecture, this requires only three or four years, and afterwards the degree of purity is kept up to the point which proves to be the most suitable for practical purposes. The complete development of the varietal character is a question restricted to ever-sporting varieties, since in white flowers and other constant varieties this degree is variable in a very small and unimportant measure. Hence the double flowers seem to afford a very good example for this discussion.

It can be decided by two facts. First by a consideration of the oldest double varieties, and secondly by that of the very youngest. Are the older ones now in a better condition than at the outset? Have they really been gradually improved during the centuries of their existence? Obviously this can only be answered by a comparison of the figures given by older writers, with the varieties as they are now in culture. Munting's drawings and descriptions are now nearly two centuries and a half old, but I do not find any real difference between his double varieties and their present representatives. So it is in other cases in which improvements by crossing or the introduction of new forms does not vitiate the evidence. Double varieties, as a rule, are exactly the same now, as they were at the time of their first introduction.

If this were otherwise one would expect that young double varieties should in the main display only slight grades of the anomaly, and that they would require centuries to reach their full development. Nothing of the kind is on record. On the contrary the newest double sorts are said to be not only equal to their predecessors, but to excel them. As a rule such claims may be exaggerated, but not to any great extent.

This is proven in the simplest way by the result of our own experiment.

In the double field-marigold we have the very first generation of a variety of pure and not hybrid origin. It shows the new attribute in its full development. It has flower-heads nearly as completely filled as the best double varieties of allied cultivated composites. In the second generation it reached heads with 200 rays each, and much larger numbers will seldom be seen in older species on heads of equal size. I have compared my novelty with the choicest double camomiles and others, but failed to discover any real difference. Improvement of the variety developed in the experiments carried on by myself seems to be excluded by the fact that it comes into conflict with the same difficulty that confronts the older cultivated species, viz.: the increasing sterility of the race.

It is perfectly evident that this double marigold is now quite constant. Continuously varying about a fixed average it may live through centuries, but the mean and the limits will always remain the same, as in the case of the ever-sporting varieties.

Throughout this lecture I have spoken of double flowers and double flower-heads of composites as of one single group. They are as nearly related from the hereditary point of view, as they are divergent in other respects. It would be superfluous to dwell any longer upon the difference between heads and flowers. But it is as well to point out, that the term double flowers indicates a motley assemblage of different phenomena. The hen-and-chicken daisy, and the corresponding variety of the garden-cineraria (*Cineraria cruenta*), are extremes on one side. The hen-and-chicken type occurs even in other families and is known to produce most curious anomalies, as with *Scabiosa*, the supernumerary heads of which may be produced on long stalks and become branched themselves in the same manner.

Petalody of the stamens is well known to be the ordinary type of doubling. But it is often accompanied by a multiplication of the organs, both of the altered stamens and of the petals themselves. This proliferation may consist in median or in lateral cleavages, and in both cases the process may be repeated one or more times. It would be quite superfluous to give more details, which may be gathered from any morphologic treatise on double flowers. But from the physiologic point of view all these cases are to be considered as one large group, complying with previously given definitions of the ever-sporting varieties. They are very variable and wholly permanent. Obviously this permanency agrees perfectly with the conception of their sudden origin.

Lecture XVIII

NEW SPECIES OF OENOTHERA

In our experiments on the origin of peloric varieties and double flowers we were guided in the choice of our material by a survey of the evidence already at hand. We chose the types known to be most commonly produced anew, either in the wild state or under the conditions of cultivation. In both instances our novelty was a variety in the ordinary sense of the word. Our pedigree-culture was mainly an experimental demonstration of the validity of conclusions, which had previously been deduced from such observations as can be made after the accidental birth of new forms.

From these facts, and even from these pedigree-experiments, it is scarcely allowable to draw conclusions as to the origin of real species. If we want to know how species originate, it is obviously necessary to have recourse to direct observation. The question is of the highest importance, both for the theory of descent, and for our conception of the real nature of systematic affinities at large. Many authors have tried to solve it on the ground of comparative studies and of speculations upon the biologic relations of plants and animals. But in vain. Contradiction and doubt still reign supreme. All our hopes now rest on the result of experiments.

Unfortunately such experiments seemed simply impossible a few years ago. What is to guide us in the choice of the material? The answer may only be expected from a consideration of elementary species. For it is obvious that they only can be observed to originate, and that the systematic species, because they are only artificial groups of lower unities, can never become the subject of successful experimental inquiry.

In previous lectures we tried to clear up the differences existing between nearly related elementary species. We have seen that they affect all of the attributes of the plants, each of them changing in some measure all of the organs. Nevertheless they were due to distinct unities and of the lowest possible degree. Such unit-steps may therefore be expected to become visible some time or other by artificial means. On the other hand, mutations as a rule make their appearance in groups, and there are many systematic species which on close inspection have been shown to be in reality composite assemblages. Roses and brambles, hawkweeds and willows are the best known examples. Violets and *Draba verna,* dandelions and helianthemums and many other instances were dealt with in previous lectures. Even wheat and barley and corn afford instances of large groups of elementary species. Formerly mixed in the fields, they became separated during the last century, and now constitute constant races, which, for brevity's sake, are dealt with under the name of varieties.

In such groups of nearly allied forms the single members must evidently be of common origin. It is not necessary for them to have originated all in the same place or at the same time. In some cases, as with *Draba verna,* the present geographic distribution points to a common birthplace, from whence the various forms may about the same period have radiated in all directions. The violets on the other hand seem to include widely diffused original forms, from which branches have started at different times and in different localities.

The origin of such groups of allied forms must therefore be the object of our research. Perhaps we might find a whole group, perhaps only part of it. In my opinion we have the right to assume that if *Draba* and violets and others have formerly mutated in this way, other species must at present be in the same changeable condition. And if mutations in groups, or such periodic mutations should be the rule, it is to be premised that these periods recur from time to time, and that many species must even now be in mutating condition, while others are not.

It is readily granted that the constant condition of species is the normal one, and that mutating periods must be the exception. This fact does not tend to increase our prospect of discovering a species in a state of mutability. Many species will have to be tested before finding an instance. On the other hand, a direct trial seems to be the only way to reach the goal. No such special guides as those that led us to the choice of pelories and double flowers are available. The only indication of value is the presumption that a condition of mutability might be combined with a general state of variability at large, and that groups of plants of very uniform features might be supposed to be constant in this respect too. On the contrary, anomalies and deviations if existent in the members of one strain, or found together in one native locality of a species, might be considered as an indication in the desired direction.

Few plants vary in the wild state in such a

measure as to give distinct indications. All have to be given a trial in the garden under conditions as similar as possible to their natural environments. Cultivated plants are of course to be excluded. Practically they have already undergone the experience in question and can not be expected to change their habits soon enough. Moreover they are often of hybrid origin. The best way is to experiment with the native plants of one's own country.

I have made such experiments with some hundred species that grow wild in Holland. Some were very variable, as for instance, the jointed charlock (*Raphanus Raphanistrum*) and the narrow-leaved plantain (*Plantago lanceolata*). Others seemed more uniform, but many species, collected without showing any malformation, subsequently produced them in my garden, either on the introduced plants themselves or among their offspring. From this initial material I have procured a long series of hereditary races, each with some peculiar anomaly for its special character. But this result was only a secondary gain, a meager consolation for the negative fact that no real mutability could be discovered.

My plants were mostly annuals or biennials, or such perennials as under adequate treatment might produce flowers and seeds during their first summer. It would be of no special use to enumerate them. The negative result does not apply to the species as such, but only to the individual strain, which I collected and cultivated. Many species, which are quite constant with us, may be expected to be mutable in other parts of their range.

Only one of all my tests met my expectations. This species proved to be in a state of mutation, producing new elementary forms continually, and it soon became the chief member of my experimental garden. It was one of the evening-primroses.

Several evening-primroses have at different times been introduced into European gardens from America. From thence they have spread into the vicinity, becoming common and exhibiting the behavior of indigenous types. *Oenothera biennis* was introduced about 1614 from Virginia, or nearly three centuries ago. *O. muricata,* with small corollas and narrow leaves, was introduced in the year 1789 by John Hunneman, and *O. suaveolens,* or sweet-scented primrose, a form very similar to the *biennis,* about the same time, in 1778, by John Fothergill. This form is met with in different parts of France, while the *biennis* and *muricata* are very common in the sandy regions of Holland, where I have observed them for more than 40 years. They are very constant and have proven so in my experiments. Besides these three species, the large-flowered evening-primrose, or *Oenothera lamarckiana,* is found in some localities in Holland and elsewhere. We know little concerning its origin. It is supposed to have come from America in the same way as its congeners, but as yet I have not been able to ascertain on what grounds this supposition rests. As far as I know, it has not been seen growing wild in this country, though it may have been overlooked. The fact that the species of this group are subject to many systematic controversies and are combined by different writers into systematic species in different ways, being often considered as varieties of one or two types, easily accounts for it having been overlooked. However, it would be of great interest to ascertain whether *O. lamarckiana* yet grows in America, and whether it is in the same state of mutability here as it is in Holland.

The large-flowered evening-primrose was also cultivated about the beginning of the last century in the gardens of the Muséum d'Histoire Naturelle, at Paris, where it was noticed by Lamarck, who at once distinguished it as an undescribed species. He wrote a complete description of it and his type specimens are still preserved in the herbarium of the Museum, where I have compared them with the plants of my own culture. Shortly afterwards it was renamed by Seringe, in honor of its eminent discoverer, whose name it now bears. So Lamarck unconsciously discovered and described himself the plant, which after a century, was to become the means of an empirical demonstration of his far-reaching views on the common origin of all living beings.

Oenothera lamarckiana is considered in Europe as a garden-plant, much prized for parks and ornamental planting. It is cultivated by seed-merchants and offered for sale. It has escaped from gardens, and having abundant means for rapid multiplication, has become wild in many places. As far as I know its known localities are small, and it is to be presumed that in each of them the plant has escaped separately from culture. It was in this state that I first met with this beautiful species.

Lamarck's evening-primrose is a stately plant, with a stout stem, attaining often a height of 1.6 meters and more. When not crowded the main stem is surrounded by a large circle of smaller branches, growing upwards from its base so as often to form a dense bush. These branches in their turn have numerous lateral branches. Most of them are crowned with flowers in summer, which regularly succeed each other, leaving behind them long spikes of young fruits. The flowers are large and of a bright yellow color, attracting immediate attention, even from a distance. They open towards evening, as the name indicates, and are pollinated by humble-bees and moths. On bright days their duration is confined to one evening, but during cloudy weather they may still be found open on the following morning. Contrary to their congeners they are dependent on visiting insects for pollination. *O. biennis* and *O. muricata* have their stigmas in immediate contact with the anthers within the flower-buds, and as the anthers open in the morning preceding the evening of the display of the petals, fecundation is usually accomplished before the insects are let in. But in *O. lamarckiana* no such self-fertilization takes place. The stigmas are above the anthers in the bud, and as the style increases in length at the time of the opening of the corolla, they are elevated above the anthers and do not receive the pollen. Ordinarily the flowers remained sterile if not visited by insects or pollinated by myself, although rare instances of self-fertilization were seen.

In falling off, the flowers leave behind them a stout ovary with four cells and a large number of young seeds. The capsule, when ripe, opens at its summit with four valves, and contains often from two to three hundred seeds. A hundred capsules on the main stem is an average estimate, and the lateral branches may ripen even still more fruits, by which a very rapid dissemination is ensured.

This striking species was found in a locality near Hilversum, in the vicinity of Amsterdam, where it grew in some thousands of individuals. Ordinarily biennial, it produces rosettes in the first, and stems in the second year. Both the stems and the rosettes were at once seen to be highly variable, and soon distinct varieties could be distinguished among them.

The first discovery of this locality was made in 1886. Afterwards I visited it many times, often weekly or even daily during the first few years, and always at least once a year up to the present time. This stately plant showed the long-sought peculiarity of producing a number of new species every year. Some of them were observed directly on the field, either as stems or as rosettes. The latter could be transplanted into my garden for further observation, and the stems yielded seeds to be sown under like control. Others were too weak to live a sufficiently long time in the field. They were discovered by sowing seed from indifferent plants

of the wild locality in the garden. A third
and last method of getting still more new species from the original strain, was the repetition
of the sowing process, by saving and sowing
the seed which ripened on the introduced
plants. These various methods have led to the
discovery of over a dozen new types, never previously observed or described.

Leaving the physiologic side of the relations of these new forms for the next lecture,
it would be profitable to give a short description of the several novelties. To this end they
may be combined under five different heads, according to their systematic value. The first
head includes those which are evidently to be
considered as varieties, in the narrower sense
of the word, as previously given. The second
and third heads indicate the real progressive
elementary species, first those which are as
strong as the parent-species, and secondly a
group of weaker types, apparently not destined
to be successful. Under the fourth head I shall
include some inconstant forms, and under the
last head those that are organically incomplete.

Of varieties with a negative attribute, or real
retrograde varieties, I have found three, all of
them in a flowering condition in the field. I
have given them the names of *laevifolia, brevistylis* and *nanella*.

The *laevifolia,* or smooth-leaved variety, was one of the very first deviating types found in the original field. This was in the summer of 1887, seventeen years ago. It formed a little group of plants growing at some distance from the main body, in the same field. I found some rosettes and some flowering stems and sowed some seed in the fall. The variety has been quite constant in the field, neither increasing in number of individual plants nor changing its place, though now closely surrounded by other Lamarckianas. In my garden it has proved to be constant from seed, never reverting to the original *lamarckiana,* provided intercrossing was excluded.

It is chiefly distinguished from Lamarck's evening-primrose by its smooth leaves, as the name indicates. The leaves of the original form show numerous sinuosities in their blades, not at the edge, but anywhere between the veins. The blade shows numbers of convexities on either surface, the whole surface being undulated in this manner; it lacks also the brightness of the ordinary evening-primrose or *Oenothera biennis.*

These undulations are lacking or at least very rare on the leaves of the new *laevifolia.* Ordinarily they are wholly wanting, but at times single leaves with slight manifestations of this character may make their appearance. They warn us that the capacity for such sinuosities is not wholly lost, but only lies dormant in the new variety. It is reduced to a latent state, exactly as are the apparently lost characters of so many ordinary horticultural varieties.

Lacking the undulations, the *laevifolia*-leaves are smooth and bright. They are a little narrower and more slender than those of the *Lamarckiana*. The convexities and concavities of leaves are said to be useful in dry seasons, but during wet summers, such as those of the last few years, they must be considered as very harmful, as they retain some of the water which falls on the plants, prolonging the action of the water on the leaves. This is considered by some writers to be of some utility after slight showers, but was observed to be a source of weakness during wet weather in my garden, preventing the leaves from drying. Whether the *laevifolia* would do better under such circumstances, remains to be tested.

The flowers of the *laevifolia* are also in a slight degree different from those of *Lamarckiana*. The yellow color is paler and the petals are smoother. Later, in the fall, on the weaker side branches these differences increase. The *laevifolia* petals become smaller and are often not emarginated at the apex, becoming ovate instead of obcordate. This shape is often the most easily recognized and most striking mark of the variety. In respect to the reproductive organs, the fertility and abundance of good seed, the *laevifolia* is by no means inferior or superior to the original species.

O. brevistylis, or the short-styled evening-primrose, is the most curious of all my new forms. It has very short styles, which bring the stigmas only up to the throat of the calyx-tube, instead of upwards of the anthers. The stigmas themselves are of a different shape, more flattened and not cylindrical. The pollen falls from the anthers abundantly on them, and germinates in the ordinary manner.

The ovary which in *lamarckiana* and in all other new forms is wholly underneath the calyx-tube, is here only partially so. This tube is inserted at some distance under its summit. The insertion divides the ovary into two parts: an upper and a lower one. The upper part is much reduced in breadth and somewhat attenuated, simulating a prolongation of the base of the style. The lower part is also reduced, but in another manner. At the time of flowering it is like the ovary of *lamarckiana,* neither smaller nor larger. But it is reached by only a very few pollen-tubes, and is therefore always incompletely fertilized. It does not fall off after the fading away of the flower, as unfertilized ovaries usually do; neither does it grow out, nor assume the upright position of normal capsules. It is checked in its development, and at the time of ripening it is nearly of the same length as in the beginning. Many of them contain no good seeds at all; from others I have succeeded in saving only a hundred seeds from thousands of capsules.

These seeds, if purely pollinated, and with the exclusion of the visits of insects, reproduce the variety entirely and without any reversion to the *lamarckiana* type.

Correlated with the detailed structures is the form of the flower-buds. They lack the high stigma placed above the anthers, which in the *lamarckiana,* by the vigorous growth of the style, extends the calyx and renders the flower-bud thinner and more slender. Those of the *brevistylis* are therefore broader and more swollen. It is quite easy to distinguish the individuals by this striking character alone, although it differs from the parent in other particulars.

The leaves of the *O. brevistylis* are more rounded at the tip, but the difference is only pronounced at times, slightly in the adult rosettes, but more clearly on the growing summits of the stems and branches. By this character, the plants may be discerned among the others, some weeks before the flowers begin to show themselves.

But the character by which the plants may be most easily recognized from a distance in the field is the failure of the fruits. They were found there nearly every year in varying, but always small numbers.

Leaving the short-styled primrose, we come now to the last of our group of retrograde varieties. This is the *O. nanella,* or the dwarf, and is a most attractive little plant. It is very short of stature, reaching often a height of only 20–30 cm., or less than one-fourth of that of the parent. It commences flowering at a height of 10–15 cm., while the parent-form often measures nearly a meter at this stage of its development. Being so very dwarfed the large flowers are all the more striking. They are hardly inferior to those of the *lamarckiana,* and agree with them in structure. When they fade away the spike is rapidly lengthened, and often becomes much longer than the lower or vegetative part of the stem.

The dwarfs are one of the most common mutations in my garden, and were observed in the native locality and also grown from seeds saved there. Once produced they are absolutely constant. I have tried many thousands of seeds from various dwarf mutants, and never observed any trace of reversion to the *lamarckiana* type. I have also cultivated them in successive generations with the same result. In a former lecture we have seen that contrary to the general run of horticultural belief, varieties are as constant as the best species, if kept free from hybrid admixtures. This is a general rule, and the exceptions, or cases of atavism are extremely rare. In this respect it is of great interest to observe that this constancy is not an acquired quality, but is to be considered as innate, because it is already fully developed at the very moment when the original mutation takes place.

From its first leaves to the rosette period, and through this to the lengthening of the stem, the dwarfs are easily distinguished from any other of their congeners. The most remarkable feature is the shape of the leaves. They are broader and shorter, and especially at the base they are broadened in such a way as to become apparently sessile. The stalk is very brittle, and any rough treatment may cause the leaves to break off. The young seedlings are recognizable by the shape of the first two or three leaves, and when more of them are produced, the rosettes become dense and strikingly different from others. Later leaves are more nearly like the parent-type, but the petioles remain short. The bases of the blades are frequently almost cordate, the laminæ themselves varying from oblong-ovate to ovate in outline.

The stems are often quite unbranched, or branched only at the base of the spike. Strong secondary stems are a striking attribute of the *lamarckiana* parent, but they are lacking, or almost so in the dwarfs. The stem is straight and short, and this, combined with the large crown of bright flowers, makes the dwarfs eminently suitable for bed or border plants. Unfortunately they are very sensitive, especially to wet weather.

Oenothera gigas and *O. rubrinervis,* or the giant, and the red-veined evening-primroses, are the names given to two robust and stout species, which seem to be equal in vigor to the parent-plant, while diverging from it in striking characters. Both are true elementary species, differentiated from *lamarckiana* in nearly all their organs and qualities, but not showing any preponderating character of a retrograde nature. Their differences may be compared with those of the elementary species of other genera, as for instance, of *Draba,* or of violets, as will be seen by their description.

The giant evening-primrose, though not taller in stature than *O. lamarckiana,* deserves its name because it is so much stouter in all respects. The stems are robust, often with twice the diameter of *lamarckiana* throughout. The internodes are shorter, and the leaves more numerous, covering the stems with a denser foliage. This shortness of the internodes extends itself to the spike, and for this reason the flowers and fruits grow closer together than on the parent-plant. Hence the crown of bright flowers, opening each evening, is more dense and more strikingly brilliant, so much the more so as the individual flowers are markedly larger than those of the parents. In connection with these characters, the flower-buds are seen to be much stouter than those of *lamarckiana*. The fruits attain only half the normal size, but are broader and contain fewer, but larger seeds.

The *rubrinervis* is in many respects a counterpart to the *gigas,* but its stature is more slender. The spikes and flowers are those of the *lamarckiana,* but the bracts are narrower. Red veins and red streaks on the fruits afford a striking differentiating mark, though they are not absolutely lacking in the parent-species. A red hue may be seen on the calyx, and even the yellow color of the petals is somewhat deepened in the same way. Young plants are often marked by the pale red tinge of the mid-veins, but in adult rosettes, or from lack of sunshine, this hue is often very faint.

The leaves are narrow, and a curious feature of this species is the great brittleness of the leaves and stems, especially in annual individuals, especially in those that make their stem and flowers in the first year. High turgidity and weak development of the mechanical and supporting tissues are the anatomical cause of this deficiency, the bast-fibers showing thinner walls than those of the parent-type under the microscope. Young stems of *rubrinervis* may be broken off by a sharp stroke, and show a smooth rupture across all the tissues, while those of *lamarckiana* are very tough and strong.

Both the giant and the red-veined species are easily recognized in the rosette-stage. Even the very young seedlings of the latter are clearly differentiated from the *lamarckiana,* but often a dozen leaves are required, before the difference may be seen. Under such circumstances the young plants must reach an age of about two months before it is possible to discern their characters, or at least before these characters have become reliable enough to enable us to judge of each individual without doubt. But the divergencies rapidly become greater. The leaves of *O. gigas* are broader, of a deeper green, the blade more sharply set off against the stalk, all the rosettes becoming stout and crowded with leaves. Those of *O. rubrinervis* on the contrary are thin, of a paler green and with a silvery white surface; the blades are elliptic, often being only 2 cm. or less in width. They are acute at the apex and gradually narrowed into the petiole.

It is quite evident that such pale narrow leaves must produce smaller quantities of organic food than the darker green and broad organs of the *gigas*. Perhaps this fact is accountable partly, at least, for the more robust growth of the giant in the second year. Perhaps also some relation exists between this difference in chemical activity and the tendency to become annual or biennial. The *gigas*, as a rule, produces far more, and the *rubrinervis* far less biennial plants than the *lamarckiana*. Annual culture for the one is as unreliable as biennial culture for the other. *Rubrinervis* may be annual in apparently all specimens, in sunny seasons, but *gigas* will ordinarily remain in the state of rosettes during the entire first summer. It would be very interesting to obtain a fuller insight into the relation of the length of life to other qualities, but as yet the facts can only be detailed as they stand.

Both of these stout species have been found

quite constant from the very first moment of their appearance. I have cultivated them from seed in large numbers, and they have never reverted to the *lamarckiana*. From this they have inherited the mutability or the capacity of producing at their turn new mutants. But they seem to have done so incompletely, changing in the direction of more absolute constancy. This was especially observed in the case of *rubrinervis*, which is not of such rare occurrence as *O. gigas*, and which it has been possible to study in large numbers of individuals. So for instance, " the red-veins " have never produced any dwarfs, notwithstanding they are produced very often by the parent-type. And in crossing experiments also the red-veins gave proof of the absence of a mutative capacity for their production.

Leaving the robust novelties, we may now take up a couple of forms, which are equally constant, and differentiated from the parent-species in exactly the same manner, though by other characters, but which are so obviously weak as to have no manifest chance of self-maintenance in the wild state. These are the whitish and the oblong-leaved evening-primroses or the *Oenothera albida* and *oblonga*.

Oenothera albida is a very weak species, with whitish, narrow leaves, which are evidently incapable of producing sufficient quantities of organic food. The young seedling-plants are soon seen to lag behind, and if no care is taken of them they are overgrown by their neighbors. It is necessary to take them out, to transplant them into pots with richly manured soil, and to give them all the care that should be given to weak and sickly plants. If this is done fully grown rosettes may be produced, which are strong enough to keep through the winter. In this case the individual leaves become stronger and broader, with oblong blades and long stalks, but retain their characteristic whitish color.

In the second year the stems become relatively stout. Not that they become equal to those of *lamarckiana,* but they become taller than might have been expected from the weakness of the plants in the previous stages. The flowers and racemes are nearly as large as those of the parent-form, the fruits only a little thinner and containing a smaller quantity of seed. From these seeds I have grown a second and a third generation, and observed that the plants remain true to their type.

O. oblonga may be grown either as an annual, or as a biennial. In the first case it is very slender and weak, bearing only small fruits and few seeds. In the alternative case however, it becomes densely branched, bearing flowers on quite a number of racemes and yielding a full harvest of seeds. But it always remains a small plant, reaching about half the height of that of *lamarckiana*.

When very young it has broader leaves, but in the adult rosettes the leaves become very narrow, but fleshy and of a bright green color. They are so crowded as to leave no space between them unoccupied. The flowering spikes of the second year bear long leaf-like bracts under the first few flowers, but those arising later are much shorter. Numerous little capsules cover the axis of the spike after the fading away of the petals, constituting a very striking differentiating mark. This species also was found to be quite constant, if grown from pure seed.

We have now given the descriptions of seven new forms, which diverge in different ways from the parent-type. All were absolutely constant from seed. Hundreds or thousands of seedlings may have arisen, but they always come true and never revert to the original *O. lamarckiana* type. From this they have inherited the condition of mutability, either completely or partly, and according to this they may be able to produce new forms themselves. But this occurs only rarely, and combinations of more than one type in one single plant seem to be limited to the admixture of the dwarf stature with the characters of the other new species.

These seven novelties do not comprise the whole range of the new productions of my *O. lamarckiana*. But they are the most interesting ones. Others, as the *O. semilata* and the *O. leptocarpa* are quite as constant and quite as distinct, but have no special claims for a closer description. Others again were sterile, or too weak to reach the adult stage and to yield seeds, and no reliable description or appreciation can be given on the ground of the appearance of a single individual.

Contrasted with these groups of constant forms are three inconstant types which we now take up. They belong to two different groups, according to the cause of their inconstancy. In one species which I call *O. lata,* the question of stability or instability must remain wholly unsolved, as only pistillate flowers are produced, and no seed can be fertilized save by the use of the pollen of another form, and therefore by hybridization. The other head comprises two fertile forms, *O. scintillans* and *O. elliptica,* which may easily be fertilized with their own pollen, but which gave a progeny only partly similar to the parents.

The *Oenothera lata* is a very distinct form

which was found more than once in the field, and recently (1902) in a luxuriant flowering specimen. It has likewise been raised from seeds collected in different years at the original station. It is also wholly pistillate. Apparently the anthers are robust, but they are dry, wrinkled and nearly devoid of contents. The inner wall of cells around the groups of pollen grow out instead of being resorbed, partly filling the cavity which is left free by the miscarriage of the pollen-grains. This miscarriage does not affect all the grains in the same degree, and under the microscope a few of them with an apparently normal structure may be seen. But the contents are not normally developed, and I have tried in vain to obtain fertilization with a large number of flowers. Only by cross-fertilization does *O. lata* produce seeds, and then as freely as the other species when self-fertilized. Of course its chance of ever founding a wild type is precluded by this defect.

O. lata is a low plant, with a limp stem, bent tips and branches, all very brittle, but with dense foliage and luxuriant growth. It has bright yellow flowers and thick flower-buds. But for an unknown reason the petals are apt to unfold only partially and to remain wrinkled throughout the flowering time. The stigmas are slightly divergent from the normal type, also being partly united with one another, and laterally with the summit of the style, but without detriment to their function.

Young seedlings of *lata* may be recognized by the very first leaves. They have a nearly orbicular shape and are very sharply set off against their stalk. The surface is very uneven, with convexities and concavities on both sides. This difference is lessened in the later leaves, but remains visible throughout the whole life of the plant, even during the flowering season. Broad, sinuate leaves with rounded tips are a sure mark of *O. lata*. On the summits of the stems and branches they are crowded so as to form rosettes.

Concerning inheritance of these characteristics nothing can be directly asserted because of the lack of pollen. The new type can only be perpetuated by crosses, either with the parent-form or some other mutant. I have fertilized it, as a rule, with *lamarckiana* pollen, but have often also used that from *nanella* and others. In doing so, the *lata* repeats its character in part of its offspring. This part seems to be independent of the nature of the pollen used, but is very variable according to external circumstances. On the average one-fourth of the offspring become *lata*, the others assuming the type of the pollen-parent, if this was a *lamarckiana* or partly this type and partly that of any other of the new species derived from *lamarckiana,* that might have been used as the pollen-parent. This average seems to be a general rule, recurring in all experiments, and remaining unchanged through a long series of successive generations. The fluctuations around this mean go up to nearly 50% and down nearly to 1%, but, as in other cases, such extreme deviations from the average are met with only exceptionally.

The second category includes the inconstant but perfectly fertile species. I have already given the names of the only two forms, which deserve to be mentioned here.

One of them is called *scintillans* or the shiny evening-primrose, because its leaves are of a deep green color with smooth surfaces, glistening in the sunshine. On the young rosettes these leaves are somewhat broader, and afterwards somewhat narrower than those of *O. lamarckiana* at the corresponding ages. The plants themselves always remain small, never reaching the stature of the ancestral type. They are likewise much less branched. They can easily be cultivated in annual generations, but then do not become as fully developed and as fertile as when flowering in the second year. The flowers have the same structure as those of the *lamarckiana,* but are of a smaller size.

Fertilizing the flowers artificially with their own pollen, excluding the visiting insects by means of paper bags, and saving and sowing the seed of each individual separately, furnishes all the requisites for the estimation of the degree of stability of this species. In the first few weeks the seed-pans do not show any unequality, and often the young plants must be replanted at wider intervals, before anything can be made out with certainty. But as soon as the rosettes begin to fill it becomes manifest that some of them are more backward than others in size. Soon the smaller ones show their deeper green and broader leaves, and thereby display the attributes of the *scintillans*. The other grow faster and stronger and exhibit all the characteristics of ordinary lamarckianas.

The numerical proportion of these two groups has been found different on different occasions. Some plants give about one-third *scintillans* and two-thirds *lamarckiana*, while the progeny of individuals of another strain show exactly the reverse proportion.

Two points deserve to be noticed. First the progeny of the *scintillans* appears to be mutable in a large degree, exceeding even the *lamarckiana*. The same forms that are produced most often by the parent-family are also most ordinarily met with among the offspring of the shiny evening-primrose. They are *oblonga*, *lata* and *nanella*. Oblonga was observed at times to constitute as much as 1% or more of the sowings of *scintillans,* while *lata* and *nanella* were commonly seen only in a few scattering individuals, although seldom lacking in experiments of a sufficient size.

Secondly the instability seems to be a constant quality, although the words themselves are at first sight, contradictory. I mean to convey the conception that the degree of instability remains unchanged during successive generations. This is a very curious fact, and strongly reminds us of the hereditary conditions of striped-flower varieties. But, on the contrary, the atavists, which are here the individuals with the stature and the characteristics of the *lamarckiana,* have become lamarckianas in their hereditary qualities, too. If their seed is saved and sown, their progeny does not contain any *scintillans,* or at least no more than might arise by ordinary mutations.

One other inconstant new species is to be noted, but as it was very rare both in the field and in my cultures, and as it was difficult of cultivation, little can as yet be said about it. It is the *Oenothera elliptica,* with narrow elliptical leaves and also with elliptical petals. It repeats its type only in a very small proportion of its seed.

All in all we thus have a group of a dozen new types, springing from an original form in one restricted locality, and seen to grow there, or arising in the garden from seeds collected from the original locality. Without any doubt the germs of the new types are fully developed within the seed, ready to be evolved at the time of germination. More favorable conditions in the field would no doubt allow all of the described new species to unfold their attributes there, and to come into competition with each other and with the common parents. But obviously this is only of secondary importance, and has no influence on the fact that a number of new types, analogous to the older swarms of *Draba, Viola* and of many other polymorphous species, have been seen to arise directly in the wild state.

Lecture XIX

EXPERIMENTAL PEDIGREE-CULTURES

The observation of the production of mutants in the field at Hilversum, and the subsequent cultivation of the new types in the garden at Amsterdam, gives ample proof of the mutability of plants. Furthermore it furnishes an analogy with the hypothetical origin of the swarms of species of *Draba* and *Viola*. Last but not least important it affords material for a complete systematic and morphologic study of the newly arisen group of forms.

The physiologic laws, however, which govern this process are only very imperfectly revealed by such a study. The instances are too few. Moreover the seeds from which the mutants spring, escape observation. It is simply impossible to tell from which individual plants they have been derived. The *laevifolia* and the *brevistylis* have been found almost every year, the first always recurring on the same spot, the second on various parts of the original field. It is therefore allowable to assume a common origin for all the observed individuals of either strain. But whether, besides this, similar strains are produced anew by the old *lamarckiana* group, it is impossible to decide on the sole ground of these field-observations.

The same holds good with the other novelties. Even if one of them should germinate repeatedly, without ever opening its flowers, the possibility could not be excluded that the seeds might have come originally from the same capsule but lain dormant in the earth during periods of unequal length.

Other objections might be cited that can only be met by direct and fully controlled experiments. Next to the native locality comes the experimental garden. Here the rule prevails that every plant must be fertilized with pollen of its own, or with pollen of other individuals of known and recorded origin. The visits of insects must be guarded against, and no seeds should be saved from flowers which have been allowed to open without this precaution. Then the seeds of each individual must be saved and sown separately, so as to admit of an appreciation, and if necessary, a numerical determination of the nature of its progeny. And last but not least the experiments should be conducted in a similar manner during a series of successive years.

I have made four such experiments, each comprising the handling of many thousands of individual plants, and lasting through five to nine generations. At the beginning the plants were biennial, as in the native locality, but later I learned to cultivate them in annual generations. They have been started from different plants and seeds, introduced from the original field into my garden at Amsterdam.

It seems sufficient to describe here one of these pedigree-cultures, as the results of all four were similar. In the fall of 1886 I took nine large rosettes from the field, planted them together on an isolated spot in the garden, and harvested their seeds the next year. These nine original plants are therefore to be considered as constituting the first generation of my race. The second generation was sown in 1888 and flowered in 1889. It at once yielded the expected result. 15000 seedlings were tested and examined, and among them 10 showed diverging characters. They were properly protected, and proved to belong to two new types. 5 of them were *lata* and 5 *nanella*. They flowered next year and displayed all the characters as described in our preceding lecture. Intermediates between them and the general type were not found, and no indication of their appearance was noted in their parents.

They came into existence at once, fully equipped, without preparation or intermediate steps. No series of generations, no selection, no struggle for existence was needed. It was a sudden leap into another type, a sport in the best acceptation of the word. It fulfilled my hopes, and at once gave proof of the possibility of the direct observation of the origin of species, and of the experimental control thereof.

The third generation was in the main a repetition of the second. I tried some 10000 seedlings and found three *lata* and three *nanella,* or nearly the same proportion as in the first instance. But besides these a *rubrinervis* made its appearance and flowered the following year. This fact at once revealed the possibility that the instability of *lamarckiana* might not be restricted to the three new types now under observation. Hence the question arose how it would be possible to obtain other types or to find them if they were present. It was necessary to have better methods of cultivation and examination of the young plants. Accordingly I devoted the three succeeding years to working on this problem.

I found that it was not at all necessary to sow any larger quantities of seed, but that the young plants must have room enough to develop into full and free rosettes. Moreover I observed that the attributes of *lata* and *nanella,* which I now studied in the offspring of my first mutants, were clearly discernible in extreme youth, while those of *rubrinervis* remained concealed some weeks longer. Hence I concluded that the young plants should be examined from time to time until they proved clearly to be only normal *lamarckiana*. Individuals exhibiting any deviation from the type, or even giving only a slight indication of it, were forthwith taken out of the beds and planted separately, under circumstances as favorable as possible. They were established in pots with well-manured soil and kept under glass, but fully exposed to sunshine. As a rule they grew very fast, and could be planted out early in June. Some of them, of course, proved to have been erroneously taken for mutants, but many exhibited new characters.

All in all I had 334 young plants which did not agree with the parental type. As I examined some 14000 seedlings altogether, the result was estimated at about 2.5%. This proportion is much larger than in the yields of the two first generations and illustrates the value of improved methods. No doubt many good mutations had been overlooked in the earlier observations.

As was to be expected, *lata* and *nanella*

were repeated in this third generation (1895). I was sure to get nearly all of them, without any important exceptions, as I now knew how to detect them at almost any age. In fact, I found many of them; as many as 60 *nanella* and 73 *lata*, or nearly .5% of each. *Rubrinervis* also recurred, and was seen in 8 specimens. It was much more rare than the two first-named types.

But the most curious fact in that year was the appearance of *oblonga*. No doubt I had often seen it in former years, but had not attached any value to the very slight differences from the type, as they then seemed to me. I knew now that any divergence was to be esteemed as important, and should be isolated for further observation. This showed that among the selected specimens not less than 176, or more than 1% belonged to the *oblonga* type. This type was at that time quite new to me, and it had to be kept through the winter, to obtain stems and flowers. It proved to be as uniform as its three predecessors, and especially as sharply contrasted with *lamarckiana*. The opportunity for the discovery of any intermediates was as favorable as could be, because the distinguishing marks were hardly beyond doubt at the time of the selection and removal of the young plants. But no connecting links were found.

The same holds good for *albida,* which appeared in 15 specimens, or in 0.1%, of the whole culture. By careful cultivation these plants proved not to be sickly, but to belong to a new, though weak type. It was evident that I had already seen them in former years, but having failed to recognize them had allowed them to be destroyed at an early age, not knowing how to protect them against adverse circumstances. Even this time I did not succeed in getting them strong enough to keep through the winter.

Besides these, two new types were observed, completing the range of all that have since been recorded to regularly occur in this family. They were *scintillans* and *gigas.* The first was obtained in the way just described. The other hardly escaped being destroyed, not having showed itself early enough, and being left in the bed after the end of the selection. But as it was necessary to keep some rosettes through the winter in order to have biennial flowering plants to furnish seeds, I selected in August about 30 of the most vigorous plants, planted them on another bed and gave them sufficient room for their stems and branches in the following summer. Most of them sent up robust shoots, but no difference was noted till the first flowers opened. One plant had a much larger crown of bright blossoms than any of the others.

As soon as these flowers faded away, and the young fruits grew out, it became clear that a new type was showing itself. On that indication I removed all the already fertilized flowers and young fruits, and protected the buds from the visits of insects. Thus the isolated flowers were fertilized with their own pollen only, and I could rely upon the purity of the seed saved. This lot of seeds was sown in the spring of 1897 and yielded a uniform crop of nearly 300 young *gigas* plants.

Having found how much depends upon the treatment, I could gradually decrease the size of my cultures. Evidently the chance of discovering new types would be lessened thereby, but the question as to the repeated production of the same new forms could more easily and more clearly be answered in this way. In the following year (1896) I sowed half as many seeds as formerly, and the result proved quite the same. With the exception of *gigas* all the described forms sprang anew from the purely fertilized ancestry of normal Lamarckianas. It was now the fifth generation of my pedigree, and thus I was absolutely sure that the descendants of the mutants of this year had been pure and without deviation for at least four successive generations.

Owing partly to improved methods of selection, partly no doubt to chance, even more mutants were found this year than in the former. Out of some 8000 seedlings I counted 377 deviating ones, or nearly 5%, which is a high proportion. Most of them were *oblonga* and *lata,* the same types that had constituted the majority in the former year.

Albida, nanella and *rubrinervis* appeared in large numbers, and even *scintillans,* of which I had but a single plant in the previous generation, was repeated sixfold.

New forms did not arise, and the capacity of my strain seemed exhausted. This conclusion was strengthened by the results of the next three generations, which were made on a much smaller scale and yielded the same, or at least the mutants most commonly seen in previous years.

Instead of giving the figures for these last two years separately, I will now summarize my whole experiment in the form of a pedigree. In this the normal *lamarckiana* was the main line, and seeds were only sown from plants after sufficient isolation either of the plants themselves, or in the latter years by means of paper bags enclosing the inflorescences. I have given the number of seedlings of *lamarckiana* which were examined each year in the table below. Of course by far the largest number of them were thrown away as soon as they showed their differentiating characters in order to make room for the remaining ones. At last only a few plants were left to blossom in order to perpetuate the race. I have indicated for each generation the number of mutants of each of the observed forms, placing them in vertical columns underneath their respective heads. The three first generations were biennial, but the five last annual.

PEDIGREE OF A MUTATING FAMILY OF OENOTHERA LAMARCKIANA IN THE EXPERIMENTAL GARDEN AT AMSTERDAM.

Gener:	O.gig.	albida	obl.	rubrin.	Lam.	nanella	lata.	scint.
VIII.		5	1	0	1700	21	1	
VII.			9	0	3000	11		
VI.		11	29	3	1800	9	5	1
V.		25	135	20	8000	49	142	6
IV.	1	15	176	8	14000	60	73	1
III.				1	10000	3	3	
II.					15000	5	5	
I.					9			

It is most striking that the various mutations of the evening-primrose display a great degree of regularity. There is no chaos of forms, no indefinite varying in all degrees and in all directions. Quite on the contrary, it is at once evident that very simple rules govern the whole phenomenon.

I shall now attempt to deduce these laws from

my experiment. Obviously they apply not only to our evening-primroses, but may be expected to be of general validity. This is at once manifest, if we compare the group of new mutants with the swarms of elementary forms which compose some of the youngest systematic species, and which, as we have seen before, are to be considered as the results of previous mutations. The difference lies in the fact that the evening-primroses have been seen to spring from their ancestors and that the drabas have not. Hence the conclusion that in comparing the two we must leave out the pedigree of the evening-primroses and consider only the group of forms as they finally show themselves. If in doing so we find sufficient similarity, we are justified in the conclusion that the drabas and others have probably originated in the same way as the evening-primroses. Minor points of course will differ, but the main lines cannot have complied with wholly different laws. All so-called swarms of elementary species obviously pertain to a single type, and this type includes our evening-primroses as the only controlled case.

Formulating the laws of mutability for the evening-primroses we therefore assume that they hold good for numerous other corresponding cases.

I. *The first law is, that new elementary species appear suddenly, without intermediate steps.*

This is a striking point, and the one that is in the most immediate contradiction to current scientific belief. The ordinary conception assumes very slow changes, in fact so slow that centuries are supposed to be required to make the differences appreciable. If this were true, all chance of ever seeing a new species arise would be hopelessly small. Fortunately the evening-primroses exhibit contrary tendencies. One of the great points of pedigree-culture is the fact that the ancestors of every mutant have been controlled and recorded. Those of the last year have seven generations of known *lamarckiana* parents preceding them. If there had been any visible preparation towards the coming mutation, it could not have escaped observation. Moreover, if visible preparation were the rule, it could hardly go on at the same time and in the same individuals in five or six diverging directions, producing from one parent, *gigas* and *nanella*, *lata* and *rubrinervis*, *oblonga* and *albida* and even *scintillans*.

On the other hand the mutants, that constitute the first representatives of their race, exhibit all the attributes of the new type in full display at once. No series of generations, no selection, no struggle for existence are needed to reach this end. In previous lectures I have mentioned that I have saved the seeds of the mutants whenever possible, and have always obtained repetitions of the prototype only. Reversions are as absolutely lacking as is also a further development of the new type. Even in the case of the inconstant forms, where part of the progeny yearly return to the stature of *lamarckiana*, intermediates are not found. So it is also with *lata*, which is pistillate and can only be propagated by cross-fertilization. But though the current belief would expect intermediates at least in this case, they do not occur. I made a pedigree-culture of *lata* during eight successive generations, pollinating them in different ways, and always obtained cultures which were partly constituted of *lata* and partly of *lamarckiana* specimens. But the latas remained *lata* in all the various and most noticeable characters, never showing any tendency to gradually revert into the original form.

Intermediate forms, if not occurring in the direct line from one species to another, might be expected to appear perhaps on lateral branches. In this case the mutants of one type, appearing in the same year, would not be a pure type, but would exhibit different degrees of deviation from the parent. The best would then have to be chosen in order to get the new type in its pure condition. Nothing of the kind, however, was observed. All the *oblonga*-mutants were pure oblongas. The pedigree shows hundreds of them in the succeeding years, but no difference was seen and no material for selection was afforded. All were as nearly equal as the individuals of old elementary species.

II. *New forms spring laterally from the main stem.*

The current conception concerning the origin of species assumes that species are slowly converted into others. The conversion is assumed to affect all the individuals in the same direction and in the same degree. The whole group changes its character, acquiring new attributes. By inter-crossing they maintain a common line of progress, one individual never being able to proceed much ahead of the others.

The birth of the new species necessarily seemed to involve the death of the old one. This last conclusion, however, is hard to understand. It may be justifiable to assume that all the individuals of one locality are ordinarily intercrossed, and are moreover subjected to the same external conditions. They might be supposed to vary in the same direction if these conditions were changed slowly. But this could of course have no possible influence on the plants of the same species growing in distant localities, and it would be improbable they should be affected in the same way. Hence we should conclude that when a species is converted into a new type in one locality this is only to be considered as one of numerous possible ones, and its alteration would not in the least change the aspect of the remainder of the species.

But even with this restriction the general belief is not supported by the evidence of the evening-primroses. There is neither a slow nor a sudden change of all the individuals. On the contrary, the vast majority remain unchanged; thousands are seen exactly repeating the original prototype yearly, both in the native field and in my garden. There is no danger that *lamarckiana* might die out from the act of mutating, nor that the mutating strain itself would be exposed to ultimate destruction from this cause.

In older swarms, such as *Draba* or *Helianthemum,* no such center, around which the various forms are grouped, is known. Are we to conclude therefore that the main strain has died out? Or is it perhaps concealed among the throng, being distinguished by no peculiar character? If our *gigas* and *rubrinervis* were growing in equal numbers with the *lamarckiana* in the native field, would it be possible to decide which of them was the progenitor of the others? Of course this could be done by long and tedious crossing-experiments, showing atavism in the progeny, and thereby indicating the common ancestor. But even this capacity seems to be doubtful and connected only with the state of mutability and to be lost afterwards. Therefore if this period of mutation were ended, probably there would be no way to decide concerning the mutual relationship of the single species.

Hence the lack of a recognizable main stem in swarms of elementary species makes it impossible to answer the question concerning their common origin.

Another phase of the opposition between the prevailing view and my own results seems far more important. According to the current belief the conversion of a group of plants growing in any locality and flowering simultaneously would be restricted to one type. In my own experiments several new species arose from the parental form at once, giving a wide range of new forms at the same time and under the same conditions.

III. *New elementary species attain their full constancy at once.*

Constancy is not the result of selection or of improvement. It is a quality of its own. It can neither be constrained by selection if it is absent from the beginning, nor does it need any natural or artificial aid if it is present. Most of my new species have proved constant from the first. Whenever possible, the original mutants have been isolated during the flowering period and artificially self-fertilized. Such plants have always given a uniform progeny, all children exhibiting the type of the parent. No atavism was observed and therefore no selection was needed or even practicable.

Briefly considering the different forms, we may state that the full experimental proof has been given for the origin of *gigas* and *rubrinervis,* for *albida* and *oblonga,* and even for *nanella,* which is to be considered as of a varietal nature; with *lata* the decisive experiment is excluded by its unisexuality. *Laevifolia* and *brevistylis* were found originally in the field, and never appeared in my cultures. No observations were made as to their origin, and seeds have only been sown from later generations. But these have yielded uniform crops, thereby showing that there is no ground for the assumption that these two older varieties might behave otherwise than the more recent derivatives.

Scintillans and *elliptica* constitute exceptions to the rule given. They repeat their character, from pure seed, only in part of the offspring. I have tried to deliver the *scintillans* from this incompleteness of heredity, but in vain. The succeeding generations, if produced from true representatives of the new type, and with pure fertilization, have repeated the splitting in the same numerical proportions. The instability seems to be here as permanent a quality as the stability in other instances. Even here no selection has been adequate to change the original form.

IV. *Some of the new strains are evidently elementary species, while others are to be considered as retrograde varieties.*

It is often difficult to decide whether a given form belongs to one or another of these two groups. I have tried to show that the best and strictest conception of varieties limits them to those forms that have probably originated by retrograde or degressive steps. Elementary species are assumed to have been produced in a progressive way, adding one new element to the store. Varieties differ from their species clearly in one point, and this is either a distinct loss, or the assumption of a character, which may be met with in other species and genera. *Laevifolia* is distinguished by the loss of the crinkling of the leaves, *brevistylis* by the partial loss of the epigynous qualities of the flowers, and *nanella* is a dwarf. These three new forms are therefore considered to constitute only retrograde steps, and no advance. This conclusion has been fully justified by some crossing experiments with *brevistylis*, which wholly complies with Mendel's law, and in one instance with *nanella*, which behaves in the same manner, if crossed with *rubrinervis*.

On the other hand, *gigas* and *rubrinervis*, *oblonga* and *albida* obviously bear the characters of progressive elementary species. They are not differentiated from *lamarckiana* by one or two main features. They diverge from it in nearly all organs, and in all in a definite though small degree. They may be recognized as soon as they have developed their first leaves and remain discernible throughout life. Their characters refer chiefly to the foliage, but no less to the stature, and even the seeds have peculiarities. There can be little doubt but that all the attributes of every new species are derived from one principal change. But why this should affect the foliage in one manner, the flowers in another and the fruits in a third direction, remains obscure. To gain ever so little an insight into the nature of these changes, we may best compare the differences of our evening-primroses with those between the two hundred elementary species of *Draba* and other similar instances. In doing so we find the same main feature, the minute differences in nearly all points.

V. *The same new species are produced in a large number of individuals.*

This is a very curious fact. It embraces two minor points, viz: the multitude of similar mutants in the same year, and the repetition thereof in succeeding generations. Obviously there must be some common cause. This cause must be assumed to lie dormant in the Lamarckianas of my strain, and probably in all of them, as no single parent-plant proved ever to be wholly destitute of mutability. Furthermore the different causes for the sundry mutations must lie latent together in the same parent-plant. They obey the same general laws, become active under similar conditions, some of them being more easily awakened than others. The germs of the *oblonga, lata* and *nanella* are especially irritable, and are ready to spring into activity at the least summons, while those of *gigas, rubrinervis* and *scintillans* are far more difficult to arouse.

These germs must be assumed to lie dormant during many successive generations. This is especially evident in the case of *lata* and *nanella*, which appeared in the first year of the pedigree-culture and which since have been repeated yearly, and have been seen to arise by mutation also during the last season (1903). Only *gigas* appeared but once, but then there is every reason to assume that in larger sowings or by a prolongation of the experiments it might have made a second appearance.

Is the number of such germs to be supposed to be limited or unlimited? My experiment has produced about a dozen new forms. Without doubt I could easily have succeeded in getting more, if I had had any definite reason to search for them. But such figures are far from favoring the assumption of indefinite mutability. The group of possible new forms is no doubt sharply circumscribed. Partly so by the morphologic peculiarities of *lamarckiana*, which seem to exclude red flowers, composite leaves, etc. No doubt there are more direct reasons for these limits, some changes having taken place initially and others later, while the present mutations are only repetitions of previous ones, and do not contribute new lines of development to those already existing. This leads us to the supposition of some common original cause, which produced a number of changes, but which itself is no longer at work, but has left the affected qualities, and only these, in the state of mutability.

In nature, repeated mutations must be of far greater significance than isolated ones. How great is the chance for a single individual to be destroyed in the struggle for life? Hundreds of thousands of seeds are produced by *lamarckiana* annually in the field, and only some slow increase of the number of specimens can be observed. Many seeds do not find the proper circumstances for germination, or the young seedlings are destroyed by lack of water, of air, or of space. Thousands of them are so crowded when becoming rosettes that only a few succeed in producing stems. Any weakness would have destroyed them. As a matter of fact they are much oftener produced in the seed than seen in the field with the usual unfavorable conditions; the careful sowing of collected seeds has given proof of this fact many times.

The experimental proof of this frequency in the origin of new types, seems to overcome many difficulties offered by the current theories on the probable origin of species at large.

VI. *The relation between mutability and fluctuating variability* has always been one of the chief difficulties of the followers of Darwin. The majority assumed that species arise by the slow accumulation of slight fluctuating deviations, and the mutations were only to be considered as extreme fluctuations, obtained, in the main, by a continuous selection of small differences in a constant direction.

My cultures show that quite the opposite is to be regarded as fact. All organs and all qualities of *lamarckiana* fluctuate and vary in a more or less evident manner, and those which I had the opportunity of examining more closely were found to comply with the general laws of fluctuation. But such oscillating changes have nothing in common with the mutations. Their essential character is the heaping up of slight deviations around a mean, and the occurrence of continuous lines of increasing deviations, linking the extremes with this group. Nothing of the kind is observed in the case of mutations. There is no mean for them to be grouped around and the extreme only is to be seen, and it is wholly unconnected with the original type. It might be supposed that on closer inspection each mutation might be brought into connection with some feature of the fluctuating variability. But this is not the case. The dwarfs are not at all the extreme variants of structure, as the fluctuation of the height of the *lamarckiana* never decreases or even approaches that of the dwarfs. There is always a gap. The smallest specimens of the tall type are commonly the weakest, according to the general rule of the relationship between nourishment and variation, but the tallest dwarfs are of course the most robust specimens of their group.

Fluctuating variability, as a rule, is subject to reversion. The seeds of the extremes do not produce an offspring which fluctuates around their parents as a center, but around some point on the line which combines their attributes with the corresponding characteristic of their ancestors, as Vilmorin has put it. No reversion accompanies mutation, and this fact is perhaps the completest contrast in which these two great types of variability are opposed to each other.

The offspring of my mutants are, of course, subject to the general laws of fluctuating variability. They vary, however, around their own mean, and this mean is simply the type of the new elementary species.

VII. *The mutations take place in nearly all directions.*

Many authors assume that the origin of species is directed by unknown causes. These causes are assumed to work in each single case for the improvement of the animals and plants, changing them in a manner corresponding in a useful way to the changes that take place in their environment. It is not easy to imagine the nature of these influences nor how they would bring about the desired effect.

This difficulty was strongly felt by Darwin, and one of the chief purposes of his selection-theory may be said to have been the attempt to surmount it. Darwin tried to replace the unknown cause by natural agencies, which lie under our immediate observation. On this point Darwin was superior to his predecessors, and it is chiefly due to the clear conception of this point that his theory has gained its deserved general acceptance. According to Darwin, changes occur in all directions, quite independently of the prevailing circumstances. Some may be favorable, others detrimental, many of them without significance, neither useful nor injurious. Some of them will sooner or later be destroyed, while others will survive, but which of them will survive, is obviously dependent upon whether their particular changes agree with the existing environic conditions or not. This is what Darwin has called the struggle for life. It is a large sieve, and it only acts as such. Some fall through and are annihilated, others remain above and are selected, as the phrase goes. Many are selected, but more are destroyed; daily observation does not leave any doubt upon this point.

How the differences originate is quite another question. It has nothing to do with the theory of natural selection nor with the struggle for life. These have an active part only in the accumulation of useful qualities, and only in so far as they protect the bearers of such characters against being crowded out by their more poorly constituted competitors.

However, the differentiating characteristics of elementary species are only very small. How widely distant they are from the beautiful adaptative organizations of orchids, of insectivorous plants and of so many others! Here the difference lies in the accumulation of numerous elementary characters, which all contribute to the same end. Chance must have produced them, and this would seem absolutely improbable, even impossible, were it not for Darwin's ingenious theory. Chance there is, but no more than anywhere else. It is not by mere chance that the variations move in the required direction. They do go, according to Darwin's view, in all directions, or at least in many. If these include the useful ones, and if this is repeated a number of times, cumulation is possible; if not, there is simply no progression, and the type remains stable through the ages. Natural selection is continually acting as a sieve, throwing out the useless changes and retaining the real improvements. Hence the accumulation in apparently predisposed directions, and hence the increasing adaptations to the more specialized conditions of life. It must be obvious to any one who can free himself from the current ideas, that this theory of natural selection leaves the question as to how the changes themselves are brought about, quite undecided. There are two possibilities, and both have been propounded by Darwin. One is the accumulation of the slight deviations of fluctuating variability, the other consists of successive sports or leaps taking place in the same direction.

In further lectures a critical comparison of the two views will be given. To-day I have only to show that the mutations of the evening-primroses, though sudden, comply with the demands made by Darwin as to the form of variability which is to be accepted as the cause of evolution and as the origin of species.

Some of my new types are stouter and others weaker than their parents, as shown by *gigas* and *albida*. Some have broader leaves and some narrower, *lata* and *oblonga*. Some have larger flowers (*gigas*) or deeper yellow ones (*rubrinervis*), or smaller blossoms (*scintillans*), or of a paler hue (*albida*). In some the capsules are longer (*rubrinervis*), or thicker (*gigas*), or more rounded (*lata*), or small (*oblonga*), and nearly destitute of seeds (*brevistylis*). The unevenness of the surface of the leaves may increase as in *lata*, or decrease as in *laevifolia*. The tendency to become annual prevails in *rubrinervis*, but *gigas* tends to become biennial. Some are rich in pollen, while *scintillans* is poor. Some have large seeds, others small. *Lata* has become pistillate, while *brevistylis* has nearly lost the faculty to produce seeds. Some undescribed forms were quite sterile, and some I observed which produced no flowers at all. From this statement it may be seen that nearly all qualities vary in opposite directions and that our group of mutants affords wide material for the sifting process of natural selection. On the original field the *laevifolia* and *brevistylis* have held their own during sixteen years and probably more, without, however, being able to increase their numbers to any noticeable extent. Others perish as soon as they make their appearance, or a few individuals are allowed to bloom, but probably leave no progeny.

But perhaps the circumstances may change, or the whole strain may be dispersed and spread to new localities with different conditions. Some of the latter might be found to be favorable to the robust *gigas,* or to *rubrinervis,* which requires a drier air, with rainfall in the springtime and sunshine during the summer. It would be worth while to see whether the climate of California, where neither *O. lamarckiana* nor *O. biennis* are found wild, would not exactly suit the requirements of the new species *rubrinervis* and *gigas*.

NOTE.—Oenotheras are native to America and all of the species growing in Europe have escaped from gardens directly, or may have arisen by mutation, or by hybridization of introduced species. A fixed hybrid between *O. cruciata* and *O. biennis* constituting a species has been in cultivation for many years. The form known as *O. biennis* in Europe, and used by de Vries in all of the experiments described in these lectures, has not yet been found growing wild in America and is not identical with the species bearing that name among American botanists. Concerning this matter Professor de Vries writes under date of Sept. 12, 1905: "The '*biennis*' which I collected in America has proved to be a motley collection of forms, which at that time I had no means of distinguishing. No one of them, so far as they are now growing in my garden is identical with our *biennis* of the sand dunes." The same appears to be the case with *O. muricata*. Plants from the Northeastern American seaboard, identifiable with the species do not entirely agree with those raised from seed received from Holland.

O. Lamarckiana has not been found growing wild in America in recent years although the evidence at hand seems to favor the conclusion that it was seen and collected in the southern states in the last century. (See MacDougal, Vail, Shull, and Small. Mutants and Hybrids of the Oenotheras. Publication 24. Carnegie Institution. Washington, D. C., 1905.)

EDITOR.

Lecture XX

THE ORIGIN OF WILD SPECIES AND VARIETIES

New species and varieties occur from time to time in the wild state. Setting aside all theoretical conceptions as to the common origin of species at large, the undoubted fact remains that new forms are sometimes met with. In the case of the peloric toad-flax the mutations are so numerous that they seem to be quite regular. The production of new species of evening-primroses was observed on the field and afterwards duplicated in the garden. There is no reason to think that these cases are isolated instances. Quite on the contrary they seem to be the prototypes of repeated occurrences in nature.

If this conception is granted, the question at once arises, how are we to deal with analogous cases, when fortune offers them, and what can we expect to learn from them?

A critical study of the existing evidence seems to be of great importance in order to ascertain the best way of dealing with new facts, and of estimating the value of the factors concerned.

It is manifest that we must be very careful and conservative in dealing with new facts that are brought to our attention, and every effort should be made to bring additional evidence to light. Many vegetable anomalies are so rare that they are met with only by the purest chance, and are then believed to be wholly new. When a white variety of some common plant is met with for the first time we generally assume that it originated on that very spot and only a short time previously. The discovery of a second locality for the same variety at once raises the question as to a common origin in the two instances. Could not the plants of the second locality have arisen from seeds transported from the first?

White varieties of many species of blue-bells and gentians are found not rarely, white-flowering plants of heather, both of *Erica Tetralix* and *Calluna vulgaris* occur on European heaths; white flowers of *Brunella vulgaris, Ononis repens, Thymus vulgaris* and others may be seen in many localities in the habitats of the colored species. Pelories of labiates seem to occur often in Austria, but are rare in Holland; white bilberries (*Vaccinium Myrtillus*) have many known localities throughout Europe, and nearly all the berry-bearing species in the large heath-family are recorded as having white varieties.

Are we to assume a single origin for all the representatives of such a variety, as we have done customarily for all the representatives of a wild species? Or can the same mutation have been repeated at different times and in distant localities? If a distinct mutation from a given species is once possible, why should it not occur twice or thrice?

A variety which seems to be new to us may only appear so, because the spot where it grows had hitherto escaped observation. *Lychnis preslii* is a smooth variety of *Lychnis diurna* and was observed for the first time in the year 1842 by Sekera. It grew abundantly in a grove near Münchengrätz in southern Hungary. It was accompanied by the ordinary hairy type of the species. Since then it has been observed to be quite constant in the same locality, and some specimens have been collected for me there lately by Dr. Němec, of Prague. No other native localities of this variety have been discovered, and there can be no doubt that it must have arisen from the ordinary campion near the spot where it still grows. But this change may have taken place some years before the first discovery, or perhaps one or more centuries ago. This could only be known if it could be proved that the locality had been satisfactorily investigated previously, and that the variety had not been met with. Even in this case only something would be discovered about the time of the change, but nothing about its real nature.

So it is in many cases. If a variety is observed in a number of specimens at the time of its first discovery, and at a locality not studied previously, it takes the aspect of an old form of limited distribution, and little can be learned as to the circumstances under which it arose. If on the contrary it occurs in very small numbers or perhaps even in a single individual, and if the spot where it is found is located so that it could hardly have escaped previous observation, then the presumption of a recent origin seems justified.

What has to be ascertained on such occasions to give them scientific value? Three points strike me as being of the highest importance. First, the constancy of the new type; secondly, the occurrence or lack of intermediates, and last, but not least, the direct observation of a repeated production.

The first two points are easily ascertained. Whether the new type is linked with its more common supposed ancestor by intermediate steps is a query which at once strikes the botanist. It is usually recorded in such cases, and we may state at once that the general result is, that such intermediates do not occur. This is of the highest importance and admits of only two explanations. One is that intermediates may be assumed to have preceded the existent developed form, and to have died out afterwards. But why should they have done so, especially in cases of recent changes? On the other hand the intermediates may be lacking because they have never existed, the change having taken place by a sudden leap, such as the mutations described in our former lectures. It is manifest that the assumption of hypothetical intermediates could only gain some probability if they had been found in some instance. Since they do not occur, the hypothesis seems wholly unsupported.

The second point is the constancy of the new type. Seeds should be saved and sown. If the plant fertilizes itself without the aid of insects, as do some evening-primroses, the seed saved from the native locality may prove wholly pure, and if it does give rise to a uniform progeny the constancy of the race may be assumed to be proved, provided that repeated trials do not bring to light any exceptions. If the offspring shows more than one type, cross-fertilization is always to be looked to as the most probable cause, and should be excluded, in order to sow pure seeds. Garden-experiments of this kind, and repeated trials, should always be combined with the discovery of a presumed mutation. In many instances the authors have realized the importance of this point, and new types have been found constant from the very beginning. Many cases are known which show no reversions and even no partial reversions. This fact throws a distinct light on our first point, as it makes the hypothesis of a slow and gradual development still more improbable.

My third point is of quite another nature and has not as yet been dealt with. But as it appeals to me as the very soul of the problem, it seems necessary to describe it in some detail. It does not refer to the new type itself, nor to any of its morphologic or hereditary attributes, but directly concerns the presumed ancestors themselves.

The peloric toad-flax in my experiment was seen to arise thrice from the same strain. Three different individuals of my original race showed a tendency to produce peloric mutations, and they did so in a number of their seeds, exactly as the mutations of the evening-primroses were repeated nearly every year. Hence the inference, that whenever we find a novelty which is really of very recent date, the parent-strain which has produced it might still be in existence on the same spot. In the case of shrubs or perennials the very parents might yet be found.

But it seems probable, and is especially proved in the case of the evening-primroses, that all or the majority of the representatives of the whole strain have the same tendency to mutate. If this were a general rule, it would suffice to take some pure seeds from specimens of the presumed parents and to sow and multiply the individuals to such an extent that the mutation might have a chance to be repeated.

Unfortunately, this has not as yet been done, but in my opinion it should be the first effort of any one who has the good luck to discover a new wild mutation. Specimens of the parents should be transplanted into a garden and fertilized under isolated conditions. Seeds saved from the wild plant would have little worth, as they might have been partly fertilized by the new type itself.

After this somewhat lengthy discussion of the value of observations surrounding the discovery of new wild mutations, we now come to the description of some of the more interesting cases. As a first example, I will take the globular-fruited shepherd's purse, described by Solms-Laubach as *Capsella heegeri*. Professor Heeger discovered one plant with deviating fruits, in a group of common shepherd's purses in the market-place near Landau in Germany, in the fall of 1897. They were nearly spherical, instead of flat and purse-shaped. Their valves were thick and fleshy, while those of the ordinary form are membranaceous and dry. The capsules hardly opened and therefore differed in this point from the shepherd's purse, which readily loosens both its valves as soon as it is ripe.

Only one plant was observed; whence it came could not be determined, nor whether it had arisen from the neighboring stock of *Capsella* or not. The discoverer took some seed to his garden and sent some to the botanical garden at Strassburg, of which Solms-Laubach is the director. The majority of the seeds of course were sowed naturally on the original spot. The following year some of the seeds germinated and repeated the novelty. The leaves, stems and flowers were those of the common shepherd's purse, but no decision could be reached concerning the type of this generation before the first flowers had faded and the rounded capsules had developed. Then it was seen that the *heegeri* came true from seed. It did so both in the gardens and on the market-place, where it was observed to have multiplied and spread in some small measure. The same was noted the following year, but then the place was covered with gravel and all the plants destroyed. It is not recorded to have been seen wild since.

Intermediate forms have not been met with. Some slight reversions may occur in the autumn on the smallest and weakest lateral branches. Such reversions, however, seem to be very rare, as I have tried in vain to produce them on large and richly branched individuals, by applying all possible inducements in the form of manure and of cutting, to stimulate the production of successive generations of weaker side branches.

This constancy was proved by the experiments of Solms-Laubach, which I have repeated in my own garden during several years with seed received from him. No atavists or deviating specimens have been found among many hundreds of flowering plants.

It is important to note that within the family of the crucifers the form of the capsule and the attributes of the valves and seeds are usually considered to furnish the characteristics of genera, and this point has been elucidated at some length by Solms-Laubach. There is, however, no sufficient reason to construe a new genus on the ground of Heeger's globular-fruited shepherd's purse; but as a true elementary species, and even as a good systematic species it has proved itself, and as such it is described by Solms-Laubach, who named it in honor of its discoverer.

Exactly analogous discoveries have been

made from time to time with other plants by different writers. Near Wageningen, in Holland, I found *Stellaria Holostea apetala* in the year 1889, and near Horn in Lippe (Germany) *Capsella Bursa-pastoris apetala*, both in a very few specimens on a single spot. Whether these were mutations or introductions remains of course uncertain. About the same time I discovered near Hilversum in Holland a smooth variety of the evening campion, *Lychnis vespertina*, forming a very small group of individuals in a field, where the hairy type was common. It was sown in my garden and proved pure and constant, without intermediates. As the locality had been repeatedly and carefully investigated by me, I trust to be justified in the assertion that I gathered the very first individuals of the variety. The stock soon was overgrown by surrounding shrubs and died out, and now only the cultivated offspring are available, as in the case of Heeger's shepherd's purse.

A very curious instance of spontaneous mutations is afforded by a peculiarity of some evening-primroses and their allies. This peculiarity is shown by the petals remaining minute and assuming a linear shape. The character is developed as a specific one in *Oenothera cruciata*. This plant owes its name to the shape of the petals, which form a slender cross in the flower, instead of displaying a bright yellow cup. *O. cruciata* grows in the Adirondack Mountains, in the states of New York and Vermont, and seems to be abundant there. It has been introduced into botanical gardens and yielded a number of hybrids, especially with *O. biennis* and *O. lamarckiana,* and the narrow petals of the parent-species may be met with in combination with the stature and vegetative characteristics of these last named species. *O. cruciata* has a purple foliage, while *biennis* and *lamarckiana* are green, and many of the hybrids may instantly be recognized by their purple color.

The curious attribute of the petals is not to be considered simply as a reduction in size. On anatomical inquiry it has been found that these narrow petals bear some characteristics which, on the normal plants, are limited to the calyx. Stomata and hairs, and the whole structure of the surface and inner tissues on some parts of these petals are exactly similar to those of the calyx, while on others they have retained the characteristics of petals. Sometimes there may even be seen by the naked eye green longitudinal stripes of calyx-like structure alternating with bright yellow petaloid parts. For these reasons the *cruciata* character may be considered as a case of sepalody of the petals, or of the petals being partly converted into sepals.

It is worth while to note that as a monstrosity this occurrence is extremely rare throughout the whole vegetable kingdom, and only very few instances have been recorded.

Two cases of sudden mutations have come to my knowledge, producing this same anomaly in allied species. One has been already alluded to; it pertains to the common evening-primrose or *Oenothera biennis,* and one is a species belonging to another genus of the same family, the great hairy willow-herb or *Epilobium hirsutum.* I propose to designate both new forms by the varietal name of *cruciata,* or *cruciatum.*

Oenothera biennis cruciata was found in a native locality of the *O. biennis* itself. It consisted of only one plant, showing in all its flowers the *cruciata* marks. In all other respects it resembled wholly the *biennis,* especially in the pure green color of its foliage, which at once excluded all suspicion of hybrid origin with the purple *O. cruciata.* Moreover in our country this last occurs only in the cultivated state in botanical gardens.

Intermediates were not seen, and as the plant bore some pods, it was possible to test its constancy. I raised about 500 plants from its seeds, out of which more than 100 flowered in the first year. The others were partly kept through the winter and flowered next year. Seeds saved in both seasons were sown on a large scale. Both the first and the succeeding generations of the offspring of the original plant came true without any exception. Intermediates are often found in hybrid cultures, and in them the character is a very variable one, but as yet they were not met with in progeny of this mutant. All these plants were exactly like *O. biennis*, with the single exception of their petals.

Epilobium hirsutum cruciatum was discovered by John Rasor near Woolpit, Bury St. Edmunds, in England. It flowered in one spot, producing about a dozen stems, among large quantities of the parent-species, which is very common there, as it is elsewhere in Europe. This species is a perennial, multiplying itself by underground runners, and the stems of the new variety were observed to stand so close to each other that they might be considered as the shoots of one individual. In this case this specimen might probably be the original mutant, as the variety had not been seen on that spot in previous years, even as it has not been found elsewhere in the vicinity.

Intermediates were not observed, though the difference is a very striking one. In the cruciate flowers the broad and bright purple petals seem at first sight to be wholly wanting. They are too weak to expand and to reflex the calyx as in the normal flowers of the species. The sepals adhere to one another, and are only opened at their summit by the protruding pistils. Even the stamens hardly come to light. At the period of full bloom the flowers convey only the idea of closed buds crowned by the conspicuous white cross of the stigma. Any intermediate form would have at once betrayed itself by larger colored petals, coming out of the calyx-sheath. The cruciate petals are small and linear and greenish, recalling thereby the color of the sepals.

Mr. Rasor having sent me some flowers and some ripe capsules of his novelty, I sowed the latter in my experimental garden, where the plant flowered in large numbers and with many thousands of flowers both in 1902 and 1903. All of these plants and all of these flowers repeated the cruciate type exactly, and not the slightest impurity or tendency to partial reversion has been observed.

Thus true and constant cruciate varieties have been produced from accidentally observed initial plants, and because of their very curious characters they will no doubt be kept in botanical gardens, even if they should eventually become lost in their native localities.

At this point I might note another observation made on the wild species of *Oenothera cruciata* from the Adirondacks. Through the kindness of Dr. MacDougal, of the New York Botanical Garden, I received seeds from Sandy Hill near Lake George. When the plants, grown from these seeds, flowered, they were not a uniform lot, but exhibited two distinct types. Some had linear petals and thin flower-buds, and in others the petals were a little broader and the buds more swollen. The difference was small, but constant on all the flowers, each single plant clearly belonging to one or the other of the two types. Probably two elementary species were intermixed here, but whether one is the systematic type and the other a mutation, remains to be seen.

Nor seem these two types to exhaust the range of variability of *Oenothera cruciata*. Dr. B. L. Robinson of Cambridge, Mass., had the kindness to send me seeds from another locality in the same region. The seeds were collected in New Hampshire and in my garden produced a true and constant *cruciata,* but with quite different secondary characters from both the aforesaid varieties. The stems and flower-spikes and even the whole foliage were much more slender, and the calyx-tubes of the flowers were noticeably more elongated. It seems not improbable that *Oenothera cruciata* includes a group of lesser unities, and may prove to comprise a swarm of elementary species, while the original strain might even now be still in a condition of mutability. A close scrutiny in the native region is likely to reveal many unexpected features.

A very interesting novelty has already been described in a former lecture. It is the *Xanthium wootoni,* discovered in the region about Las Vegas, New Mexico, by T. D. A. Cockerell. It is similar in all respects to *X. commune,* but the burrs are more slender and the prickles much less numerous, and mostly stouter at their base. It grows in the same localities as the *X. commune,* and is not recorded to occur elsewhere. Whether it is an old variety or a recent mutation it is of course impossible to decide. In a culture made in my garden from the seed sent me by Mr. Cockerell, I observed (1903) that both forms had a subvariety with brownish foliage, and, besides this, one of a pure green. Possibly this species, too, is still in a mutable condition.

Perhaps the same may be asserted concerning the beautiful shrub, *Hibiscus Moscheutos,* observed in quite a number of divergent types by John W. Harshberger. They grew in a small meadow at Seaside Park, New Jersey, in a locality which had been undisturbed for years. They differed from each other in nearly all the organs, in size, in the diameter of the stems, which were woody in some and more fleshy in others, in the shape of the foliage and in the flowers. More than twenty types could be distinguished and seeds were saved from a number of them, in order to ascertain whether they are constant, or whether perhaps a main stem in a mutating condition might be found among them. If this should prove to be the case, the relations between the observed forms would probably be analogous to those between the *O. lamarckiana* and its derivatives.

Many other varieties have sprung from the type-species under similar conditions from time to time. A fern-leaved mercury, *Mercurialis annua laciniata,* was discovered in the year 1719 by Marchant. The type was quite new at the time and maintained itself during a series of years. The yellow deadly nightshade or *Atropa Belladonna lutea* was found about 1850 in the Black Forest in Germany in a single spot, and has since been multiplied by seeds. It is now dispersed in botanical gardens, and seems to be quite constant. A dwarf variety of a bean, *Phaseolus lunatus,* was observed to spring from the ordinary type by a sudden leap about 1895 by W. W. Tracy, and many similar cases could be given.

The annual habit is not very favorable for

is now so universally cultivated. I take the following statements from an interesting historical essay of Prof. Jäggi. He describes three original localities. One is near the Swiss village, Buch am Irchel, and is located on the Stammberg. During the 17th century five purple beeches are recorded to have grown on this spot. Four of them have died, but one is still alive. Seedlings have germinated around this little group, and have been mostly dug up and transplanted into neighboring gardens. Nothing is known about the real origin of these plants, but according to an old document, it seems that about the year 1190 the purple beeches of Buch were already enjoying some renown, and attracting large numbers of pilgrims, owing to some old legend. The church of Embrach is said to have been built in connection with this legend, and was a goal for pilgrimages during many centuries.

A second native locality of the purple beech is found in a forest near Sondershausen in Thüringen, Germany, where a fine group of these trees is to be seen. They were mentioned for the first time in the latter half of the eighteenth century, but must have been old specimens long before that time. The third locality seems to be of much later origin. It is a forest near Roveredo in South Tyrol, where a new university is being erected. It is only a century ago that the first specimens of the purple beech were discovered there.

As it is very improbable that the two last named localities should have received their purple beeches from the first named forest, it seems reasonable to assume that the variety must have been produced at least thrice.

The purple beech is now exceedingly common in cultivation. But Jäggi succeeded in showing that all the plants owe their origin to the original trees mentioned above, and are, including nearly all cultivated specimens with the sole exception of the vicinity of Buch, probably derived from the trees in Thüringen. They are easily multiplied by grafting, and come true from seed, at least often, and in a high proportion. Whether the original trees would yield a pure progeny if fertilized by their own pollen has as yet not been tested. The young seedlings have purple seed-leaves, and may easily be selected by this character, but they seem to be always subjected in a large measure to vicinism.

Many other instances of trees and shrubs, found in accidental specimens constituting a new variety in the wild state, might be given. The oak-leaved beech has been found in a forest of Lippe-Detmold in Germany and near Versailles, whence it was introduced into horticulture by Carrière. Similarly divided and cleft leaves seem to have occurred more often in the wild state, and cut-leaved hazels are recorded from Rouen in France, birches and alders from Sweden and Lapland, where both are said to have been met with in several forests. The purple barberry was found about 1830 by Bertin, near Versailles. Weeping varieties of ashes were found wild in England and in Germany, and broom-like oaks, *Quercus pedunculata fastigiata,* are recorded from Hessen-Darmstadt, Calabria, the Pyrenees and other localities. About the real origin of all these varieties nothing is definitely known.

The " single-leaved " strawberry is a variety often seen in botanical gardens, as it is easily propagated by its runners. It was discovered wild in Lapland at the time of Linnaeus, and appeared afterwards unexpectedly in a nursery near Versailles. This happened about the year 1760 and Duchesne tested it from seeds and found it constant. This strain, however, seems to have died out before the end of the 18th century. In a picture painted by Holbein (1495-1543), strawberry leaves can be seen agreeing exactly with the monophyllous type. The variety may thus be assumed to have arisen independently at least thrice, at different periods and in distant localities.

From all these statements and a good many others which can be found in horticultural and botanical literature, it may be inferred that mutations are not so very rare in nature as is often supposed. Moreover we may conclude that it is a general rule that they are neither preceded nor accompanied by intermediate steps, and that they are ordinarily constant from seed from the first.

Why then are they not met with more often? In my opinion it is the struggle for life which is the cause of this apparent rarity; which is nothing else than the premature death of all the individuals that so vary from the common type of their species as to be incapable of development under prevailing circumstances. It is obviously without consequence whether these deviations are of a fluctuating or of a mutating nature. Hence we may conclude that useless mutations will soon die out and will disappear without leaving any progeny. Even if they are produced again and again by the same strain, but under the same unfavorable conditions, there will be no appreciable result.

Thousands of mutations may perhaps take place yearly among the plants of our immediate vicinity without any chance of being discovered.

We are trained to the appreciation of the differentiating marks of systematic species. When we have succeeded in discerning these as given by our local flora lists, we rest content. Meeting them again we are in the habit of greeting them with their proper names. Such is the satisfaction ensuing from this knowledge that we do not feel any inclination for further inquiry. Striking deviations, such as many varietal characters, may be remarked, but then they are considered as being of only secondary interest. Our minds are turned from the delicately shaded features which differentiate elementary species.

Even in the native field of the evening-primroses, no botanist would have discovered the rosettes with smaller or paler leaves, constituting the first signs of the new species. Only by the guidance of a distinct theoretical idea were they discovered, and having once been pointed out a closer inspection soon disclosed their number.

Variability seems to us to be very general, but very limited. The limits however, are distinctly drawn by the struggle for existence. Of course the chance for useful mutations is a very small one. We have seen that the same mutations are as a rule repeated from time to time by the same species. Now, if a useful mutation, or even a wholly indifferent one, might easily be produced, it would have been so, long ago, and would at the present time simply exist as a systematic variety. If produced anew somewhere the botanist would take it for the old variety and would omit to make any inquiry as to its local origin.

Thousands of seeds with perhaps wide circles of variability are ripened each year, but only those that belong to the existing old narrow circles survive. How different would Nature appear to us if she were free to evolve all her potentialities!

Darwin himself was struck with this lack of harmony between common observations and the probable real state of things. He discussed it in connection with the cranesbill of the Pyrenees (*Geranium pyrenaicum*). He described how this fine little plant, which has never been extensively cultivated, had escaped from a garden in Staffordshire and had succeeded in multiplying itself so as to occupy a large area. In doing so it had evidently found place for an uncommonly large number of plantlets from its seeds and correspondingly it had commenced to vary in almost all organs and qualities and nearly in all imaginable directions. It displayed under these exceptional circumstances a capacity which never had been exceeded and which of course would have remained concealed if its multiplication had been checked in the ordinary way.

Many species have had occasion to invade new regions and cover them with hundreds of thousands of individuals. First are to be cited those species which have been introduced from America into Europe since the time of Columbus, or from Europe into this country. Some of them have become very common. In my own country the evening-primroses and Canada fleabane or *Erigeron canadensis* are examples, and many others could be given. They should be expected to vary under these circumstances in a larger degree. Have they done so? Manifestly they have not struck out useful new characters that would enable their bearers to found new elementary species. At least none have been observed. But poor types might have been produced, and periods of mutability might have been gone through similar to that which is now under observation for Lamarck's evening-primrose in Holland.

From this discussion we may infer that the chances of discovering new mutating species are great enough to justify the utmost efforts to secure them. It is only necessary to observe large numbers of plants, grown under circumstances which allow the best opportunities for all the seeds. And as nature affords such opportunities only at rare intervals, we should make use of artificial methods. Large quantities of seed should be gathered from wild plants and sowed under very favorable conditions, giving all the nourishment and space required to the young seedlings. It is recommended that they be sown under glass, either in a glass-house or protected against cold and rain by glass-frames. The same lot of seed will be seen to yield twice or thrice as many seedlings if thus protected, compared with what it would have produced when sown in the field or in the garden. I have nearly wholly given up sowing seeds in my garden, as circumstances can be controlled and determined with greater exactitude when the sowing is done in a glass-house.

The best proof perhaps, of the unfavorable influence of external conditions for slightly deteriorated deviations is afforded by variegated leaves. Many beautiful varieties are seen in our gardens and parks, and even corn has a variety with striped leaves. They are easily reproduced, both by buds and by seeds, and they are the most ordinary of all varietal deviations. They may be expected to occur wild also. But no real variegated species, nor even good varieties with this attribute occurs in nature.

On the other hand occasional specimens with a single variegated leaf, or with some few of them, are actually met with, and if attention is once drawn to this question, perhaps a dozen or so instances might be brought together in a summer. But they never seem to be capable of further evolution, or of reproducing themselves sufficiently and of repeating their peculiarity in their progeny. They make their appearance, are seen during a season, and then disappear. Even this slight incompleteness of some spots on one or two leaves may be enough to be their doom.

It is a common belief that new varieties owe their origin to the direct action of external conditions and moreover it is often assumed that similar deviations must have similar causes, and that these causes may act repeatedly in the same species, or in allied, or even systematically distant genera. No doubt in the end all things must have their causes, and the same causes will lead under the same circumstances to the same results. But we are not justified in deducing a direct relation between the external conditions and the internal changes of plants. These relations may be of so remote a nature that they cannot as yet be guessed at. Therefore only direct experience may be our guide.

Summing up the result of our facts and discussions we may state that wild new elementary species and varieties are recorded to have appeared from time to time. Invariably this happened by sudden leaps and without intermediates. The mutants are constant when propagated by seed, and at once constitute a new race. In rare instances this may be of sufficient superiority to win a place for itself in nature, but more often it has qualities which have led to its introduction into gardens as an ornamental plant or into botanical gardens by reason of the interest afforded by their novelty, or by their anomaly.

Many more mutations may be supposed to be taking place all around us, but artificial sowings on a large scale, combined with a close examination of the seedlings and a keen appreciation of the slightest indications of deviation seem required to bring them to light.

Lecture XXI

MUTATIONS IN HORTICULTURE

It is well known that Darwin based his theory of natural selection to a large extent upon the experience of breeders. Natural and artificial selection exhibit the same general features, yet it was impossible in Darwin's time to make a critical and comparative analysis of the two processes.

In accordance with our present conception there is selection of species and selection within the species. The struggle for life determines which of a group of elementary species shall survive and which shall disappear. In agricultural practice the corresponding process is usually designated by the name of variety-testing. Within the species, or within the variety, the sieve of natural selection is constantly eliminating poor specimens and preserving those that are best adapted to live under the given conditions. Some amelioration and some local races are the result, but this does not appear to be of much importance. On the contrary, the selection within the race holds a prominent place in agriculture, where it is known by the imposing term, race-breeding.

Experience and methods in horticulture differ from those in agriculture in many points. Garden-varieties have been tested and separated for a long time, but neither vegetables nor flowers are known to exhibit such motley groups of types as may be seen in large forage crops.

New varieties which appear from time to time may be ornamental or otherwise in flowers, and more or less profitable than their parents in vegetables and fruits. In either case the difference is usually striking, or if not, its culture would be unprofitable.

The recognition of useful new varieties being thus made easy, the whole attention of the breeder is reduced to isolating the seeds of the mutants that are to be saved and sown separately, and this process must be repeated during a few years, in order to produce the quantity of seed that is needed for a profitable introduction of the variety into commerce. In proportion to the abundance of the harvest of each year this period is shorter for some and longer for other species.

Isolation in practice is not so simple nor so easy an affair as it is in the experimental garden. Hence we have constant and nearly unavoidable cross-fertilizations with the parent-form, or with neighboring varieties, and consequent impurity of the new strain. This impurity we have called vicinism, and in a previous lecture have shown its effects upon the horticultural races on one hand, and on the other, on the scientific value that can be ascribed to the experience of the breeder. We have established the general rule that stability is seldom met with, but that the observed instability is always open to the objection of being the result of vicinism. Often this last agency is its sole cause; or it may be complicated with other factors without our being able to discern them.

Though our assertion that the practice of the horticulturist in producing new varieties is limited to isolation, whenever chance affords them, is theoretically valid, it is not always so. We may discern between the two chief groups of varieties. The retrograde varieties are constant, the individuals not differing more from one another than those of any ordinary species. The highly variable varieties play an important part in horticulture. Double flowers, striped flowers, variegated leaves and some others yield the most striking instances. Such forms have been included in previous lectures among the ever-sporting varieties, because their peculiar characters oscillate between two extremes, viz.:

the new one of the variety and the corresponding character of the original species.

In such cases isolation is usually accompanied by selection: rarely has the first of a double, striped or variegated race well filled or richly striped flowers or highly spotted leaves. Usually minor degrees of the anomaly are seen first, and the breeder expects the novelty to develop its features more completely and more beautifully in subsequent generations. Some varieties need selection only in the beginning, in others the most perfect specimens must be chosen every year as seed-bearers. For striped flowers, it has been prescribed by Vilmorin, that seeds should be taken only from those with the smallest stripes, because there is always reversion. Mixed seed or seed from medium types would soon yield plants with too broad stripes, and therefore less diversified flowers.

In horticulture, new varieties, both retrograde and ever-sporting, are known to occur almost yearly. Nevertheless, not every novelty of the gardener is to be considered as a mutation in the scientific sense of the word. First of all, the novelties of perennial and woody species are to be excluded. Any extreme case of fluctuating variability may be preserved and multiplied in the vegetative way. Such types are designated in horticulture as varieties, though obviously they are of quite another nature than the varieties reproduced by seed. Secondly, a large number, no doubt the greater number of novelties, are of hybrid origin. Here we may discern two cases. Hybrids may be produced by the crossing of old types, either of two old cultivated forms or newly introduced species, or ordinarily between an old and an introduced variety. Such novelties are excluded from our present discussion. Secondly, hybrids may be produced between a true, new mutation and some of the already existing varieties of the same species. Examples of this obvious and usual practice will be given further on, but it must be pointed out now that by such crosses a single mutation may produce as many novelties as there are available varieties of the same species.

Summarizing these introductory remarks we must lay stress on the fact that only a small part of the horticultural novelties are real mutations, although they do occur from time to time. If useful, they are as a rule isolated and multiplied, and if necessary, improved by selection. They are in many instances, as constant from seed as the unavoidable influence of vicinism allows them to be. Exact observations on the origin, or on the degree of constancy, are usually lacking, the notes being ordinarily made for commercial purposes, and often only at the date of introduction into trade, when the preceding stages of the novelty may have been partly forgotten.

With this necessary prelude I will now give a condensed survey of the historical facts relating to the origin of new horticultural varieties. An ample description has been given recently by Korshinsky, a Russian writer, who has brought together considerable historical material as evidence of the sudden appearance of novelties throughout the whole realm of garden-plants.

The oldest known, and at the same time one of the most accurately described mutations is the origin of the cut-leaved variety of the greater celandine or *Chelidonium majus*. This variety has been described either as such, or as a distinct species, called *Chelidonium laciniatum* Miller.

It is distinguished from the ordinary species, by the leaves being cut into narrow lobes, with almost linear tips, a character which is, as we have seen on a previous occasion, repeated in the petals. It is at present nearly as commonly cultivated in botanical gardens as the *C. majus*, and has escaped in many localities and is observed to thrive as readily as the native wild plants. It was not known until a few years before the close of the 16th century. Its history has been described by the French botanist, Rose.

It was seen for the first time in the garden of Sprenger, an apothecary of Heidelberg, where the *C. majus* had been cultivated for many years. Sprenger discovered it in the year 1590, and was struck by its peculiar and sharply deviating characters. He was anxious to know whether it was a new plant and sent specimens to Clusius and to Plater, the last of whom transmitted them to Caspar Bauhin. These botanists recognized the type as quite new and Bauhin described it some years afterwards in his Phytopinax under the name of *Chelidonium majus foliis quernis,* or oak-leaved celandine. The new variety soon provoked general interest and was introduced into most of the botanical gardens of Europe. It was recognized as quite new, and repeated search has been made for it in a wild state, but in vain. No other origin has been discovered than that of Sprenger's garden. Afterwards it became naturalized in England and elsewhere, but there is not the least doubt as to its derivation in all the observed cases.

Hence its origin at Heidelberg is to be considered as historically proven, and it is of course only legitimate to assume that it originated in the year 1590 from the seeds of the *C. majus*. Nevertheless, this was not ascertained by Sprenger, and some doubt as to a possible introduction from elsewhere might arise. If not, then the mutation must have been sudden, occurring without visible preparation and without the appearance of intermediates.

From the very first, the cut-leaved celandine has been constant from seed. Or at least it has been propagated by seed largely and without difficulty. Nothing, however, is known about it in the first few years of its existence. Later careful tests were made by Miller, Rose and others and later by myself, which have shown its stability to be absolute and without reversion, and it has probably been so from the beginning. The fact of its constancy has led to its specific distinction by Miller, as varieties were in his time universally, and up to the present time not rarely, though erroneously, believed to be less stable than true species.

Before leaving the laciniate celandine it is to be noted that in crosses with *C. majus* it follows the law of Mendel, and for this reason should be considered as a retrograde variety, the more so, as it is also treated as such from a morphological point of view by Stahl and others.

We now come to an enumeration of those cases in which the date of the first appearance of a new horticultural variety has been recorded, and I must apologize for the necessity of again quoting many variations, which have previously been dealt with from another point of view. In such cases I shall limit myself as closely as possible to historical facts. They have been recorded chiefly by Verlot and Carrière, who wrote in Paris shortly after the middle of the past century, and afterwards by Darwin, Korshinsky, and others. It is from their writings and from horticultural literature at large that the following evidence is brought together.

A very well-known instance is that of the dwarf variety of *Tagetes signata,* which arose in the nursery of Vilmorin in the year 1860. It was observed for the first time in a single individual among a lot of the ordinary *Tagetes signata.* It was found impossible to isolate it, but the seeds were saved separately. The majority of the offspring returned to the parental type, but two plants were true dwarfs. From these the requisite degree of purity for commercial purposes was reached, the vicinists not being more numerous than 10% of the entire number. The same mutation had been observed a year earlier in the same nursery in a lot of *Saponaria calabrica.* The seeds of this dwarf repeated the variety in the next generation, but in the third none were observed. Then the variety was thought to be lost, and the culture was given up, as the Mendelian law of the splitting of varietal hybrids was not known. According to our present knowledge we might expect the atavistic descendants of the first dwarf to be hybrids, and to be liable to split in their progeny into one-fourth dwarfs and three-fourths normal specimens. From this it is obvious that the dwarfs would have appeared a second time if the strain had been continued by means of the seeds of the vicinistic progeny.

In order to avoid a return to this phase of the question, another use of the vicinists should at once be pointed out. It is the possibility of increasing the yield of the new variety. If space admits of sowing the seeds of the vicinists, a quarter of the progeny may be expected to come true to the new type, and if they were partly pollinated by the dwarfs, even a larger number would do so. Hence it should be made a rule to sow these seeds also, at least when those of the true representatives of the novelty do not give seed enough for a rapid multiplication.

Other dwarfs are recorded to have sprung from species in the same sudden and unexpected manner, as for instance *Ageratum coeruleum* of the same nursery, further *Clematis Viticella nana* and *Acer campestre nanum*. *Prunus Mahaleb nana* was discovered in 1828 in one specimen near Orléans by Mme LeBrun in a large culture of *Mahaleb*. *Lonicera tatarica nana* appeared in 1825 at Fontenay-aux-Roses. A tall variety of the strawberry is called "Giant of Zuidwijk" and originated at Boskoop in Holland in the nursery of Mr. van de Water, in a lot of seedlings of the ordinary strawberry. It was very large, but produced few runners, and was propagated with much difficulty, for after six years only 15 plants were available. It proved to be a late variety with abundant large fruit, and was sold at a high price. For a long time it was prominent in cultures in Holland only.

Varieties without prickles are known to have originated all of a sudden in sundry cases. *Gleditschia sinensis*, introduced in 1774 from China, gave two seedlings without spines in the year 1823, in the nursery of Caumzet. It is curious in being one of the rare instances where a simultaneous mutation in two specimens is acknowledged, because as a rule, such records comply with the prevailing, though inexact, belief that horticultural mutations always appear in single individuals.

From Korshinsky's survey of varieties with cut leaves or laciniate forms the following cases may be quoted. In the year 1830 a nurseryman named Jacques had sown a large lot of elms,

Ulmus pedunculata. One of the seedlings had cut leaves. He multiplied it by grafting and gave it to the trade under the name of *U. pedunculata urticaefolia.* It has since been lost.

Laciniate alders seem to have been produced by mutation at sundry times. Mirbel says that the *Alnus glutinosa laciniata* is found wild in Normandy and in the forests of Montmorency near Paris. A similar variety has been met with in a nursery near Orléans in the year 1855. In connection with this discovery some discussion has arisen concerning the question whether it was probable that the Orléans strain was a new mutation, or derived in some way from the trees cited by Mirbel. Of course, as always in such cases, any doubt, once pronounced, affects the importance of the observation for all time, since it is impossible to gather sufficient historical evidence to fully decide the point. The same variety had appeared under similar circumstances in a nursery at Lyons previously (1812).

Laciniated maples are said to be of relatively frequent occurrence in nurseries, among seedlings of the typical species. Loudon says that once 100 laciniated seedlings were seen to originate from seed of some normal trees. But in this case it is rather probable that the presumed normal parents were in reality hybrids between the type and the laciniated form, and simply split according to Mendel's law. This hypothesis is partly founded on general considerations and partly on experiments made by myself with the cut-leaved celandine, previously alluded to, which I crossed with the type. The hybrids repeated the features of the species and showed no signs of their internal hybrid constitution. But the following year one-fourth of their progeny returned to the cut-leaved form. If the same thing has taken place in the case of Loudon's maples, but without their hybrid origin being known, the result would have been precisely what he observed.

Broussonetia papyrifera dissecta originated about 1830 at Lyons, and a second time in 1866 at Fontenay-aux-Roses. The cut-leaved hazelnuts, birches, beeches and others have mostly been found in the wild state, as I have already pointed out in a previous lecture. A similar variety of the elder, *Sambucus nigra laciniata*, and its near ally, *Sambucus racemosa laciniata*, are often to be seen in our gardens. They have been on record since 1886 and come true from seed, but their exact origin seems to have been forgotten. Cut-leaved walnuts have been known since 1812; they come true from seed, but are extremely liable to vicinism, a nuisance which is ascribed by some authors to the fact that often on the same tree the male catkins flower and fall off several weeks before the ripening of the pistils of the other form of flowers.

Weeping varieties afford similar instances. *Sophora japonica pendula* originated about 1850, and *Gleditschia triacanthos pendula* some time later in a nursery at Chateau-Thierry (Aisne, France). In the year 1821 the bird's cherry, or *Prunus Padus*, produced a weeping variety, and in 1847 the same mutation was observed for the allied *Prunus Mahaleb*. Numerous other instances of the sudden origin of weeping trees, both of conifers and of others, have been brought together in Korshinsky's paper. This striking type of variation includes perhaps the best examples of the whole historical evidence. As a rule they appear in large sowings, only one, or only a few at a time. Many of them have not been observed during their youth, but only after having been planted out in parks and forests, since the weeping characters show only after several years.

The monophyllous bastard-acacia originated in the same way. Its peculiarities will be dealt with on another occasion, but the circumstances of its birth may as well be given here. In 1855 in the nursery of Deniau, at Brain-sur-l'Authion (Maine et Loire), it appeared in a lot of

the discovery of new forms in the wild state. New varieties may appear, but may be crowded out the first year. The chances are much greater with perennials, and still greater with shrubs or trees. A single aberrant specimen may live for years and even for centuries, and under such conditions is pretty sure to be discovered sooner or later. Hence it is no wonder that many such cases are on record. They have this in common that the original plant of the variety has been found among a vast majority of representatives of the corresponding species. Nothing of course is directly known about its origin. Intermediate links have as a rule been wanting, and the seeds, which have often been sown, have not yielded reliable results, as no care was taken to preserve the blossoms from intercrossing with their parent-forms.

Stress should be laid upon one feature of these curious occurrences. Relatively often the same novelty has been found twice or thrice, or even more frequently, and under conditions which make it very improbable that any relation between such occurrences might exist. The same mutation must have taken place more than once from the same main stem.

The most interesting of these facts are connected with the origin of the purple beech, which

seedlings of the typical species in a single individual. This was transplanted into the Jardin des Plantes at Paris, where it flowered and bore seeds in 1865. It must have been partly pollinated by the surrounding normal representatives of the species, since the seeds yielded only one-fourth of true offspring. This proportion, however, has varied in succeeding years. Briot remarks that the monophyllous bastard-acacia is liable to petaloid alterations of its stamens, which deficiency may encroach upon its fertility and accordingly upon the purity of its offspring.

Broom-like varieties often occur among trees, and some are known for their very striking reversions by buds, as we have seen on a previous occasion. They are ordinarily called pyramidal or fastigiate forms, and as far as their history goes, they arise suddenly in large sowings of the normal species. The fastigiate birch was produced in this way by Baumann, the *Abies concolor fastigiata* by Thibault and Keteleer at Paris, the pyramidal cedar by Paillat, the analogous form of *Wellingtonia* by Otin. Other instances could easily be added, though of course some of the most highly prized broom-like trees are so old that nothing is known about their origin. This, for instance, is the case with the pyramidal yew-tree, *Taxus baccata fastigiata*.

Others have been found wild, as already mentioned in a former lecture.

An analogous case is afforded by the purple-leaved plums, of which the most known form is *Prunus Pissardi*. It is said to be a purple variety of *Prunus cerasifera*, and was introduced at the close of the seventies from Persia, where it is said to have been found in Täbris. A similar variety arose independently and unexpectedly in the nursery of Späth, near Berlin, about 1880, but it seems to differ in some minor points from the Persian prototype.

A white variety of *Cyclamen vernum* made its appearance in the year 1836 in Holland. A single individual was observed for the first time among a large lot of seedlings, in a nursery near Haarlem. It yielded a satisfactory amount of seed, and the progeny was true to the new type. Such plants propagate slowly, and it was only twenty-seven years later (1863) that the bulbs were offered for sale by the Haarlem firm of Krelage & Son. The price of each bulb was $5.00 in that year, but soon afterwards was reduced to $1.00 each, which was about thrice the ordinary price of the red variety.

The firm of Messrs. Krelage & Son has brought into commerce a wide range of new bulb-varieties, all due to occasional mutations, some by seed and others by buds, or to the accidental transference of new qualities into the already existing varieties by cross-pollination through the agency of insects. Instead of giving long lists of these novelties, I may cite the black tulips, which cost during the first few years of their introduction about $25.00 apiece.

Horticultural mutations are as a rule very rare, especially in genera or species which have not yet been brought to a high degree of variability. In these the wide range of varieties and the large scale in which they are multiplied of course give a greater chance for new varieties. But then the possibilities of crossing are likewise much larger, and apparent changes due to this cause may easily be taken for original mutations.

The rarity of the mutations is often proved by the lapse of time between the introduction of a species and its first sport. Some instances may be given. They afford a proof of the length of the period during which the species remained unaltered, although some of these alterations may be due to a cross with an allied form. *Erythrina Crista-galli* was introduced about 1770, and produced its first sport in 1884, after more than a century of cultivation. *Begonia semperflorens* has been cultivated since 1829, and for half a century before it commenced sporting. The same length of time has elapsed between the first culture and the first variation of *Crambe maritima*. Other cases are on record in which the variability exhibited itself much sooner, perhaps within a few years after the original discovery of the species. But such instances seem, as a rule, to be subject to doubt as to the concurrence of hybridization. So for instance the *Iris lortetii*, introduced in the year 1895 from the Lebanon, which produced a white variety from its very first seeds. If by chance the introduced plants were natural hybrids between the species and the white variety, this apparent and rather improbable mutation would find a very simple explanation. The length of the period preceding the first signs of variability is largely, of course, due to divergent methods of culture. Such species as *Erythrina*, which are perennial and only sown on a small scale, should not be expected to show varieties very soon. Annual species, which are cultivated yearly in thousands or even hundreds of thousands of individuals, have a much better chance. Perhaps the observed differences are largely due to this cause.

Monstrosities have, from time to time, given rise to cultivated races. The cockscomb or *Celosia* is one of the most notorious instances. Cauliflowers, turnips and varieties of cabbages are recorded by De Candolle to have arisen in culture, more than a century ago, as isolated monstrous individuals. They come true from seed, but show deviations from time to time which seem to be intimately linked with their abnormal characters. Apetalous flowers may be considered as another form of monstrosity, and in *Salpiglossis sinuata* such a variety without a corolla made its appearance in the year 1892 in the nursery of Vilmorin. It appeared suddenly, yielded a good crop of seed and was constant from the outset, without any sign of vicinism or impurity.

In several cases the origin of a variety is obscure, while the subsequent historical evidence is such as to make an original sudden appearance quite probable. Although these instances offer but indirect evidence, and will sooner or later lose their importance, it seems desirable to lay some stress on them here, because most of these cases are very obvious and more striking than purely historical facts. Sterile varieties belong to this heading. Sometimes they bear fruit without kernels, sometimes flowers without sexual organs, or even no flowers at all. Instances have been given in the lecture on retrograde varieties; they are ordinarily assumed to have originated by a leap, because it is not quite clear how a loss of the capacity for the formation of seeds could have been slowly accumulated in preceding generations. An interesting case is afforded by a sterile variety of corn, which originated some time ago in my own pedigree-cultures made for another purpose, and which had begun with an ear of 1886. The first generation from the original seeds showed nothing particular, but the second at once produced quite a number of sterile plants. The sterility was caused by the total lack of branches, including those bearing the pistillate flowers. The terminal spikes themselves were reduced to naked spindles, without branches, without flowers and even almost without bracts.

In some individuals, however, this negative character was seen to give way at the tip, showing a few small naked branches. Of course it was impossible to propagate this curious form, but my observations showed that it sprang into existence from known ancestors by a single step or sudden leap. This leap, however, was not confined to a single specimen; on the contrary it affected 40 plants out of a culture of 340 individuals. The same phenomenon was repeated from the seeds of the normal plants in the following year, but afterwards the monstrosity disappeared.

The Italian poplar affords another instance. It is considered by some authors as a distinct species, *Populus italica*, and by others as a broom-like variety of the *Populus nigra,* from which it is distinguished by its erect branches and other characters of minor importance. It is often called the pyramidal or fastigiate poplar. Its origin is absolutely unknown and it occurs only in the cultivated state. In Italy it seems to have been cultivated from the earliest historical times, but it was not introduced into other countries till the eighteenth century. In 1749 it was brought into France, and in 1758 into England, and to-day it may be seen along roads throughout central Europe and in a large part of Asia. But the most curious fact is that it is only observed in staminate specimens; pistillate trees have not been found, although often sought for. This circumstance makes it very probable that the origin of the broom-like poplar was a sudden mutation, producing only one individual. This being staminate, it has been propagated exclusively by cuttings. It is to be admitted, however, that no material evidence is at hand to prove that it is not an original wild species, the pistillate form of which has been lost by vegetative multiplication. One form only of many dioecious plants is to be found in cultivation, as for instance some South American species of *Ribes*.

Total lack of historical evidence concerning

the origin of a variety has sometimes been considered as sufficient proof of a sudden origin. The best known instance is that of the renowned cactus-dahlia with its recurved instead of incurved ray-florets. It was introduced from Mexico into the Netherlands by Van den Berg of Jutphaas, under the following remarkable circumstances. In the autumn of 1872 one of his friends had sent him a small case, containing seeds, bulbs and roots from Mexico. From one of these roots a Dahlia shoot developed. It was cultivated with great care and bloomed next year. It surprised all who saw it by the unexpected peculiarity of its large rich crimson flowers, the rays of which were reversed tubular. The margins of the narrow rays were curved backwards, showing the bright color of the upper surface. It was a very showy novelty, rapidly multiplied by cuttings, and was soon introduced into commerce. It has since been crossed with nearly all other available varieties of the *Dahlia,* giving a large and rich group of forms, bound together by the curious curling of the petals. It has never been observed to grow in Mexico, either wild or in gardens, and thus the introduced individual has come to be considered as the first of its race.

I have already mentioned that the rapid production of large numbers of new varieties, by means of the crossing of the offspring of a single mutant with previously existing sorts, is a very common feature in horticultural practice. It warns us that only a small part of the novelties introduced yearly are due to real mutations. Further instances of novelties with such a common origin are the purple-leaved dahlias, the gooseberries without prickles, the double petunias, erect gloxinias and many others. Accumulation of characters, acquired in different races of a species, may easily be effected in this way; in fact it is one of the important factors in the breeding of horticultural novelties.

I have alluded more than once in this lecture to the question, whether it is probable that mutations occur in one individual or in more. The common belief among horticulturists is that, as a rule, they appear in a single plant. This belief is so widespread that whenever a novelty is seen for the first time in two or more specimens it is at once suggested that it might have originated and been overlooked in a previous generation. Not caring to confess a lack of close observation, the number of mutants in such cases is usually kept secret. At least this statement has been made to me by some of the horticulturists at Erfurt, whom I visited some years ago in order to learn as much as possible about the methods of production of their novelties. Hence it is simply impossible to decide the question on the basis of the experience of the breeders. Even in the case of the same novelty arising in sundry varieties of the same species, the question as to common origin, by means of crossing, is often hard to decide, as for instance in moss-roses and nectarines. On the other hand, instances are on record where the same novelty has appeared at different times, often at long intervals. Such is the case with the butterfly-cyclamen, a form with wide-spreading petals which originated in Martin's nursery in England. The first time it was seen it was thought to be of no value, and was thrown away, but when appearing for a second time it was multiplied and eventually placed on the market. Other varieties of *Cyclamen*, as for instance the crested forms, are also known to have originated repeatedly.

In concluding this series of examples of horticultural mutations, I might mention two cases, which have occurred in my own experimental garden. The first refers to a tubular dahlia. It has ray-florets, the ligules of which have their margins grown together so as to form tubes, with the outer surface corresponding to the pale under-surface of the corolla.

This novelty originated in a single plant in a

culture from the seed of the dwarf variety "Jules Chrétien." The seeds were taken from introduced plants in my garden, and as the sport has no ornamental value it is uncertain whether this was the first instance or whether it had previously occurred in the nursery at Lyons, from whence the bulbs were secured. Afterwards it proved true from seed, but was very variable, exhibiting rather the features of an ever-sporting variety.

Another novelty was seen the first time in several individuals. It was a pink sport of the European cranesbill, *Geranium pratense*. It arose quite unexpectedly in the summer of 1902 from a striped variety of the blue species. It was seen in seven specimens out of a lot of about a hundred plants. This strain was introduced into my garden in 1897, when I bought two plants under the name of *Geranium pratense album*, which however proved to belong to the striped variety. From their seeds I sowed in 1898 a first generation, of which a hundred plants flowered the next year, and from their seeds I sowed in 1900 the lot which produced the sport. Neither the introduced plants nor their offspring had exhibited the least sign of a color-variation, besides the blue and white stripes. Hence it is very probable that my novelty was a true first mutation, the more probably so since a pink variety would without doubt have a certain horticultural value and would have been preserved if it had occurred. But as far as I have been able to ascertain, it is as yet unknown, nor has it been described until to-day.

Summing up the results of this long, though very incomplete, list of horticultural novelties with a more or less well-known origin, we see that sudden appearances are the rule. Having once sprung into existence the new varieties are ordinarily constant, except as affected by vicinism. Details concerning the process are mostly unavailable or at least are of very doubtful value. And to this it should be added that really progressive mutations have hardly been observed in horticulture. Hence the theoretical value of the facts is far less than might have been expected.

Lecture XXII

SYSTEMATIC ATAVISM

The steady coöperation of progression and retrogression is one of the important principles of organic evolution. I have dwelt upon this point more than once in previous lectures. I have tried to show that both in the more important lines of the general pedigree of the vegetable kingdom, and in the numerous lateral branches ending in the genera and species within the families, progression and retrogression are nearly always at work together. Your attention has been directed to the monocotyledons as an example, where retrogression is everywhere so active that it can almost be said to be the prevailing movement. Reduction in the vegetative and generative organs, in the anatomical structure and growth of the stems, and in sundry other ways is the method by which the monocotyledons have originated as a group from their supposed ancestors among the lower dicotyledonous families. Retrogression is the leading idea in the larger families of the group, as for instance in the aroids and the grasses. Retrograde evolution is also typical in the highest and most highly differentiated family of the monocotyledons, the orchids, which have but one or two stamens. In the second place I have had occasion more than once to assert that retrogression, though seemingly consisting in the disappearance of some quality, need not, as a rule, be considered as a complete loss. Quite on the contrary, it is very probable that real losses are extremely rare, if not wholly lacking. Ordinarily the loss is only apparent, the capacity becomes inactive only, but is not destroyed. The character has become latent, as it is commonly stated, and therefore may return to activity and to the full display of its peculiarity, whenever occasion offers.

Such a return to activity was formerly called atavism. But as we have seen, when dealing with the phenomena of latency at large, sundry cases of latency are to be distinguished, in order to get a clear insight into these difficult processes.

So it is with atavism, too. If any plant reverts to a known ancestor, we have a positive and simple case. But ancestors with alternate specific marks are as a rule neither historically nor experimentally manifest. They are only reputed to be such, and the presumption rests upon the systematic affinity between the derivative species and its nearest probable allies. Such reversions are now to be examined at some length and may be adequately treated under the head of systematic atavism. To this form of atavism pertain, on the basis of our definition, those phenomena by which species assume one or more characters of allies, from which they are understood to have descended by the loss of the character under discussion. The phenomena themselves consist in the production of anomalies and varieties, and as the genetic relation of the latter is often hardly beyond doubt, the anomalies seem to afford the best instances for the study of systematic atavism. This study has for its chief aim the demonstration of the presence of the latent characters, and to show that they return to activity suddenly and not by a slow and gradual recovery of the former features. It supports the assertion that the visible elementary characters are essentially an external display of qualities carried by the bearers of heredity, and that these bearers are separate entities, which may be mingled together, but are not fused into a chaotic primitive life-substance. Systematic atavism by this means leads us to a closer examination of the internal and concealed causes, which rule the affinities and divergencies of allied species. It brings before us, and emphasizes the importance of the conception of the so-called unit-characters.

The primrose will serve as an example. In the second lecture we have seen that the old species of Linnaeus, the *Primula veris,* was split up by Jacquin into three smaller ones, which are called *P. officinalis, P. elatior* and *P. acaulis.* From this systematic treatment we can infer that these three forms are assumed to be derived from a common ancestor. Now two of them bear their flowers in bracted whorls, condensed into umbels at the summits of a scape. The scapes themselves are inserted in the axils of the basal leaves, and produce the flowers above them. In the third species, *Primula acaulis,* this scape is lacking and the flowers are inserted singly in the axils on long slender stalks. For this reason the species is called acaulescent, indicating that it has no other stem than the subterranean rootstock. But on closer inspection we observe that the flower-stalks are combined into little groups, each group occupying the axil of one of the basal leaves. This fact at once points to an analogy with the umbellate allies, and induces us to examine the insertion of the flowers more critically. In doing so we find that they are united at their base so as to constitute a sessile umbel.

The scapes are not absolutely lacking, but only reduced to almost invisible rudiments.

Relying upon this conclusion we infer that all of the three elementary species have umbels, some pedunculate and the others not. On this point they agree with the majority of the allied species in the genus and in other genera, as for instance in *Androsace*. Hence the conclusion that the common ancestors were perennial plants with a rootstock bearing their flowers in umbels or whorls on scapes. Lacking in the *Primula veris*, these scapes must obviously have been lost at the time of the evolution of this form.

Proceeding on this line of speculation we at once see that a very adequate opportunity for systematic atavism is offered here. According to our general conception the apparent loss of a scape is no proof of a corresponding internal loss, but might as well be caused simply by the reduction of the scape-growing capacity to a latent or inactive state. It might be awakened afterwards by some unknown agency, and return to activity.

Now this is exactly what happens from time to time. In Holland the acaulescent primrose is quite a common plant, filling the woods in the spring with thousands of clusters of bright yellow flowers. It is a very uniform type, but in some years it is seen to return to atavistic conditions in some rare individuals. More than once I have observed such cases myself, and found that the variation is only a partial one, producing one or rarely two umbels on the same plant, and liable to fail of repetition when the varying specimens are transplanted into the garden for further observation. But the fact remains that scapes occur. The scapes themselves are of varying length, often very short, and seldom long, and their umbels display the involucre of bracts in a manner quite analogous to that of the *Primula officinalis* and *P. elatior*. To my mind this curious anomaly strongly supports the view of the latent condition of the scape in the acaulescent species, and that such a dormant character must be due to a descent from ancestors with active scapes, seems to be in no need of further reiteration. Returning to activity the scapes at once show a full development, in no way inferior to that of the allied forms, and only unstable in respect to their length.

A second example is afforded by the bracts of the crucifers. This group is easily distinguished by its cruciform petals and the grouping of the flowers into long racemes. In other families each flower of such an inflorescence would be subtended by a bract, according to the general rule that in the higher plants side branches are situated in the axils of leaves. Bracts are reduced leaves, but the spikes of the cruciferous plants are generally devoid of them. The flower-stalks, with naked bases, seem to arise from the common axis at indefinite points.

Hence the inference that crucifers are an exception to a general rule, and that they must have originated from other types which did comply with this rule, and accordingly were in the possession of floral bracts. Or, in other words, that the bracts must have been lost during the original evolution of the whole family. This conclusion being accepted, the accidental re-apparition of bracts within the family must be considered as a case of systematic atavism, quite analogous to the re-appearance of the scapes in the acaulescent primrose. The systematic importance of this phenomenon, however, is far greater than in the first case, in which we had only to deal with a specific character, while the abolition of the bracts has become a feature of a whole family.

This reversion is observed to take place according to two widely different principles. On one hand, bracts may be met with in a few stray species, assuming the rank of a specific character. On the other hand they may be seen to occur as an anomaly, incompletely developed, often very rare and with all the appearance of an accidental variation, but sometimes so common as to seem nearly normal.

Coming now to particular instances, we may turn our attention in the first place to the genus *Sisymbrium*. This is a group of about 50 species, of wide geographic distribution, among which the hedge mustard (*S. officinalis*) is perhaps the most common of weeds. Two species are reputed to have bracts, *Sisymbrium hirsutum* and *S. supinum*. Each flower-stalk of their long racemes is situated in the axil of such a bract, and the peculiarity is quite a natural one, corresponding exactly to what is seen in the inflorescence of other families. Besides the *Sisymbrium* some six other genera afford similar structures.

Erucastrum pollichii has been already alluded to in a former lecture when dealing with the same problem from another point of view. As previously stated, it is one of the most manifest and most easily accessible examples of a latent character becoming active through systematic atavism. In fact, its bracts are found so often as to be considered by some authors as of quite normal occurrence. Contrasted with those of the above mentioned species of *Sisymbrium*, they are not seen at the base of all the flower-stalks, but are limited to the lowermost part of the raceme, adorning a few, often ten or twelve, and rarely more flower-stalks. Moreover they exhibit a feature which is indicative of the presence of an abnormality. They are not all of the same size, but decrease in length from the base of the raceme upward, and finally slowly disappear.

Besides these rare cases there are quite a number of cruciferous species on record, which have been observed to bear bracts. Penzig in his valuable work on teratology gives a list of 33 such genera, many of them repeating the anomaly in more than one species. Ordinary cabbages are perhaps the best known instance, and any unusual abundance of nourishment, or anomalous cause of growth seems to be liable to incite the development of bracts. The hedge garlic or garlic mustard (*Alliaria*), the shepherd's purse, the wormseed or *Erysimum cheiranthoides* and many others afford instances. In my cultures of Heeger's shepherd's purse, the new species derived at Landau in Germany from the common shepherd's purse, the anomaly was observed to occur more than once, showing that the mutation, which changed the fruits, had not in the least affected this subordinate anomalous peculiarity. In all these cases the bracts behave as with the *Eru-*

castrum, being limited to the base of the spike, and decreasing in size from the lower flowers upward. Connected with these atavistic bracts is a feature of minor importance, which however, by its almost universal accompaniment of the bracts, deserves our attention, as it is indicative of another latent character. As a rule, the bracts are grown together with their axillary flower-stalk. This cohesion is not complete, nor is it always developed in the same degree. Sometimes it extends over a large part of the two organs, leaving only their tips free, but on other occasions it is limited to a small part of the base. But it is very interesting that this same cohesion is to be seen in the shepherd's purse, in the wormseed and in the cabbage, as well as in the case of the *Erucastrum* and most of the other observed cases of atavistic bracts. This fact suggests the idea of a common origin for these anomalies, and would lead to the hypothesis that the original ancestors of the whole family, before losing the bracts, exhibited this peculiar mode of cohesion.

Bracts and analogous organs afford similar cases of systematic atavism in quite a number of other families. Aroids sometimes produce long bracts from various places on their spadix, as may be seen in the cultivated greenhouse species, *Anthurium scherzerianum.*

Poppies have been recorded to bear bracts analogous to the little scales on the flower-stalks of the pansies, on the middle of their flower-stalks. A similar case is shown by the yellow foxglove or *Digitalis parviflora*. The foxgloves as a rule have naked flower-stalks, without the two little opposite leafy organs seen in so many other instances. The yellow species, however, has been seen to produce such scales from time to time. The honeysuckle genus is, as a rule, devoid of the stipules at the base of the petiole, but *Lonicera etrusca* has been observed to develop such organs, which were seen to be free in some, but in other specimens were adnate to the base of the leaf, and even connate with those of the opposite leaf.

Other instances could be given proving that bracts and stipules, when systematically lacking, are liable to reappear as anomalies. In doing so, they generally assume the peculiar characters that would be expected of them by comparison with allied genera in which they are of normal occurrence. There can be no doubt that their absence is due to an apparent loss, resulting from the reduction of a formerly active quality to inactivity. Resuming this effective state, the case attains the value and significance accorded to systematic atavism.

A very curious instance of reduced bracts, developing to unusual size, is afforded by a variety of corn, which is called *Zea Mays cryptosperma,* or *Zea Mays tunicata.* In ordinary corn the kernels are surrounded by small and thin, inconspicuous and membranaceous scales. Invisible on the integrate spikes, when ripe, they are easily detected by pulling the kernels out. In *cryptosperma* they are so strongly developed as to completely hide the kernels. Obviously they constitute a case of reversion to the characters of some unknown ancestor, since the corn is the only member of the grass-family with naked kernels. The var. *tunicata,* for this same reason, has been considered to be the original wild form, from which the other varieties of corn have originated. But as no historical evidence on this point is at hand, we must leave it as it is, notwithstanding the high degree of attractiveness attached to the suggestion.

The horsetail-family may be taken as a further support of our assertion. Some species have stems of two kinds, the fertile being brownish and appearing in early spring before the green or sterile ones. In others the stems are all alike, green and crowned with a cone-like spike of sporangia-bearing scales. Manifestly the dimorphous cases are to be considered as the younger ones, partly because they are obvious exceptions to the common rule, and partly because the division of labor is indicative of a higher degree of evolution. But sometimes these dimorphic species are seen to revert to the primary condition, developing a fertile cone at the summit of the green summer-stem. I have had the opportunity of collecting an instance of this anomaly on the tall *Equisetum telmateja* in Switzerland, and other cases are on record in teratological literature. It is an obvious example of systematic atavism, occurring suddenly and with the full development of all the qualities needed for the normal production of sporangia and spores. All of these must be concealed in a latent condition within the young tissues of the green stems.

More than once I have had occasion to deal with the phenomenon of torsions, as exhibited by the teasels and some other plants. This anomaly has been shown to be analogous to the cases described as double adaptations. The capacity of evolving antagonistic characters is prominent in both. The antagonists are assumed to lie quietly together while inactive. But as soon as evolution calls them into activity they become mutually exclusive, because only one of them can come to full display in the same organ. External influences decide which of the two becomes dominant and which remains dormant. This decision must take place separately for each stem and each branch, but as a rule, the stronger axes are more liable to furnish anomalies than the weaker.

Exactly the same thing is true of double adaptations. Every bud of the water-persicaria may develop either into an erect or into a floating stem, according as it is surrounded by water or by relatively dry soil. In other cases utility is often less manifest, but some use may either be proved, or shown to be very probable. At all events the term adaptation includes the idea of utility, and obviously useless contrivances could hardly be brought under the same head.

We have also dealt with the question of heredity. It is obvious that from the flowers of the floating and erect stems of the water-persicaria seeds will result, each capable of yielding both forms. Quite the same thing was the case with the teasels. Some 40% of the progeny produce beautifully twisted stems, but whether the seed was saved from the most completely twisted specimens or from the straight plants of the race was of no importance.

This phenomenon of twisting may now be considered from quite another point of view. It is a case of systematic atavism, or of the reacquirement of some ancient and long-lost quality. This quality is the alternate position of the leaves, which has been replaced in the teasel-family by a grouping in pairs. In order to prove the validity of this assertion, it will be necessary to discuss two points separately, viz.: relative positions of the leaves, and the manner in which the alternate position causes the stems to become twisted.

Leaves are affixed to their stems and branches in various ways. Among them one is of wide occurrence throughout the whole realm of the higher plants, while all the others are more rare. Moreover these subordinate arrangements are, as a rule, confined to definite systematic groups. Such groups may be large, as for instance, the monocotyledons, that have their leaves arranged in two opposite rows in many families, or small, as genera or subdivisions of genera. Apart from these special cases the main stem and the greater part of the branches of the pedigree of the higher plants exhibit a spiral condition or a screw arrangement, all leaves being inserted at different points and on different sides of the stem. This condition is assumed to be the original one, from which the more specialized types have been derived. As is usual with characters in general, it is seen to vary around an average, the spiral becoming narrower and looser. A narrow spiral condenses the leaves, while a loose one disperses them. According to such fluctuating deviations the number of leaves, inserted upon a given number of spiral circuits, is different in different species. In a vast majority of cases 13 leaves are found on 5 circuits, and as we have only to deal with this proportion in the teasels we will not consider others.

In the teasels this screw-arrangement has disappeared, and has been replaced by a decussate grouping. The leaves are combined into pairs, each pair occupying the opposite sides of one node. The succeeding pairs alternate with one another, so as to place their leaves at right angles. The leaves are thus arranged on the whole stem in four equidistant rows.

On the normal stem of a teasel the two members of a pair are tied to one another in a comparatively complicated way. The leaves are broadly sessile and their bases are united so as to constitute a sort of cup. The margins of these cups are bent upward, thereby enabling them to hold water, and after a rainfall they may be seen filled to the brim. It is believed that these little reservoirs are useful to the plant during the flowering period, because they keep the ants away from the honey. Considering the internal structure of the stem at the base of these cups we find that the vascular bundles of the two opposite leaves are strongly connected with one another, constituting a ring which narrowly surrounds the stem, and which would impede an increase in thickness, if such were in the nature of the plant. But since the stems end their existence during the summer of their development, this structure is of no real harm.

The grouping of the leaves in alternate pairs may be seen within the bud as well as on the adult stems. In order to do this, it is necessary to make transverse sections through the heart of the rosette of the leaves of the first year. If cut through the base, the pair exhibit connate wings, corresponding to the water-cups; if cut above these, the leaves seem to be free from one another.

In order to compare the position of leaves of the twisted plants with this normal arrangement, the best way is to make a corresponding section through the heart of the rosette of the first year. It is not necessary to make a microscopic preparation. In the fall the changed disposition may at once be seen to affect the central leaves of the group. All the rosettes of the whole race commence with opposite leaves; those that are to produce straight stems remain in this condition, but the preparation for twisting begins at the end of the first year as shown by a special arrangement of the leaves. This disposition may then be seen to extend to the very center of the rosette, by use of microscopical sections. Examining sections made in the spring, the original arrangement of the leaves of the stem is observed to continue until the beginning of the growth of the shoot. It is easy to estimate the number of leaves corresponding to a given number of spiral circuits in these sections and the proportion is found to indicate 13 leaves on 5 turns. These figures are the same as those given above for the ordinary arrangement of alternate leaves in the main lines of the pedigree of the vegetable kingdom.

Leaving aside for the moment the subsequent changes of this spiral arrangement, it becomes at once clear that here we have a case of systematic atavism. The twisted teasels lose their decussation, but in doing so the leaves are not left in a disorderly dispersion, but a distinct new arrangement takes its place, which is to be assumed as the normal one for the ancestors of the teasel family. The case is to be considered as one of atavism. Obviously no other explanation is possible, than the supposition that the 5–13 spiral is still latent, though not displayed by the teasels. But in the very moment when the faculty of decussation disappears, it resumes its place, and becomes as prominent as it must once have been in the ancestors, and is still in that part of their offspring, which has not become changed in this respect. Thus the proof of our assertion of systematic atavism is, in this case, not obtained by the inspection of the adult, but by the investigation of the conditions in an early stage. It remains to be explained how the twisting may finally be caused by this incipient grouping of the leaves. Before doing so, it may be as well to state that the case of the teasel is not an isolated one, and that the same conclusions are supported by the valerian, and a large number of other examples. In early spring some rosettes show a special condition of the leaves, indicating thereby at once their atavism and their tendency to become twisted as soon as they begin to expand. The Sweet William or *Dianthus barbatus* affords another instance; it is very interesting because a twisted race is available, which may produce thousands of instances developed in all imaginable degrees, in a single lot of plants. *Viscaria oculata* is another instance belonging to the same family.

The bedstraw (*Galium*) also includes many species which from time to time produce twisted stems. I have found them myself in Holland on *Galium verum* and *G. Aparine*. Both seem to be of rare occurrence, as I have not succeeded in getting any repetition by prolonged culture.

Species, which generally bear their leaves in whorls, are also subjected to casual atavisms of this kind, as for instance the tall European horsetail, *Equisetum Telmateja,* which occasionally bears cones on its green summer stems. Its whorls are changed on the twisted parts into clearly visible spirals. The ironwood or *Casuarina quadrivalvis* is sometimes observed to produce the same anomaly on its smaller lateral branches.

Coming now to the discussion of the way in which the twisting is the result of the spiral disposition of the leaves, we may consider this arrangement on stems in the adult state. These at once show the spiral line and it is easy to follow this line from the base up to the apex. In the most marked cases it continues without interruption, not rarely however, ending in a whorl of three leaves and a subsequent straight internode, of which there may even be two or three. The spiral exhibits the basal parts of the leaves, with the axillary lateral branches. The direction of the screw is opposed to that of the twisting, and the spiral ribs are seen to cross the line of insertion of the leaves at nearly right angles. On this line the leaves are nearer to one another than would correspond to the original proportion of 5 turns for 13 leaves. In fact, 10 or even 13 leaves may not rarely be counted on a single turn. Or the twist may become so strong locally as to change the spiral into a longitudinal line. On this line all inserted leaves extend themselves in the same direction, resembling an extended flag.

The spiral on the stem is simply the continuation of the spiral line from within the rosettes of the first year. Accordingly it is seen to become gradually less steep at the base. For this reason it must be one and the same with this line, and in extreme youth it must have produced its leaves at the same mutual distances as this line. Transverse sections of the growing summits of the stems support this conclusion.

From these several facts we may infer that the steepness of the spiral line increases on the stem, as it is gradually changed into a screw. Originally 5 turns were needed for 13 leaves, but this number diminishes and 4 or 3 or even 2 turns may take the same number of foliar organs, until the screw itself is changed into a straight line.

This change consists in an unwinding of the whole spiral, and in order to effect this the stem must become wound up in the opposite direction. The winding of the foliar screw must curve the longitudinal ribs. The straighter and steeper the screw becomes, the more the ribs will become twisted. That this happens in the opposite direction is obvious, without further discussion. The twisting is the inevitable consequence of the reversal of the screw.

Two points remain to be dealt with. One is the direct proof of the reversal of the screw, the other the discussion of its cause. The first may be observed by a simple experiment. Of course it proceeds only slowly, but all that is necessary is to mark the position of one of the younger leaves of a growing stem of a twisting individual and to observe the change in its position in a few hours. It will be seen to have turned some way around the stem, and finally may be seen to make a complete revolution in the direction opposite to the screw, and thereby demonstrating the fact of its uncurling.

The cause of this phenomenon is to be sought in the intimate connection of the basal parts of the leaves, which we have detailed above. The fibrovascular strands constitute a strong rope, which is twisted around the stem along the line on which the leaves are inserted. The strengthening of the internodes may stretch this rope to some extent, but it is too strong to be rent asunder. Hence it opposes the normal growth, and the only manner in which the internodes may adjust themselves to the forces which tend to cause their expansion is by straightening the rope. In doing so they may find the required space, by growing out in an unusual direction, bending their axes and twisting the ribs.

To prove the validity of this explanation, a simple experiment may be given. If the fibrovascular rope is the mechanical impediment which hinders the normal growth, we may try the effect of cutting through this rope. By this means the hindrance may at least locally be removed. Now, of course, the operation must be made in an early stage before, or at the beginning of the period of growth, in every case before the uncurling of the rope begins. Wounds made at this time are apt to give rise to malformations, but notwithstanding this difficulty I have succeeded in giving the necessary proof. Stems operated upon become straight where the rope is cut through, though above and under the wounded part they go on twisting in the usual way.

Sometimes the plants themselves succeed in tearing the rope asunder, and long straight internodes divide the twisted stems in two or more parts in a very striking manner. A line of torn leaf-bases connects the two parts of the screw and gives testimony of what has passed within the tissues. At other times the straightening may have taken place directly internal to a leaf, and it is torn and may be seen to be attached to the stem by two distinct bases.

Summing up this description of the hereditary qualities of our twisted teasels and of their mechanical consequences, we may say that the loss of the normal decussation is the cause of all the observed changes. This special adaptation, which places the leaves in alternating pairs, replaced and concealed the old and universal arrangement on a screw line. In disappearing, it leaves the latter free, and according to the rule of systematic atavism, this now becomes active and takes its place. If the fibrovascular connection of the leaf-bases were lost at the same time the stems would grow and become straight and tall. This change however, does not occur, and the bases of the leaves now constitute a continuous rope instead of separate rings, and thereby impede the stretching of the internodes. These in their turn avoid the difficulty by twisting themselves in a direction opposite to that of the spiral of the leaves.

As a last example of systematic atavism I will refer to the reversionary changes, afforded by the tomatoes. Though the culture of this plant is a recent one, it seems to be at present in a state of mutability, producing new strains, or assuming the features of their presumable ancestors. In his work " The Survival of the Unlike," Bailey has given a detailed description of these various types. Moreover, he has closely studied the causes of the changes, and shown the great tendency of the tomatoes to vicinism. By far the larger part of the observed cases of running out of varieties are caused by accidental crosses through the agency of insects. Even improvements are not rarely due to this cause. Besides these common and often unavoidable changes, others of greater importance occur from time to time. Two of them deserve to be mentioned. They are called the " Upright " and the " Mikado " types, and differ as much or even more from their parents than the latter do from any one of their wild congeners. Their characters come true from seed. The " Mikado " race or the *Lycopersicum grandifolium* (*L. latifolium*) has larger and fewer leaflets than the slender and somewhat flimsy foliage of the common form. Flat or plane blades with decurrent margins constitute another character. This variety, however, does not concern our present discussion. The upright type has stiff and self-sustaining stems and branches, resembling rather a potato-plant than a tomato. Hence the name *Lycopersicum solanopsis* or *L. validum,* under which it is usually described.

The foliage of the plant is so distinct as to yield botanical characters of sufficient importance to justify this specific designation. The leaflets are reduced in numbers and greatly modified, and the flowers in the inflorescence are reduced to two or three. This curious race came in suddenly, without any premonition, and the locality and date of its mutation are still on record. Until some years ago it had not made its appearance for a second time. Obviously it is to be considered as a reversionary form. The limp stems of the common tomatoes are in all respects indicative of the cultivated condition. They cannot hold themselves erect, but must be tied up to supports. The color of the leaves is a paler green than should be expected from a wild plant. Considering other species of the genus *Solanum,* of which the *Lycopersicum* is a subdivision, the stems are as a rule erect and self-supporting, with some few exceptions. These, however, are special adaptations as shown by the winding stems of the bitter-sweet.

From this discussion we seem justified in concluding that the original appearance of the upright type was of the nature of systematic atavism. It differs however, from the already detailed cases in that it is not a monstrosity, nor an ever-sporting race, but is as constant a form as the best variety or species. Even on this ground it must be considered as a representative of a separate group of instances of the universal rule of systematic reversions.

Of late the same mutation has occurred in the garden of C. A. White at Washington. The parent form in this case was the "Acme," of the ordinary weak and spreading habit of growth. It is known as one of the best and most stable of the varieties and was grown by Mr. White for many years, and had not given any sign of a tendency towards change. Seeds from some of the best plants in 1899 were sown the following spring, and the young seedlings unexpectedly exhibited a marked difference from their parents. From the very outset they were more strong and erect, more compact and of a darker green than the "Acme." When they reached the fruiting stage they had developed into typical representatives of the *Lycopersicum solanopsis* or upright division. The whole lot of plants comprised only some 30 specimens, and this number, of course, is too small to base far-reaching conclusions upon. But all of the lot showed this type, no true "Acme" being seen among them. The fruit differed in flavor, consistency and color from that of the parent, and it also ripened earlier than the latter. No seed was saved from these plants, but the following year the "Acme" was sown again and found true to its type. Seeds saved from this generation in 1900 have, however, repeated the mutation, giving rise to exactly the same new upright form in 1901. This was called by its originator "The Washington." Seeds from this second mutation were kindly sent to me by Mr. White, and proved true to their type when sown in my garden.

Obviously it is to be assumed in the case of the tomatoes as well as in instances from other genera cited, that characters of ancestors, which are not displayed in their progeny, have not been entirely lost, but are still present, though in a latent condition. They may resume their activity unexpectedly, and at once develop all the features which they formerly had borne.

Latency, from this point of view, must be one of the most common things in nature. All organisms are to be considered as internally formed of a host of units, partly active and partly inactive. Extremely minute and almost inconceivably numerous, these units must have their material representatives within the most intimate parts of the cells.

Lecture XXIII

TAXONOMIC ANOMALIES

The theory of descent is founded mainly on comparative studies, which have the advantage of affording a broad base and the convincing effect of concurrent evidence brought together from widely different sources. The theory of mutation on the other hand rests directly upon experimental investigations, and facts concerning the actual descent of one form from another are as yet exceedingly rare. It is always difficult to estimate the validity of conclusions drawn from isolated instances selected from the whole range of contingent phenomena, and this is especially true of the present case. Systematic and physiologic facts seem to indicate the existence of universal laws, and it is not probable that the process of production of new species would be different in the various parts of the animal and vegetable kingdoms. Moreover the principle of unit-characters, the pre-eminent significance of which has come to be more fully recognized of late, is in full harmony with the theory of sudden mutations. Together these two conceptions go to strengthen the probability of the sudden origin of all specific characters.

Experimental researches are limited in their extent, and the number of cases of direct observation of the process of mutation will probably never become large enough to cover the whole field of the theory of descent. Therefore it will always be necessary to show that the similarity between observed and other cases is such as to lift above all doubt the assertion of their resulting from the same causes.

Besides the direct comparison of the mutations described in our former lectures, with the analogous cases of the horticultural and natural production of species and varieties at large, another way is open to obtain the required proof. It is the study of the phenomena, designated by Casimir de Candolle by the name of taxonomic anomalies. It is the assertion that characters, which are specific in one case, may be observed to arise as anomalies or as varieties in other instances. If they can be shown to be identical or nearly so in both, it is obviously allowable to assume the same origin for the specific character and for the anomaly. In other terms, the specific marks may be considered as having originated according to the laws

that govern the production of anomalies, and
we may assume them to lie within reach of our
experiments. The experimental treatment of
the origin of species may also be looked upon as
a method within our grasp.

The validity and the significance of these
considerations will at once become clear, if we
choose a definite example. The broadest and
most convincing one appears to me to be afforded by the cohesion of the petals in gamopetalous flowers. According to the current
views the families with the petals of their
flowers united are regarded as one or two main
branches of the whole pedigree of the vegetable kingdom. Eichler and others assume
them to constitute one branch, and therefore one
large subdivision of the system. Bessey, on the
other hand, has shown the probability of a separate origin for those groups which have inferior ovaries. Apart from such divergencies
the connation of the petals is universally recognized as one of the most important systematic
characters.

How may this character have originated?
The heath-family or the *Ericaceae* and their
nearest allies are usually considered to be the
lowest of the gamopetalous plants. In them the
cohesion of the petals is still subject to reversionary exceptions. Such cases of atavism may

be observed either as specific marks, or in the way of anomalies. *Ledum, Monotropa* and *Pyrola,* or the Labrador tea, the Indian pipe and wintergreen are instances of reversionary gamopetalism with free petals. In heaths (*Erica Tetralix*) and in rhododendrons the same deviation is observed to occur from time to time as an anomaly, and even the common *Rhododendron ponticum* of our gardens has a variety in which the corolla is more or less split. Sometimes it exhibits five free petals, while at other times only one or two are entirely free, the remaining four being incompletely loosened.

Such cases of atavism make it probable that the coherence of the petals has originally arisen by the same method, but by action in the opposite direction. The direct proof of this conclusion is afforded by a curious observation, made by Vilmorin upon the bright and large-flowered garden-poppy, *Papaver bracteatum.* Like all poppies it has four petals, which are free from one another. In the fields of Messrs. Vilmorin, where it is largely cultivated for its seeds, individuals occur from time to time which are anomalous in this respect. They exhibit a tendency to produce connate petals. Their flowers become monopetalous, and the whole strain is designated by the name of *Papaver bracteatum monopetalum*. Henry de Vilmorin had the kindness to send me some of these plants, and they have flowered in my garden during several years. The anomaly is highly variable. Some flowers are quite normal, exhibiting no sign of connation; others are wholly gamopetalous, the four petals being united from their base to the very margin of the cup formed. In consequence of the broadness of the petals however, this cup is so wide as to be very shallow.

Intermediate states occur, and not infrequently. Sometimes only two or three petals are united, or the connation does not extend the entire length of the petals. These cases are quite analogous to the imperfect splitting of the corolla of the rhododendron. Giving free rein to our imagination, we may for a moment assume the possibility of a new subdivision of the vegetable kingdom, arising from Vilmorin's poppy and having gamopetalous flowers for its chief character. If the character became fixed, so as to lose its present state of variability, such a group of supposititious gamopetalous plants might be quite analogous to the corresponding real gamopetalous families. Hence there can be no objection to the view, that the heaths have arisen in an analogous manner from their polypetalous ancestors. Other species of the same genus have also been recorded to produce gamopetalous flowers, as for instance, *Papaver hybridum,* by Hoffmann. Poppies are not the sole example of accidental gamopetaly. Linnaeus observed the same deviation long ago for *Saponaria officinalis,* and since, it has been seen in *Clematis Vitalba* by Jaeger, in *Peltaria alliacea* by Schimper, in *Silene annulata* by Boreau and in other instances. No doubt it is not at all of rare occurrence, and the origin of the present gamopetalous families is to be considered as nothing extraordinary. It is, as a matter of fact, remarkable that it has not taken place in more numerous instances, and the mallows show that such opportunities have been available at least more than once.

Other instances of taxonomic anomalies are afforded by leaves. Many genera, the species of which mainly bear pinnate or palmate leaves, have stray types with undivided leaves. Among the brambles, *Rubus odoratus* and *R. flexuosus* may be cited, among the aralias, *Aralia crassifolia* and *A. papyrifera,* and among the jasmines, the deliciously scented sambac (*Jasminum Sambac*). But the most curious instance is that of the telegraph-plant, or *Desmodium gyrans,* each complete leaf of which consists of a large terminal leaflet and two little lateral ones. These latter keep up, night and day, an irregular jerking movement, which has been compared to the movements of a semaphore. *Desmodium* is a papilionaceous plant and closely allied to the genus *Hedysarum,* which has pinnate leaves with numerous pairs of leaflets. Its place in the system leaves no doubt concerning its origin from pinnate-leaved ancestors. At the time of its origination its leaves must have become reduced as to the number of the blades, while the size of the terminal leaflet was correspondingly increased.

It might seem difficult to imagine this great change taking place suddenly. However, we are compelled to familiarize ourselves with such hypothetical assumptions. Strange as they may seem to those who are accustomed to the conception of continuous slow improvements, they are nevertheless in complete agreement with what really occurs. Fortunately the direct proof of this assertion can be given, and in a case which is narrowly related, and quite parallel to that of the *Desmodium,* since it affects a plant of the same family. It is the case of the monophyllous variety of the bastard-acacia or *Robinia Pseud-Acacia.* In a previous lecture we have seen that it originated suddenly in a French nursery in the year 1855. It can be propagated by seed, and exhibits a curious degree of variability of its leaves. In some instances these are one-bladed, the blade reaching a length of 15 cm., and hardly resembling those of the common bastard-acacia. Other leaves produce one or two small leaflets at the base of the large terminal one, and by this contrivance are seen to be very similar to those of the *Desmodium*, repeating its chief characters nearly exactly, and only differing somewhat in the relative size of the various parts. Lastly real intermediates are seen between the monophyllous and the pinnate types. As far as I have been able to ascertain, these are produced on weak twigs under unfavorable conditions; the size of the terminal leaflet decreases and the number of the lateral blades increases, showing thereby the presence of the original pinnate type in a latent condition.

The sudden origin of this " one-leaved " acacia in a nursery may be taken as a prototype of the ancient origin of *Desmodium*. Of course the comparison only relates to a single character, and the movements of the leaflets are not affected by it. But the monophylly, or rather the size of the terminal blade and the reduction of the lateral ones, may be held to be sufficiently illustrated by the bastard-acacia. It is worth while to state, that analogous varieties have also arisen in other genera. The " one-leaved" strawberry has already been referred to. It originated from the ordinary type in Norway and at Paris. The walnut likewise, has its monophyllous variety. It was mentioned for the first time as a cultivated tree about 1864, but its origin is unknown. A similar variety of the walnut, with "one-bladed" leaves but of varying shapes, was found wild in a forest near Dieppe in France some years ago, and appeared to be due to a sudden mutation.

Something more is known concerning the "one-bladed" ashes, varieties of which are often seen in our parks and gardens. The common form has broad and deeply serrate leaves, which are far more rounded than the leaflets of the ordinary ash. The majority of the leaves are simple, but some produce one or two smaller leaflets at their base, closely corresponding in this respect to the variations of the "one-bladed" bastard-acacia, and evidently indicating the same latent and atavistic character. In some instances this analogy goes still further, and incompletely pinnate leaves are produced with two or more pairs of leaflets. Besides this variable type another has been described by Willdenow. It has single leaves exclusively, never producing smaller lateral leaflets, and it is said to be absolutely constant from seed, while the more variable types seem to be also more inconstant when propagated sexually. The difference is so striking and affords such a reliable feature that Koch proposed to make two distinct varieties of them, calling the pure type *Fraxinus excelsior monophylla,* and the varying trees *F. excel. exheterophylla.* Some writers, and among them Willdenow, have preferred to separate the " one-leaved " forms from the species, and to call them *Fraxinus simplicifolia.*

According to Smith and to Loudon, the " one-leaved " ashes are found wild in different districts in England. Intermediate forms have not been recorded from these localities. This mode of origin is that already detailed for the laciniate varieties of alders and so many other trees. Hence it may be assumed that the " one-leaved " ashes have sprung suddenly but frequently from the original pinnate species. The pure type of Willdenow should, in this case, be considered as due to a slightly different mutation, perhaps as a pure retrograde variety, while the varying strains may only be ever-sporting forms. This would likewise explain part of their observed inconstancy.

In this respect the historic dates, as collected by Korshinsky, are not very convincing. Vicinism has of course, almost never been excluded, and part of the multiformity of the offspring must obviously be due to this most universal agency. Indirect vicinism also plays some part, and probably affords the explanation of some reputed mutative productions of the variety. So, for instance, in the case of Sinning, who after sowing the seeds of the common ash, got as large a proportion as 2% of monophyllous trees in a culture of some thousand plants. It is probable that his seeds were taken partly from normal plants, and partly from hybrids between the normal and the " one-bladed " type, assuming that these hybrids have pinnate leaves like their specific parent, and bear the characters of the other parent only in a latent condition.

Our third example relates to peltate leaves. They have the stalk inserted in the middle of the blade, a contrivance produced by the connation of the two basal lobes. The water-lilies are a well known instance, exhibiting sagittate leaves in the juvenile stage and changing in many species, into nearly circular peltate forms, of which *Victoria regia* is a very good example, although its younger stages do not always excite all the interest they deserve. The Indian cress (*Tropaeolum*), the marsh-pennywort or *Hydrocotyle,* and many other instances could be quoted. Sometimes the peltate leaves are not at all orbicular, but are elongated, oblong or elliptic, and with only the lobes at the base united. The lemon-scented *Eucalyptus citriodora* is one of the most widely known cases. In other instances the peltate leaves become more or less hollow, constituting broad ascidia as in the case of the crassulaceous genus *Umbilicus*.

This connation of the basal lobes is universally considered as a good and normal specific character. Nevertheless it has its manifest analogy in the realm of the anomalies. This is the pitcher or *ascidium*. On some trees it is of quite common occurrence, as on the lime-tree (*Tilia parvifolia*) and the magnolia (*Magnolia obovata* and its hybrids). It is probable that both these forms have varieties with, and others without, ascidia. Of the lime-tree, instances are known of single trees which produce hundreds of such anomalous leaves yearly, and one such a tree is growing in the neighborhood of Amsterdam at Lage Vuursche. I have alluded to these cases more than once, but on this occasion a closer inspection of the structure of the ascidium is required. For this purpose we may take the lime-tree as an example. Take the shape of the normal leaves in the first place. These are cordate at their base and mainly inequilateral, but the general shape varies to a considerable extent. This variation is closely related to the position of the leaves on the twigs, and shows distinct indications of complying with the general law of periodicity. The first leaves are smaller, with more rounded lobes, the subsequent leaves attain a larger size, and their lobes slightly change their forms. In the first leaves the lobes are so broad as to touch one another along a large part of their margins, but in organs formed later this contact gradually diminishes and the typical leaves have the lobes widely separated. Now it is easily understood that the contact or the separation of the lobes must play a part in the construction of the ascidia, as soon as the margins grow together. Leaves which touch one another, may be affected by the connation without any further malformation. They remain flat, become peltate and exhibit a shape which in some way holds a middle position between the pennyworts and the lemon-scented eucalyptus. Here we have the repetition of the specific characters of these plants by the anomaly of another. Whenever the margins are not in contact, and become connate, notwithstanding their separation, the blade must be folded together in some slight degree, in order to produce the required contact. This is the origin of the ascidium. It is quite superfluous to insist upon the fact that their width or narrowness must depend upon the corresponding normal form. The more distant the lobes, the deeper the ascidium will become. It should be added that this explanation of the different shapes of ascidia is of general validity.

Ascidia of the snake-plantain or *Plantago lanceolata* are narrow tubes, because the leaves are oblong or lanceolate, while those of the broad leaved species of arrowhead, as for instance, the *Sagittaria japonica,* are of a conical shape.

From the evidence of the lime-tree we may conclude that normal peltate leaves may have originated in the same way. And from the fact that pitchers are one of the most frequent anomalies, we may conclude that the chance of producing peltate leaves must have been a very great one, and wholly sufficient to account for all observed cases. In every instance the previously existing shape of the leaf must have decided whether peltate or pitcher-like leaves would be formed. As far as we can judge peltate anomalies are quite uninjurious, while ascidia are forms which must impede the effect of the light on the leaf, as they conceal quite an important part of the upper surface. In this way it is easily conceivable that peltate leaves are a frequent specific character, while ascidia are not, as they only appear in the special cases of limited adaptation, as in the instances of the so called pitcher-plants. The genera *Nepenthes,*

Sarracenia and some others are very well known and perhaps even the bladderworts or *Utricularia* might be included here.

The reproduction of specific characters by anomalous ascidia is not at all limited to the general case as described above. More minute details may be seen to be duplicated in the same way. Proofs are afforded on one side by incomplete ascidia, and on the other by the double cups.

Incomplete ascidia are those of the *Nepenthes*. The leaf is divided into three parts, a blade, a tendril and the pitcher. Or in other words, the limb produces a tendril at its summit, by means of which the plant is enabled to fasten itself to surrounding shrubs and to climb between their branches. But the end of this tendril bears a well-formed urn, which however, is produced only after the revolving and grasping movements of the tendril have been made. Some species have more rounded and some more elongated ascidia and often the shape is seen to change with the development of the stem. The mouth of the urn is strengthened by a thick rim and covered with a lid. Numerous curious contrivances in these structures to catch ants and other insects have been described, but as they have no relation to our present discussion, we shall abstain from dealing with them.

Likewise we must refrain from a consideration of the physiologic qualities of the tendril, and confine our attention to the combination of a limb, a naked midvein and an ascidium. This combination is to be the basis of our discussion. It is liable to be produced all of a sudden. This assertion is proved by its occurrence as a varietal mark in one of our most ordinary cultivated plants. It is the group known as *Croton,* belonging to the genus *Codiaeum.* A variety is called *interruptum* and another *appendiculatum,* and these names both relate to the interruption of the leaves by a naked midvein. The leaves are seen to be built up of three parts. The lower half retains the aspect of a limb; it is crowned by a vein without lateral nerves or blade-like expansions, and this stalk in its turn bears a short limb on its summit. The base of this apical limb exhibits two connate lobes, forming together a wide cup or ascidium. It should be stated that these *interruptum* varieties are highly variable, especially in the relative size of the three principal parts of the leaf. Though it is of course conceded that the ascidium of *Nepenthes* has many secondary devices which are lacking in *Croton,* it seems hardly allowable to deny the possibility of an analogous origin for both. Those of the *Croton,* according to our knowledge regarding similar cases, must have arisen at once, and hence the conclusion that the ascidia of *Nepenthes* are also originally due to a sudden mutation. Interrupted leaves, with an ascidium on a naked prolongation of the midvein, are by no means limited to the *Croton* varieties. As stray anomalies they have often been observed, and I myself had the opportunity of collecting them on magnolia, on clover and on some other species. They are additional evidence in support of the explanation given above.

In the same way double ascidia may be made use of to explain the foliar cups of the teasels and some other plants, as for instance, some European snakeroots (*Eryngium maritimum* and *E. campestre*), or the floral leaves of the honeysuckle. The leaves on the stems of the teasels are disposed in pairs, and the bases of the two leaves of each pair are connate so as to constitute large cups. We have already mentioned these cups, and recall them in the present connection to use them as a prototype of the double ascidia. These are constituted of two opposite leaves, accidentally connated at their base or along some part of their margins. If the leaves are sessile, the analogy with the teasels is complete, as shown, for instance, in a case of *Cotyledon*, a crassulaceous plant which is known to produce such cups from time to time. They are narrower than those of the teasel, but this depends, as we have seen for the "one-leaved" ascidium, on the shape of the original leaf. In other respects they exactly imitate the teasel cups, showing thereby how these cups may probably have originated.

In numerous cases of anomalies some accidental structures are parallel to specific characters, while others are not, being obviously injurious to their bearers. So it is also with the double ascidia. In the case of stalked leaves the two opposite stalks must, of course, constitute a long and very narrow tube, when growing together. This tube must bear at its summit the conical ascidium produced by the two connate limbs. At its base however, it includes the terminal bud of the stem, and frequently the tube is so narrow as to impede its further development. By this contrivance the double ascidium assumes a terminal position. Instances have been observed on magnolia, in *Boehmeria* and in other cases.

Flowers on leaves are of rare occurrence. Notwithstanding this, they constitute specific characters in some instances, accidental anomalies in others. *Helwingia rusciflora* is the most curious and best known instance. It is a little shrub, belonging to the *Cornaceae*, and has broad elliptical undivided leaves. On the middle of the midvein these leaves are seen to bear small clusters of flowers; indeed this is the only place where flowers are produced. Each cluster has from 13 – 15 flowers, of which some are staminate and borne on stalks, while others are pistillate and nearly sessile. These flowers are small and of a pale greenish color and yield small stone-fruits, with a thin coating of pulpy tissue. As the name indicates, this mode of flowering is closely similar to that of *Ruscus,* which however, does not bear its flowers and berries on real leaves, but on leaf-like expansions of the twigs. *Phyllonoma ruscifolia,* a saxifragaceous plant, bears the same specific name, indicating a similar origin of the flowers. Other instances have been collected by Casimir de Candolle, but their number is very small.

As a varietal mark, flowers on leaves likewise rarely occur. One instance however, is very remarkable, and we have already dealt with it, when treating of constant varieties, and of the lack of vicinism in the case of species with exclusive self-fertilization.

It is the " Nepaul-barley " or *Hordeum trifurcatum.* The leaves, which in this case bear the adventitious flowers, are the inner scales of the spikelets, and not on green leaves as in the cases already alluded to. But this of course makes no real difference. The character is variable to a high degree, and this fact indicates its varietal nature, though it should be recalled that at least with the *Helwingia,* the majority of the leaves are destitute of flowers, and that in this way some degree of variability is present in this normal case too.

All in all there are three sorts of "Nepaul-barley." They have the same varietal mark, but belong to different species of barley. These are differentiated according to the number of the rows in which the grains are seen on the spikes. These numbers may be two, four or six, giving rise to the specific names of *Hordeum distichum, tetrastichum* and *hexastichum.* Whether these three varieties are of independent, but parallel origin, or are to be considered as due to a single mutation and subsequent crosses is not known, all of them being of ancient origin. Historic evidence concerning their birth is wholly wanting. From analogy it would seem probable that the character had arisen by a mutation in one of the three named species, and had been transferred to others by means of accidental crosses, even as it has been artificially transmitted of late to quite a number of other sorts. But however admissible this conception may seem, there is of course no real objection to the assumption of independent and parallel mutations.

For the purpose of a comparison with the *Helwingia* type we are however, not at all concerned with the species to which the *trifurcatum* variety belongs, but only with the varietal mark itself. The spikelets may be one-, two- or three-flowered, according to the species. If we choose for further consideration the *hexastichum* type, each spikelet produces three normal flowers and afterwards three normal grains. Morphologically however, the spikelet is not homologous to those parts of other grasses which have the same name. It is constituted of three real spikelets, and thus deserves the name of a triple construction. Each of these three little organs has its normal pair of outer scales or glumae. These are linear and short, ending in a long and narrow spine. Those of the middle-most spikelets stand on its outer side, while those of the lateral part are placed transversely. In this way they form a kind of involucre around the central parts. The latter consist of the inner and outer palets or scales, each two of which include one of the flowers. The outer palet is to be considered as the metamorphosed leaf, in the axil of which the flower is produced. In the common sorts of barley it bears a long awn, giving thereby its typical aspect to the whole spike. The axillary flower is protected on the opposite side by a two-keeled inner palet. Each flower exhibits three stamens and an ovary. In the six-rowed barley all the three flowers of a triple spikelet are fertile, and each of them has a long awn on the top of the outer palet. But in the two-rowed species only the middle-most flower is normal and has an awn, the two remaining being sterile and more or less rudimentary and with only very short awns. From this description it is easily seen that the species of barley may be distinguished from one another, even at a casual glance, by the number of the rows of the awns, and therefore by the shape of the entire spikes. This striking feature, however, does not exist in the "Nepaul-barley." The awns are replaced by curiously shaped appendices, which are three-lobed. The central lobe is oblong and hollow, and forms a kind of hood, which covers a small supernumerary floret. The two lateral lobes are narrower, often linear and extended into a smaller or longer awn. These awns are mostly turned away from the center of the spike. The central lobe may sometimes bear two small florets, but ordinarily only one is to be found, and this is often incomplete, having only one or two stamens, or is different in some other way.

These narrow lateral lobes heighten the abnormal aspect of the whole spike.

They are only produced at a somewhat advanced stage of the development of the palet, are united to one another and to the central part by strong veins, which form transversal anastomoses at their insertion. The length of these awns is very variable, and this quality is perhaps the most striking of the whole variety. Often they reach only 1 – 2 mm., or the majority may become longer and attain even 1 cm., while here and there, between them, longer ones are inserted, extending in some instances even as far as 3 cm. from the spike. Their transverse position in such cases is strikingly contrasted with the ordinary erect type of the awns.

These lateral lobes are to be regarded, from the morphologic point of view, as differentiated parts of the blade of the leaf. Before they are formed, or coincidently with the beginning of their development, the summit of the central lobe becomes hollow, and the development of the supernumerary flower commences. In different varieties, and especially in the most recent crosses of them, this development is excessively variable.

The accidental flower arises at some distance beneath the summit of the scale, on its middle vein. The development begins with the protrusion of a little scale, and the flower itself is situated beneath this scale, and is to be protected by it and by the primary scale, but is turned upside down at the same time. Opposite to this organ, which represents the outer palet of the adventitious flower, two little swollen bodies are evolved. In the normal flowers of barley and other grains and grasses their function is to open the flowers by swelling, and afterwards collapse and allow them to close.

In the adventitious flowers of the "Nepaul-barley," however, this function is quite superfluous. The stamens occur in varying numbers; typically there are three, but not rarely less, or more, are seen. In some instances the complete double whorl of six, corresponding to the ancestral monocotyledonous type, has been found. This is a very curious case of systematic atavism, quite analogous to the *Iris pallida abavia*, previously alluded to, which likewise has six stamens, and to the cases given in a previous lecture. But for our present discussion it is of no further interest. The ovary is situated in the middle of the flower, and in some instances two have been observed. This is also to be considered as a case of atavism.

All these parts of the adventitious flower are more or less subject to arrest of development in a later stage. They may even sometimes become abnormal. Stamens may unite into pairs, or carpels bear four stigmas. The pollen-sacs are as a rule barren, the mother-cells undergoing atrophy, while normal grains are seen but rarely. Likewise the ovaries are rudimentary, but Wittmack has observed the occasional production of ripe grains from these abnormal florets.

The scale is seldom seen to extend any farther upwards than the supernumerary flower. But in the rare instances where it does prolong its growth, it may repeat the abnormality and bear a second floret above the first. This of course is generally much weaker, and more rudimentary.

Raciborsky, who has lately given a full and very accurate description of this anomaly, lays great stress upon the fact that it is quite useless. It is perhaps the most obviously useless structure in the whole vegetable kingdom. Notwithstanding this, it has come to be as completely hereditary as any of the most beautiful adaptations in nature. Therefore it is one of the most serious objections to the hypothesis of slow and gradual improvements on the sole ground of their usefulness. The struggle for life and natural selection are manifestly inadequate to give even the slightest indication of an explanation of this case. It is simply impossible to imagine the causes that might have produced such a character. The only way out of this difficulty is to assume that it has arisen at once, in its present apparently differentiated and very variable condition, and that, being quite uninjurious and since it does not decrease the fertility of the race, it has never been subjected to natural selection, and so has saved itself from destruction.

But if we once grant the probability of the origin of the " Nepaul-barley " by a sudden mutation, we obviously must assume the same in the case of the *Helwingia* and other normal instances. In this way we gain a further support for our assertion, that even the strangest specific characters may have arisen suddenly.

After having detailed at some length those proofs which seem to be the most striking, and which had not been previously described with sufficient detail, we may now take a hasty survey of other contingent cases. In the first place the cruciate flowers of some onagraceous plants should be remembered. Small linear petals occur as a specific character in *Oenothera cruciata* of the Adirondacks, but have been seen to arise as sudden mutations in the common evening-primrose (*O. biennis*) in Holland, and in the willow-herb (*Epilobium hirsutum*) in England.

Leaves placed in whorls of three are very rare. The oleander, juniper and some few other plants have ternate whorls as a specific character. As an anomaly, ternate whorls are far more common, and perhaps any plant with opposite leaves may from time to time produce them. Races rich in this abnormality are found in the wild state in the yellow loosestrife or *Lysimachia vulgaris,* in which it is a very variable specific character, the whorls varying from two to four leaves. In the cultivated state it is met with in the myrtle or *Myrtus communis,* where it has come to be of some importance in Israelitic ritual. Crisped leaves are known in a mallow, *Malva crispa,* and as a variety in cabbages, parsley, lettuce and others. The orbicular fruits of Heeger's shepherd's purse (*Capsella heegeri*) recall similar fruits of other cruciferous genera, as for instance, *Camelina.* Screw-like stems with wide spirals are specific in the flower-stalks of *Cyclamen* and *Vallisneria,* varietal in *Juncus effusus spiralis* and accidental in *Scirpus lacustris.* Dormant buds or small bulbs in inflorescences are normal for wild onions, *Polygonum viviparum* and others, varietal in *Poa alpina vivipara* and perhaps in *Agave vivipara,* and accidental in plantains (*Plantago lanceolata*), *Saxifraga umbrosa* and others.

Cleft leaves, one of the most general anomalies, are typical in *Boehmeria biloba*. The adnation of the peduncles of the inflorescences to the stem is typical in *Solanum* and accidental in many other cases.

It seems quite superfluous to add further proof. It is a very general phenomenon that specific characters occur in other genera as anomalies, and under such circumstances that the idea of a slow evolution on the ground of utility is absolutely excluded. No other explanation remains than that of a sudden mutation, and once granted for the abnormal cases, this explanation must obviously likewise be granted for the analogous specific characters.

Our whole discussion shows that mutations, once observed in definite instances, afford the most probable basis for the explanation of specific characters at large.

Lecture XXIV

THE HYPOTHESIS OF PERIODIC MUTATIONS

The prevailing belief that slow and gradual, nearly invisible changes constitute the process of evolution in the animal and vegetable kingdom, did not offer a strong stimulus for experimental research. No appreciable response to any external agency was of course to be expected. Responses were supposed to be produced, but the corresponding outward changes would be too small to betray themselves to the investigator.

The direct observation of the mutations of the evening-primrose has changed the whole aspect of the problem at once. It is no longer a matter dealing with purely hypothetical conditions. Instead of the vague notions, uncertain hopes, and *a priori* conceptions, that have hitherto confused the investigator, methods of observation have been formulated, suitable for the attainment of definite results, the general nature of which is already known.

To my mind the real value of the discovery

of the mutability of the evening-primrose lies in its usefulness as a guide for further work. The view that it might be an isolated case, lying outside of the usual procedure of nature, can hardly be sustained. On such a supposition it would be far too rare to be disclosed by the investigation of a small number of plants from a limited area. Its appearance within the limited field of inquiry of a single man would have been almost a miracle.

The assumption seems justified that analogous cases will be met with, perhaps even in larger numbers, when similar methods of observation are used in the investigation of plants of other regions. The mutable condition may not be predicated of the evening-primroses alone. It must be a universal phenomenon, although affecting a small proportion of the inhabitants of any region at one time: perhaps not more than one in a hundred species, or perhaps not more than one in a thousand, or even fewer may be expected to exhibit it. The exact proportion is immaterial, because the number of mutable instances among the many thousands of species in existence must be far too large for all of them to be submitted to close scrutiny.

It is evident from the above discussion that next in importance to the discovery of the prototype of mutation is the formulation of methods for bringing additional instances to light. These methods may direct effort toward two different modes of investigation. We may search for mutable plants in nature, or we may hope to induce species to become mutable by artificial methods. The first promises to yield results most quickly, but the scope of the second is much greater and it may yield results of far more importance. Indeed, if it should once become possible to bring plants to mutate at our will and perhaps even in arbitrarily chosen directions, there is no limit to the power we may finally hope to gain over nature.

What is to guide us in this new line of work? Is it the minute inspection of the features of the process in the case of the evening-primroses? Or are we to base our hopes and our methods on broader conceptions of nature's laws? Is it the systematic study of species and varieties, and the biologic inquiry into their real hereditary units? Or is the theory of descent to be our starting-point? Are we to rest our conceptions on the experience of the breeder, or is perhaps the geologic pedigree of all organic life to open to us better prospects of success?

The answer to all such questions is a very simple one. All possibilities must be considered, and no line of investigation ignored. For myself I have based my field-researches and my testing of native plants on the hypothesis of unit-characters as deduced from Darwin's Pangenesis. This conception led to the expectation of two different kinds of variability, one slow and one sudden. The sudden ones known at the time were considered as sports, and seemed limited to retrograde changes, or to cases of minor importance. The idea that sudden steps might be taken as the principal method of evolution could be derived from the hypothesis of unit-characters, but the evidence might be too remote for a starting point for experimental investigation.

The success of my test has given proof to the contrary. Hence the assertion that no evidence is to be considered as inadequate for the purpose under discussion. Sometime a method of discovering, or of producing, mutable plants may be found, but until this is done, all facts of whatever nature or direction must be made use of. A very slight indication may change forever the whole aspect of the problem.

The probabilities are now greatly in favor of our finding out the causes of evolution by a close scrutiny of what really happens in nature. A persistent study of the physiologic factors of this evolution is the chief condition of success. To this study field-observations may contribute as well as direct experiments, microscopical investigations as well as extended pedigree-cultures. The cooperation of many workers is required to cover the field. Somewhere no doubt the desired principle lies hidden, but until it is discovered, all methods must be tried.

With this conception as the best starting-point for further investigation, we may now make a brief survey of the other phase of the problem. We shall try to connect our observations on the evening-primroses with the theory of descent at large.

We start with two main facts. One is the mutability of Lamarck's primrose, and the second is the immutable condition of quite a number of other species. Among them are some of its near allies, the common and the small-flowered evening-primrose, or *Oenothera biennis* and *O. muricata*.

From these facts, a very important question arises in connection with the theory of descent. Is the mutability of our evening-primroses temporary, or is it a permanent condition? A discussion of this problem will give us the means of reaching a definite idea as to the scope of our inquiries.

Let us consider the present first. If mutability is a permanent condition, it has of course no beginning, and moreover is not due to the agency of external circumstances. Should this be granted for the evening-primrose, it would have to be predicated for other species found in a mutable state. Then, of course, it would be useless to investigate the causes of mutability at large, and we should have to limit ourselves to the testing of large numbers of plants in order to ascertain which are mutable and which not.

If, on the other hand, mutability is not a permanent feature, it must once have had a beginning, and this beginning itself must have had an external cause. The amount of mutability and its possible directions may be assumed to be due to internal causes. The determination of the moment at which they will become active can never be the result of internal causes. It must be assigned to some external factor, and as soon as this is discovered the way for experimental investigation is open.

In the second place we must consider the past. On the supposition of permanency all the ancestors of the evening-primrose must have been mutable. By the alternative view mutability must have been a periodic phenomenon, producing at times new qualities, and at other times leaving the plants unchanged during long successions of generations. The present mutable state must then have been preceded by an immutable condition, but of course thousands of mutations must have been required to produce the evening-primroses from their most remote ancestors.

If we take the species into consideration that are not mutable at present, we may ask how we are to harmonize them with each of the two theories proposed. If mutability is permanent, it is manifest that the whole pedigree of the animal and vegetable kingdom is to be considered as built up of main mutable lines, and that the thousands of constant species can only be taken to represent lateral branches of the genealogic tree.

These lateral branches would have lost the capacity of mutating, possessed by all their ancestors. And as the principle of the hypothesis under discussion does not allow a resumption of this habit, they would be doomed to eternal constancy until they finally die out. Loss of mutability, under this conception, means loss of the capacity for all further development. Only those lines of the main pedigree which have retained this capacity would have a future; all others would die out without any chance of progression.

If, on the other hand, mutability is not permanent, but a periodic condition, all lines of the genealogic tree must be assumed to show alternatively mutating and constant species. Some lines may be mutating at the present moment; others may momentarily be constant. The mutating lines will probably sooner or later revert to the inactive state, while the powers of development now dormant may then become awakened on other branches.

The view of permanency represents life as being surrounded with unavoidable death, the principle of periodicity, on the contrary, follows the idea of resurrection, granting the possibility of future progression for all living beings. At the same time it yields a more hopeful prospect for experimental inquiry.

Experience must decide between the two main theories. It demonstrates the existence of polymorphous genera, such as *Draba* and *Viola* and hundreds of others. They clearly indicate a previous state of mutability. Their systematic relation is exactly what would be expected, if they were the result of such a period. Perhaps mutability has not wholly ceased in them, but might be found to survive in some of their members. Such very rich genera however, are not the rule, but are exceptional cases, indicating the rarity of powerful mutative changes.

On the other hand, species may remain in a state of constancy during long, apparently during indefinite, ages.

Many facts plead in favor of the constancy of species. This principle has always been recognized by systematists. Temporarily the current form of the theory of natural selection has assumed species to be inconstant, ever changing and continuously being improved and adapted to the requirements of the life-conditions. The followers of the theory of descent believed that this conclusion was unavoidable, and were induced to deny the manifest fact that species are constant entities. The mutation theory gives a clew to the final combination of the two contending ideas. Reducing the changeability of the species to distinct and probably short periods, it at once explains how the stability of species perfectly agrees with the principle of descent through modification.

On the other hand, the hypothesis of mutative periods is by no means irreconcilable with the observed facts of constancy. Such casual changes can be proved by observations such as those upon the evening-primrose, but it is obvious that a disproof can never be given. The principle grants the present constancy of the vast majority of living forms, and only claims the exceptional occurrence of definite changes.

Proofs of the constancy of species have been given in different ways. The high degree of similarity of the individuals of most of our species has never been denied. It is observed throughout extended localities, and during long series of years. Other proofs are afforded by those plants which have been transported to distant localities some time since, but do not exhibit any change as a result of this migration. Widely dispersed plants remain the same throughout their range, provided that they belong to a single elementary species. Many species have been introduced from America into Europe and have spread rapidly and widely. The Canadian horsetail (*Erigeron canadensis*), the evening-primrose and many other instances could be given. They have not developed any special European features after their introduction. Though exposed to other environmental conditions and to competition with other species, they have not succeeded in developing a new character. Such species as proved adequate to the new environment have succeeded, while those which did not have succumbed.

Much farther back is the separation of the species which now live both in arctic regions and on the summits of our highest mountain-tops. If we compare the alpine flora with the arctic plants, a high degree of similarity at once strikes us. Some forms are quite identical; others are slightly different, manifestly representing elementary species of the same systematic type. Still others are more distant or even belong to different genera. The latter, and even the diverging, though nearly allied, elementary species, do not yield adequate evidence in any direction.

They may as well have lived together in the long ages before the separation of the now widely distant floras, or have sprung from a common ancestor living at that time, and subsequently have changed their habits. After excluding these unreliable instances, a good number of species remain, which are quite the same in the arctic and alpine regions and on the summits of distant mountain-ranges. As no transportation over such large distances can have brought them from one locality to the other, no other explanation is left than that they have been wholly constant and unchanged ever since the glacial period which separated them. Obviously they must have been subjected to widely changing conditions. The fact of their stability through all these outward changes is the best proof that the ordinary external conditions do not necessarily have an influence on specific evolution. They may have such a result in some instances, in others they obviously have not. Many arctic forms bearing the specific name of *alpinus* justify this conclusion. *Astragalus alpinus, Phleum alpinum, Hieracium alpinum* and others from the northern parts of Norway may be cited as examples.

Thus *Primula imperialis* has been found in the Himalayas, and many other plants of the high mountains of Java, Ceylon and northern India are identical forms. Some species from the Cameroons and from Abyssinia have been found on the mountains of Madagascar. Some peculiar Australian types are represented on the summit of Kini Balu in Borneo. None of these species, of course, are found in the intervening lowlands, and the only possible explanation of their identity is the conception of a common post-glacial origin, coupled with complete stability. This stability is all the more remarkable as nearly allied but slightly divergent forms have also been reported from almost all of these localities. Other evidence is obtained by the comparison of ancient plants with their living representatives. The remains in tombs of ancient Egypt have always afforded strong support of the views of the adherents of the theory of stability, and to my mind they still do so. The cereals and fruits and even the flowers and leaves in the funeral wreaths of Rameses and Amen-Hotep are the same that are still now cultivated in Egypt. Nearly a hundred or more species have been identified. Flowers of *Acacia,* leaves of *Mimu-*

sops, petals of *Nymphaea* may be cited as instances, and they are as perfectly preserved as the best herbarium-specimens of the present time. The petals and stamens retain their original colors, displaying them as brightly as is consistent with their dry state.

Paleontologic evidence points to the same conclusion. Of course the remains are incomplete, and rarely adequate for a close comparison. The range of fluctuating variability should be examined first, but the test of elementary species given by their constancy from seed cannot, of course, be applied. Apart from these difficulties, paleontologists agree in recognizing the very great age of large numbers of species. It would require a too close survey of geologic facts to go into details on this point. Suffice it to say that in more recent Tertiary deposits many species have been identified with living forms. In the Miocene period especially, the similarity of the types of phanerogamic plants with their present offspring, becomes so striking that in a large number of cases specific distinctions rest in greater part on theoretical conceptions rather than on real facts. For a long time the idea prevailed that the same species could not have existed through more than one geologic period. Many distinctions founded on this belief have since had to be abandoned.

Species of algae belonging to the well-preserved group of the diatoms, are said to have remained unchanged from the Carboniferous period up to the present time.

Summing up the results of this very hasty survey, we may assert that species remain unchanged for indefinite periods, while at times they are in the alternative condition. Then at once they produce new forms often in large numbers, giving rise to swarms of subspecies. All facts point to the conclusion that these periods of stability and mutability alternate more or less regularly with one another. Of course a direct proof of this view cannot, as yet, be given, but this conclusion is forced upon us by a consideration of known facts bearing on the principle of constancy and evolution.

If we are right in this general conception, we may ask further, what is to be the exact place of our group of new evening-primroses in this theory? In order to give an adequate answer, we must consider the whole range of the observations from a broader point of view. First of all it is evident that the real mutating period must be assumed to be much longer than the time covered by my observations. Neither the beginning nor the end have been seen. It is quite obvious that *Oenothera lamarckiana* was in a mutating condition when I first saw it, seventeen years ago. How long had it been so? Had it commenced to mutate after its introduction into Europe, some time ago, or was it already previously in this state? It is as yet impossible to decide this point. Perhaps the mutable state is very old, and dates from the time of the first importation of the species into Europe.

Apart from all such considerations the period of the direct observations, and the possible duration of the mutability through even more than a century, would constitute only a moment, if compared with the whole geologic time. Starting from this conception the pedigree of our mutations must be considered as only one small group. Instead of figuring a fan of mutants for each year, we must condense all the succeeding swarms into one single fan, as might be done also for *Draba verna* and other polymorphous species. In *Oenothera* the main stem is prolonged upwards beyond the fan; in the others the main stem is lacking or at least undiscernible, but this feature manifestly is only of secondary importance. We might even prefer the image of a fan, adjusted laterally to a stem, which itself is not interrupted by this branch.

On this principle two further considerations are to be discussed. First the structure of the fan itself, and secondly the combination of succeeding fans into a common genealogic tree.

The composition of the fan as a whole includes more than is directly indicated by the facts concerning the birth of new species. They arise in considerable quantities, and each of them in large numbers of individuals, either in the same or in succeeding years. This multiple origin must obviously have the effect of strengthening the new types, and of heightening their chances in the struggle for life. Arising in a single specimen they would have little chance of success, since in the field among thousands of seeds perhaps one only survives and attains complete development. Thousands or at least hundreds of mutated seeds are thus required to produce one mutated individual, and then, how small are its chances of surviving! The mutations proceed in all directions, as I have pointed out in a former lecture. Some are useful, others might become so if the circumstances were accidentally changed in definite directions, or if a migration from the original locality might take place. Many others are without any real worth, or even injurious. Harmless or even slightly useless ones have been seen to maintain themselves in the field during the seventeen years of my research, as proved by *Oenothera laevifolia* and *Oeno-*

thera brevistylis. Most of the others quickly disappear.

This failure of a large part of the productions of nature deserves to be considered at some length. It may be elevated to a principle, and may be made use of to explain many difficult points of the theory of descent. If, in order to secure one good novelty, nature must produce ten or twenty or perhaps more bad ones at the same time, the possibility of improvements coming by pure chance must be granted at once. All hypotheses concerning the direct causes of adaptation at once become superfluous, and the great principle enunciated by Darwin once more reigns supreme.

In this way too, the mutation-period of the evening-primrose is to be considered as a prototype. Assuming it as such provisionally, it may aid us in arranging the facts of descent so as to allow of a deeper insight and a closer scrutiny. All swarms of elementary species are the remains of far larger initial groups. All species containing only a few subspecies may be supposed to have thrown off at the outset far more numerous lateral branches, out of which however, the greater part have been lost, being unfit for the surrounding conditions. It is the principle of the struggle for life between elementary species, followed by the survival of the fittest, the law of the selection of species, which we have already laid stress upon more than once.

Our second consideration is also based upon the frequent repetition of the several mutations. Obviously a common cause must prevail. The faculty of producing *nanella* or *lata* remains the same through all the years. This faculty must be one and the same for all the hundreds of mutative productions of the same form. When and how did it originate? At the outset it must have been produced in a latent condition, and even yet it must be assumed to be continuously present in this state, and only to become active at distant intervals. But it is manifest that the original production of the characters of *Oenothera gigas* was a phenomenon of far greater importance than the subsequent accidental transition of this quality into the active state. Hence the conclusion that at the beginning of each series of analogous mutations there must have been one greater and more intrinsic mutation, which opened the possibility to all its successors. This was the origination of the new character itself, and it is easily seen that this incipient change is to be considered as the real one. All others are only its visible expressions.

Considering the mutative period of our evening-primrose as one unit-stride section in the great genealogic tree, this period includes two nearly related, but not identical changes. One is the production of new specific characters in the latent condition, and the other is the bringing of them to light and putting them into active existence. These two main factors are consequently to be assumed in all hypothetic conceptions of previous mutative periods.

Are all mutations to be considered as limited to such periods? Of course not. Stray mutations may occur as well. Our knowledge concerning this point is inadequate for any definite statement. Swarms of variable species are easily recognized, if the remnants are not too few. But if only one or two new species have survived, how can we tell whether they have originated alone or together with others. This difficulty is still more pronounced in regard to paleontologic facts, as the remains of geologic swarms are often found, but the absence of numerous mutations can hardly be proved in any case.

I have more than once found occasion to lay stress on the importance of a distinction between progressive and retrograde mutations in previous lectures. All improvement is, of course, by the first of these modes of evolution, but apparent losses of organs or qualities are perhaps of still more universal occurrence. Progression and regression are seen to go hand in hand everywhere. No large group and probably even no genus or large species has been evolved without the joint agency of these two great principles. In the mutation-period of the evening-primroses the observed facts give direct support to this conclusion, since some of the new species proved, on closer inspection, to be retrograde varieties, while others manifestly owe their origin to progressive steps. Such steps may be small and in a wrong direction; notwithstanding this they may be due to the acquisition of a wholly new character and therefore belong to the process of progression at large.

Between them however, there is a definite contrast, which possibly is in intimate connection with the question of periodic and stray mutations. Obviously each progressive change is dependent upon the production of a new character, for whenever this is lacking, no such mutation is possible. Retrograde changes, on the other hand, do not require such elaborate preliminary work. Each character may be converted into the latent condition, and for all we know, a special preparation for this purpose is not at all necessary. It is readily granted that such special preparation may occur, because the great numbers in which our dwarf variety of the *Oenothera* are yearly produced are suggestive of such a condition. On the other hand, the *laevifolia* and *brevistylis* mutations have not been repeated, at least not in a visible way.

From this discussion we may infer that it is quite possible that a large part of the progressive changes, and a smaller part of the retrograde mutations, are combined into groups, owing their origin to common external agencies. The periods in which such groups occur would constitute the mutative periods. Besides them the majority of the retrograde changes and some progressive steps might occur separately, each being due to some special cause. Degressive mutations, or those which arise by the return of latent qualities to activity, would of course belong with the latter group.

This assumption of a stray and isolated production of varieties is to a large degree supported by experience in horticulture. Here there are no real swarms of mutations. Sudden leaps in variability are not rare, but then they are due to hybridization. Apart from this mixture of characters, varieties as a rule appear separately, often with intervals of dozens of years, and without the least suggestion of a common cause. It is quite superfluous to go into details, as we have dealt with the horticultural mutations at sufficient length on a previous occasion. Only the instance of the peloric toadflax might be recalled here, because the historic and geographic evidence, combined with the results of our pedigree-experiment, plainly show that peloric mutations are quite independent of any periodic condition. They may occur anywhere in the wide range of the toad-flax, and the capacity of repeatedly producing them has lasted some centuries at least, and is perhaps even as old as the species itself.

Leaving aside such stray mutations, we may now consider the probable constitution of the great lines of the genealogic tree of the evening-primroses, and of the whole vegetable and animal kingdom at large. The idea of drawing up a pedigree for the chief groups of living organisms is originally due to Haeckel, who used this graphic method to support the Darwinian theory of descent. Of course, Haeckel's genealogic trees are of a purely hypothetic nature, and have no other purpose than to convey a clear conception of the notion of descent, and of the great lines of evolution at large. Obviously all details are subject to doubt, and many have accordingly been changed by his successors. These changes may be considered as partial improvements, and the somewhat picturesque form of Haeckel's pedigree might well be replaced by more simple plans. But the changes have by no means removed the doubts, nor have they been able to supplant the general impression of distinct groups, united by broad lines. This feature is very essential, and it is easily seen to correspond with the conception of swarms, as we have deduced it from the study of the lesser groups.

Genealogic trees are the result of comparative studies; they are far removed from the results of experimental inquiry concerning the origin of species. What are the links which bind them together? Obviously they must be sought in the mutative periods, which have immediately preceded the present one. In the case of the evening-primrose the systematic arrangement of the allied species readily guides us in the delimitations of such periods. For manifestly the species of the large genus of *Oenothera* are grouped in swarms, the youngest or most recent of which we have under observation. Its immediate predecessor must have been the subgenus *Onagra,* which is considered by some authors as consisting of a single systematic species, *Oenothera biennis*. Its multifarious forms point to a common origin, not only morphologically but also historically. Following this line backward or downward we reach another apparent mutation-period, which includes the origin of the group called *Oenothera*, with a large number of species of the same general type as the *Onagra*-forms. Still farther downward comes the old genus *Oenothera* itself, with numerous subgenera diverging in sundry characters and directions.

Proceeding still farther we might easily construct a main stem with numerous succeeding fans of lateral branches, and thus reach, from our new empirical point of view, the theoretical conclusion already formulated.

Paleontologic facts readily agree with this conception. The swarms of species and varieties are found to succeed one another like so many stories. The same images are repeated, and the single stories seem to be connected by the main stems, which in each tier produce the whole number of allied forms. Only a few prevailing lines are prolonged through numerous geologic periods; the vast majority of the lateral branches are limited each to its own storey. It is simply the extension of the pedigree of the evening-primroses backward through ages, with the same construction and the same leading features. There can be no doubt that we are quite justified in assuming that evolution has followed the same general laws through the whole duration of life on earth. Only a moment of their lifetime is disclosed to us, but it is quite sufficient to enable us to discern the laws and to conjecture the outlines of the whole scheme of evolution.

A grave objection which has often, and from the very outset, been urged against Darwin's conception of very slow and nearly imperceptible changes, is the enormously long time required. If evolution does not proceed any faster than what we can see at present, and if the process must be assumed to have gone on in the same slow manner always, thousands of millions of years would have been needed to develop the higher types of animals and plants from their earliest ancestors.

Now it is not at all probable that the duration of life on earth includes such an incredibly long time. Quite on the contrary the lifetime of the earth seems to be limited to a few millions of years. The researches of Lord Kelvin and other eminent physicists seem to leave no doubt on this point. Of course all estimates of this kind are only vague and approximate, but for our present purposes they may be considered as sufficiently exact.

In a paper published in 1862 Sir William Thomson (now Lord Kelvin) first endeavored to show that great limitation had to be put upon the enormous demand for time made by Lyell, Darwin and other biologists. From a consideration of the secular cooling of the earth, as deduced from the increasing temperature in deep mines, he concluded that the entire age of the earth must have been more than twenty and less than forty millions of years, and probably much nearer twenty than forty. His views have been much criticised by other physicists, but in the main they have gained an ever-increasing support in the way of evidence. New mines of greater depth have been bored, and their temperatures have proved that the figures of Lord Kelvin are strikingly near the truth. George Darwin has calculated that the separation of the moon from the earth must have taken place some fifty-six millions of years ago. Geikie has estimated the existence of the solid crust of the earth at the most as a hundred million years. The first appearance of the crust must soon have been succeeded by the formation of the seas, and a long time does not seem to have been required to cool the seas to such a degree that life became possible. It is very probable that life originally commenced in the great seas, and that the forms which are now usually included in the plankton or floating-life included the very first living beings. According to Brooks, life must have existed in this floating condition during long primeval epochs, and evolved nearly all the main branches of the animal and vegetable kingdom before sinking to the bottom of the sea, and later producing the vast number of diverse forms which now adorn the sea and land.

All these evolutions, however, must have been very rapid, especially at the beginning, and together cannot have taken more time than the figures given above.

The agency of the larger streams, and the deposits which they bring into the seas, afford further evidence. The amount of dissolved salts, especially of sodium chloride, has been made the subject of a calculation by Joly, and the amount of lime has been estimated by Eugène Dubois. Joly found fifty-five and Dubois thirty-six millions of years as the probable duration of the age of the rivers, and both figures correspond to the above dates as closely as might be expected from the discussion of evidence so very incomplete and limited.

All in all it seems evident that the duration of life does not comply with the demands of the conception of very slow and continuous evolution. Now it is easily seen, that the idea of successive mutations is quite independent of this difficulty. Even assuming that some thousands of characters must have been acquired in order to produce the higher animals and plants of the present time, no valid objection is raised. The demands of the biologists and the results of the physicists are harmonized on the ground of the theory of mutation.

The steps may be surmised to have never been essentially larger than in the mutations now going on under our eyes, and some thousands of them may be estimated as sufficient to account for the entire organization of the higher forms. Granting between twenty and forty millions of years since the beginning of life, the intervals between two successive mutations may have been centuries and even thousands of years. As yet there has been no objection cited against this assumption, and hence we see that the lack of harmony between the demands of biologists and the results of the physicists disappears in the light of the theory of mutation.

Summing up the results of this discussion, we may justifiably assert that the conclusions derived from the observations and experiments made with evening-primroses and other plants in the main agree satisfactorily with the inferences drawn from paleontologic, geologic and systematic evidence. Obviously these experiments are wonderfully supported by the whole of our knowledge concerning evolution. For this reason the laws discovered in the experimental garden may be considered of great importance, and they may guide us in our further inquiries. Without doubt many minor points are in need of correction and elaboration, but such improvements of our knowledge will gradually increase our means of discovering new instances and new proofs.

The conception of mutation periods producing swarms of species from time to time, among which only a few have a chance of survival, promises to become the basis for speculative pedigree-diagrams, as well as for experimental investigations.

F. FLUCTUATION

Lecture XXV

GENERAL LAWS OF FLUCTUATION

The principle of unit-characters and of elementary species leads at once to the recognition of two kinds of variability. The changes of wider amplitude consist of the acquisition of new units, or the loss of already existing ones. The lesser variations are due to the degree of activity of the units themselves.

Facts illustrative of these distinctions were almost wholly lacking at the time of the first publication of Darwin's theories. It was a bold conception to point out the necessity for such distinction on purely theoretical grounds. Of course some sports were well known and fluctuations were evident, but no exact analysis of the details was possible, a fact that was of great importance in the demonstration of the theory of descent. The lack of more definite knowledge upon this matter was keenly felt by Darwin, and exercised much influence upon his views at various times.

Quetelet's famous discovery of the law of fluctuating variability changed the entire situation and cleared up many difficulties. While a clear conception of fluctuations was thus gained, mutations were excluded from consideration, being considered as very rare, or non-existent. They seemed wholly superfluous for the theory of descent, and very little importance was attached to their study. Current scientific belief in the matter has changed only in recent years. Mendel's law of varietal hybrids is based upon the principle of unit-characters, and the validity of this conception has thus been brought home to many investigators.

A study of fluctuating or individual variability, as it was formerly called, is now carried on chiefly by mathematical methods. It is not my purpose to go into details, as it would require a separate course of lectures. I shall consider the limits between fluctuation and mutation only, and attempt to set forth an adequate idea of the principles of the first as far as they touch these limits. The mathematical treatment of the facts is no doubt of very great value, but the violent discussions now going on between mathematicians such as Pearson, Kapteyn and others should warn biologists to abstain from the use of methods which are not necessary for the furtherance of experimental work.

Fortunately, Quetelet's law is a very clear and simple one, and quite sufficient for our considerations. It claims that for biologic phenomena the deviations from the average comply with the same laws as the deviations from the average in any other case, if ruled by chance only. The meaning of this assertion will become clear by a further discussion of the facts.

First of all, fluctuating variability is an almost universal phenomenon. Every organ and every quality may exhibit it. Some are very variable, while others seem quite constant. Shape and size vary almost indefinitely, and the chemical composition is subject to the same law, as is well known for the amount of sugar in sugar-beets. Numbers are of course less liable to changes, but the numbers of the rays of umbels, or ray-florets in the composites, of pairs of blades in pinnate leaves, and even of stamens and carpels are known to be often exceedingly variable. The smaller numbers however, are more constant, and deviations from the quinate structure of flowers are rare. Complicated structures are generally capable of only slight deviations.

From a broad point of view, fluctuating variability falls under two heads. They obey quite the same laws and are therefore easily confused, but with respect to questions of heredity they should be carefully separated. They are designated by the terms individual and partial fluctuation. Individual variability indicates the differences between individuals, while partial variability is limited to the deviations shown by the parts of one organism from the average structure. The same qualities in some cases vary individually and in others partially. Even stature, which is as markedly individual for annual and biennial plants as it is for man, becomes partially variant in the case of perennial herbs with numbers of stems. Often a character is only developed once in the whole course of evolution, as for instance, the degree of connation of the seed-leaves in tricotyls and in numerous cases it is impossible to tell whether a character is individual or partial. Consequently such minute details are generally considered to have no real importance for the hereditary transmission of the character under discussion.

Fluctuations are observed to take place only in two directions. The quality may increase or decrease, but is not seen to vary in any other way. This rule is now widely established by numerous investigations, and is fundamental to the whole method of statistical investigation. It is equally important for the discussion of the contrast between fluctuations and mutations, and for the appreciation of their part in the general progress of organization. Mutations are going on in all directions, producing, if they are progressive, something quite new every time. Fluctuations are limited to increase and decrease of what is already available. They may produce plants with higher stems, more petals in the flowers, larger and more palatable fruits, but obviously the first petal and the first berry cannot have originated by the simple increase of some older quality. Intermediates may be found, and they may mark the limit, but the demonstration of the absence of a limit is quite another question. It would require the two extremes to be shown to belong to one unit, complying with the simple law of Quetelet.

Nourishment is the potent factor of fluctuating variability. Of course in thousands of cases our knowledge is not sufficient to allow us to analyze this relation, and a number of phases of the phenomenon have been discovered only quite recently. But the fact itself is thoroughly manifest, and its appreciation is as old as horticultural science. Knight, who lived at the beginning of the last century, has laid great stress upon it, and it has since influenced practice in a large measure. Moreover, Knight pointed out more than once that it is the amount of nourishment, not the quality of the various factors, that exercises the determinative influence. Nourishment is to be taken in the widest sense of the word, including all favorable and injurious elements. Light and temperature, soil and space, water and salts are equally active, and it is the harmonious cooperation of them all that rules growth.

We treated this important question at some length, when dealing with the anomalies of the opium-poppies, consisting of the conversion of stamens into supernumerary pistils. The dependency upon external influences which this change exhibited is quite the same as that shown by fluctuating variability at large. We inquired into the influence of good and bad soil, of sunlight and moisture and of other concurrent factors. Especial emphasis was laid upon the great differences to which the various individuals of the same lot may be exposed, if moisture and manure differ on different portions of the same bed in a way unavoidable even by the most careful preparation. Some seeds germinate on moist and rich spots, while their neighbors are impeded by local dryness, or by distance from manure. Some come to light on a sunny day, and increase their first leaves rapidly, while on the following day the weather may be unfavorable and greatly retard growth. The individual differences seem to be due, at least in a very great measure, to such apparent trifles.

On the other hand partial differences are often manifestly due to similar causes. Considering the various stems of plants, which multiply themselves by runners or by buds on the roots, the assertion is in no need of further proof. The same holds good for all cases of artificial multiplication by cuttings, or by other vegetative methods. But even if we limit ourselves to the leaves of a single tree, or the branches of a shrub, or the flowers on a plant, the same rule prevails. The development of the leaves is dependent on their position, whether inserted on strong or weak branches, exposed to more or less light, or nourished by strong or weak roots. The vigor of the axillary buds and of the branches which they may produce is dependent upon the growth and activity of the leaves to which the buds are axillary.

This dependency on local nutrition leads to the general law of periodicity, which, broadly speaking, governs the occurrence of the fluctuating deviations of the organs. This law of periodicity involves the general principle that every axis, as a rule, increases in strength when growing, but sooner or later reaches a maximum and may afterwards decrease.

This periodic augmentation and declination is often boldly manifest, though in other cases it may be hidden by the effect of alternate influences. Pinnate leaves generally have their lower blades smaller than the upper ones, the longest being seen sometimes near the apex and sometimes at a distance from it. Branches bearing their leaves in two rows often afford quite as obvious examples, and shoots in general comply with the same rule. Germinating plants are very easy of observation on this point. When they are very weak they produce only small leaves. But their strength gradually increases and the subsequent organs reach fuller dimensions until the maximum is attained. The phenomenon is so common that its importance is usually overlooked. It should be considered as only one instance of a rule, which holds good for all stems and all branches, and which is everywhere dependent on the relation of growth to nutrition.

The rule of periodicity not only affects the size of the organs, but also their number, whenever these are largely variable. Umbellate plants have numerous rays on the umbels of strong stems, but the number is seen to decrease and to become very small on the weakest lateral branches. The same holds good for the number of ray-florets in the flower-heads of the composites, even for the number of stigmas on the ovaries of the poppies, which on weak branches may be reduced to as few as three or four. Many other instances could be given.

One of the best authenticated cases is the dependency of partial fluctuation on the season and on the weather. Flowers decline when the season comes to an end, become smaller and less brightly colored. The number of ray-florets in the flower-heads is seen to decrease towards the fall. Extremes become rarer, and often the deviations from the average seem nearly to disappear. Double flowers comply with this rule very closely, and many other cases will easily occur to any student of nature.

Of course, the relation to nourishment is different for individual and partial fluctuations. Concerning the first, the period of development of the germ within the seed is decisive. Even the sexual cells may be in widely different conditions at the moment of fusion, and perhaps this state of the sexual cells includes the whole matter of the decision for the average characters of the new individual. Partial fluctuation commences as soon as the leaves and buds begin to form, and all later changes in nutrition can only cause partial differences. All leaves, buds, branches, and flowers must come under the influence of external conditions during the juvenile period, and so are liable to attain a development determined in part by the action of these factors.

Before leaving these general considerations, we must direct our attention to the question of utility. Obviously, fluctuating variability is a very useful contrivance, in many cases at least. It appears all the more so, as its relation to nutrition becomes manifest. Here two aspects are intimately combined. More nutrient matter produces larger leaves and these are in their turn more fit to profit by the abundance of nourishment. So it is with the number of flowers and flower-groups, and even with the numbers of their constituent organs. Better nourishment produces more of them, and thereby makes the plant adequate to make a fuller use of the available nutrient substances. Without fluctuation such an adjustment would hardly be possible, and from all our notions of usefulness in nature, we therefore must recognize the efficiency of this form of variability.

In other respects the fluctuations often strike us as quite useless or even as injurious. The numbers of stamens, or of carpels are dependent on nutrition, but their fluctuation is not known to have any attraction for the visiting insects.

If the deviations become greater, they might even become detrimental. The flowers of the St. Johnswort, or *Hypericum perforatum*, usually have five petals, but the number varies from three to eight or more. Bees could hardly be misled by such deviations. The carpels of buttercups and columbines, the cells in the capsules of cotton and many other plants are variable in number. The number of seeds is thereby regulated in accordance with the available nourishment, but whether any other useful purpose is served, remains an open question. Variations in the honey-guides or in the pattern of color-designs might easily become injurious by deceiving insects, and such instances as the great variability of the spots on the corolla of some cultivated species of monkey-flowers, for instance, the *Mimulus quinquevulnerus*, could hardly be expected to occur in wild plants. For here the dark brown spots vary between nearly complete deficiency up to such predominancy as almost to hide the pale yellow ground-color.

After this hasty survey of the causes of fluctuating variability, we now come to a discussion of Quetelet's law. It asserts that the deviations from the average obey the law of probability. They behave as if they were dependent on chance only.

Everyone knows that the law of Quetelet can

be demonstrated the most readily by placing a sufficient number of adult men in a row, arranging them according to their size. The line passing over their heads proves to be identical with that given by the law of probability. Quite in the same way, stems and branches, leaves and petals and even fruits can be arranged, and they will in the main exhibit the same line of variability. Such groups are very striking, and at the first glance show that the large majority of the specimens deviate from the mean only to a very small extent. Wider deviations are far more rare, and their number lessens, the greater the deviation, as is shown by the curvature of the line. It is almost straight and horizontal in the middle portion, while at the ends it rapidly declines, going sharply downward at one extreme and upward at the other.

It is obvious however, that in these groups the leaves and other organs could conveniently be replaced by simple lines, indicating their size. The result would be quite the same, and the lines could be placed at arbitrary, but equal distances. Or the sizes could be expressed by figures, the compliance of which with the general law could be demonstrated by simple methods of calculation. In this manner the variability of different organs can easily be compared.

Another method of demonstration consists in

grouping the deviations into previously fixed divisions. For this purpose the variations are measured by standard units, and all the instances that fall between two limits are considered to constitute one group. Seeds and small fruits, berries and many other organs may conveniently be dealt with in this way. As an example we take ordinary beans and select them according to their size. This can be done in different ways. On a small piece of board a long wedge-shaped slit is made, into which seeds are pushed as far as possible. The margin of the wedge is calibrated in such a manner that the figures indicate the width of the wedge at the corresponding place. By this device the figure up to which a bean is pushed at once shows its length. Fractions of millimeters are neglected, and the beans, after having been measured, are thrown into cylindrical glasses of the same width, each glass receiving only beans of equal length. It is clear that by this method the height to which beans fill the glasses is approximately a measure of their number. If now the glasses are put in a row in the proper sequence, they at once exhibit the shape of a line which corresponds to the law of chance. In this case however, the line is drawn in a different manner from the first. It is to be pointed out that the glasses may be replaced by lines indicating the height of their contents, and that, in order to reach a more easy and correct statement, the length of the lines may simply be made proportionate to the number of the beans in each glass. If such lines are erected on a common base and at equal distances, the line which unites their upper ends will be the expression of the fluctuating variability of the character under discussion.

The same inquiry may be made with other seeds, with fruits, or other organs. It is quite superfluous to arrange the objects themselves, and it is sufficient to arrange the figures indicating their value. In order to do this a basal line is divided into equal parts, the demarcations corresponding to the standard-units chosen for the test. The observed values are then written above this line, each finding its place between the two demarcations, which include its value. It is very interesting and stimulating to construct such a group. The first figures may fall here and there, but very soon the vertical rows on the middle part of the basal line begin to increase. Sometimes ten or twenty measurements will suffice to make the line of chance appear, but often indentations will remain. With the increasing number of the observations the irregularities gradually disappear, and the line becomes smoother and more uniformly curved.

This method of arranging the figures directly on a basal line is very convenient, whenever observations are made in the field or garden. Very few instances need be recorded to obtain an appreciation of the mean value, and to show what may be expected from a continuance of the test. The method is so simple and so striking, and so wholly independent of any mathematical development that it should be applied in all cases in which it is desired to ascertain the average value of any organ, and the measure of the attendant deviations.

I cite an instance, secured by counting the ray-florets on the flower-heads of the corn-marigold or *Chrysanthemum segetum*. It was that, by which I was enabled to select the plant, which afterwards showed the first signs of a double head. I noted them in this way:

```
         47
         47 52
         41 54 68
         44 50 62 75
      36 45 58 65 72 — 99
```

Of course the figures might be replaced in this work by equidistant dots or by lines, but experience teaches that the chance of making mistakes is noticeably lessened by writing down the figures themselves. Whenever decimals are made use of it is obviously the best plan to keep the figures themselves. For afterwards it often becomes necessary to arrange them according to a somewhat different standard.

Uniting the heads of the vertical rows of figures by a line, the form corresponding to Quetelet's law is easily seen. In the main it is always the same as the line shown by the measurements of beans and seeds. It proves a dense crowding of the single instances around the average, and on both sides of the mass of the observations, a few wide deviations. These become more rare in proportion to the amount of their divergency. On both sides of the average the line begins by falling very rapidly, but then bends slowly so as to assume a nearly horizontal direction. It reaches the basal line only beyond the extreme instances.

It is quite evident that all qualities, which can be expressed by figures, may be treated in this way. First of all the organs occurring in varying numbers, as for instance the ray-florets of composites, the rays of umbels, the blades of pinnate and palmate leaves, the numbers of veins, etc., are easily shown to comply with the same general rule. Likewise the amount of chemical substances can be expressed in percentage numbers, as is done on a large scale with sugar in beets and sugar-cane, with starch in potatoes and in other instances. These figures are also found to follow the same law.

All qualities which are seen to increase and to decrease may be dealt with in the same manner, if a standard unit for their measurement can be fixed. Even the colors of flowers may not escape our inquiry.

If we now compare the lines, compiled from the most divergent cases, they will be found to exhibit the same features in the main. Ordinarily the curve is symmetrical, the line sloping down on both sides after the same manner. But it is not at all rare that the inclination is steep on one side and gradual on the other. This is noticeably the case if the observations relate to numbers, the average of which is near zero. Here of course the allowance for variation is only small on one side, while it may increase without distinct limits on the alternate slope. So it is for instance with the numbers of ray-florets in the example given on p. 729. Such divergent cases, however, are to be considered as exceptions to the rule, due to some unknown cause.

Heretofore we have discussed the empirical side of the problem only. For the purpose of experimental study of questions of heredity this is ordinarily quite sufficient. The inquiry into the phenomenon of regression, or of the relation of the degree of deviation of the progeny to that of their parents, and the selection of extreme instances for multiplication are obviously independent of mathematical considerations. On the other hand an important inquiry lies in the statistical treatment of these phenomena, and such treatment requires the use of mathematical methods.

Statistics however, are not included in the object of these lectures, and therefore I shall refrain from an explanation of the method of their preparation and limit myself to a general comparison of the observed lines with the law of chance. Before going into the details, it should be repeated once more that the empirical result is quite the same for individual and for partial fluctuations. As a rule, the latter occur in far greater number, and are thus more easily investigated, but individual or personal averages have also been studied.

Newton discovered that the law of chance can be expressed by very simple mathematical calculations. Without going into details, we may at once state that these calculations are based upon his binomium. If the form $(a + b)^n$ is calculated for some value of the exponent, and if the values of the coefficients after development are alone considered, they yield the basis for the construction of what is called the line or curve of probability. For this construction the coefficients are used as ordinates, the length of which is to be made proportionate to their value. If this is done, and the ordinates are arranged at equal distances, the line which unites their summits is the desired curve. At first glance it exhibits a form quite analogous to the curves of fluctuating variability, obtained by the measurements of beans and in other instances. Both lines are symmetrical and slope rapidly down in the region of the average, while with increasing distance they gradually lose their steep inclination, becoming nearly parallel to the base at their termination.

This similarity between such empirical and theoretical lines is in itself an empirical fact. The causes of chance are assumed to be innumerable, and the whole calculation is based on this assumption. The causes of the fluctuations of biological phenomena have not as yet been critically examined to such an extent as to allow of definite conceptions. The term nourishment manifestly includes quite a number of separate factors, as light, space, temperature, moisture, the physical and chemical conditions of the soil and the changes of the weather. Without doubt the single factors are very numerous, but whether they are numerous enough to be treated as innumerable, and thereby to explain the laws of fluctuations, remains uncertain. Of course the easiest way is to assume that they combine in the same manner as the causes of chance, and that this is the ground of the similarity of the curves. On the other hand, it is manifestly of the highest importance to inquire into the part the several factors play in the determination of the curves. It is not at all improbable that some of them have a larger influence on individual, and others on partial, fluctuations. If this were the case, their importance with respect to questions of heredity might be widely different. In the present state of our knowledge the fluctuation-curves do not contribute in any large measure to an elucidation of the causes. Where these are obvious, they are so without statistics, exactly as they were, previous to Quetelet's discovery.

In behalf of a large number of questions concerning heredity and selection, it is very desirable to have a somewhat closer knowledge of these curves. Therefore I shall try to point out their more essential features, as far as this can be done without mathematical calculations.

At a first glance three points strike us, the average or the summit of the curve, and the extremes. If the general shape is once denoted by the results of observations or by the coefficients of the binomium, all further details seem to depend upon them. In respect to the average this is no doubt the case; it is an empirical value without need of any further discussion. The more the number of the observations increases, the more assured and the more correct is this mean value, but generally it is the same for smaller and for larger groups of observations.

This however, is not the case with the extremes. It is quite evident that small groups have a chance of containing neither of them. The more the number of the observations increases, the larger is the chance of extremes. As a rule, and excluding exceptional cases, the extreme deviations will increase in proportion to the number of cases examined. In a hundred thousand beans the smallest one and the largest one may be expected to differ more widely from one another than in a few hundred beans of the same sample. Hence the conclusion that extremes are not a safe criterion for the discussion of the curves, and not at all adequate for calculations, which must be based upon more definite values.

A real standard is afforded by the steepness of the slope. This may be unequal on the two sides of one curve, and likewise it may differ for different cases. This steepness is usually measured by means of a point on the half curve and for this purpose a point is chosen which lies exactly half way between the average and the extreme. Not however half way with respect to the amplitude of the extreme deviation, for on this ground it would partake of the uncertainty of the extreme itself. It is the point on the curve which is surpassed by half the number, and not reached by the other half of the number of the observations included in the half of the curve. This point corresponds to the important value called the probable error, and was designated by Galton as the quartile. For it is evident that the average and the two quartiles divide the whole of the observations into four equal parts.

Choosing the quartiles as the basis for calculations we are independent of all the secondary causes of error, which necessarily are inherent in the extremes. At a casual examination, or for demonstrative purposes, the extremes may be prominent, but for all further considerations the quartiles are the real values upon which to rest calculations.

Moreover if the agreement with the law of probability is once conceded, the whole curve is defined by the average and the quartiles, and the result of hundreds of measurements or countings may be summed up in three, or, in the case of symmetrical curves, perhaps in two figures.

Also in comparing different curves with one another, the quartiles are of great importance. Whenever an empirical fluctuation-curve is to be compared with the theoretical form, or when two or more cases of variability are to be considered under one head, the lines are to be drawn on the same base. It is manifest that the averages must be brought upon the same ordinate, but as to the steepness of the line, much depends on the manner of plotting. Here we must remember that the mutual distance of the ordinates has been a wholly arbitrary one in all our previous considerations. And so it is, as long as only one curve is considered at a time. But as soon as two are to be compared, it is obvious that free choice is no longer allowed. The comparison must be made on a common basis, and to this effect the quartiles must be brought together. They are to lie on the same ordinates. If this is done, each division of the base corresponds to the same proportionate number of individuals, and a complete comparison is made possible.

On the ground of such a comparison we may thus assert that fluctuations, however different the organs or qualities observed, are the same whenever their curves are seen to overlap one another. Furthermore, whenever an empirical curve agrees in this manner with the theoretical one, the fluctuation complies with Quetelet's law, and may be ascribed to quite ordinary and universal causes. But if it seems to diverge from this line, the cause of this divergence should be inquired into.

Such abnormal curves occur from time to time, but are rare. Unsymmetrical instances have already been alluded to, and seem to be quite frequent. Another deviation from the rule is the presence of more than one summit. This case falls under two headings. If the ray-florets of a composite are counted, and the figures brought into a curve, a prominent summit usually corresponds to the average. But next to this, and on both sides, smaller summits are to be seen. On a close inspection these summits are observed to fall on the same ordinates, on which, in the case of allied species, the main apex lies. The specific character of one form is thus repeated as a secondary character on an allied species. Ludwig discovered that these secondary summits comply with the rule discovered by Braun and Schimper, stating the relation of the subsequent figures of the series. This series gives the terms of the disposition of leaves in general, and of the bracts and flowers on the composite flower-heads in our particular case. It is the series to which we have already alluded when dealing with the arrangement of the leaves on the twisted teasels. It commences with 1 and 2 and each following figure is equal to the sum of its two precedents. The most common figures are 3, 5, 8, 13, 18, 21, higher cases seldom coming under observation. Now the secondary summits of the ray-curves of the composites are seen to agree, as a rule, with these figures. Other instances could readily be given.

Our second heading includes those cases which exhibit two summits of equal or nearly equal height. Such cases occur when different races are mixed, each retaining its own average and its own curve-summit. We have already demonstrated such a case when dealing with the origin of our double corn-chrysanthemum. The wild species culminates with 13 rays, and the *grandiflorum* variety with 21. Often the latter is found to be impure, being mixed with the typical species to a varying extent. This is not easily ascertained by a casual inspection of the cultures, but the true condition will promptly betray itself, if curves are constructed. In this way curves may in many instances be made use of to discover mixed races.

Double curves may also result from the investigation of true double races, or ever-sporting varieties. The striped snapdragon shows a curve of its stripes with two summits, one corresponding to the average striped flowers, and the other to the pure red ones. Such cases may be discovered by means of curves, but the constituents cannot be separated by culture-experiments.

A curious peculiarity is afforded by half-curves. The number of petals is often seen to vary only in one direction from what should be expected to be the mean condition. With buttercups and brambles and many others there is only an increase above the typical five; quaternate flowers are wanting or at least are very rare. With weigelias and many others the number of the tips of the corolla varies downwards, going from five to four and three. Hundreds of flowers show the typical five, and determine the summit of the curve. This drops down on one side only, indicating unilateral variability, which in many cases is due to a very intimate connection of a concealed secondary summit and the main one. In the case of the bulbous buttercup, *Ranunculus bulbosus,* I have succeeded in isolating this secondary summit, although not in a separate variety, but only in a form corresponding to the type of ever-sporting varieties.

Recapitulating the results of this too condensed discussion, we may state that fluctuations are linear, being limited to an increase and to a decrease of the characters. These changes are mainly due to differences in nourishment, either of the whole organism or of its parts. In the first case, the deviations from the mean are called individual; they are of great importance for the hereditary characters of the offspring. In the second case the deviations are far more universal and far more striking, but of lesser importance. They are called partial fluctuations.

All these fluctuations comply, in the main, with the law of probability, and behave as if their causes were influenced only by chance.

Lecture XXVI

ASEXUAL MULTIPLICATION OF EXTREMES

Fluctuating variability may be regarded from two different points of view. The multiformity of a bed of flowers is often a desirable feature, and all means which widen the range of fluctuation are therefore used to enhance this feature, and variability affords specimens, which surpass the average, by yielding a better or larger product.

In the case of fruits and other cultivated forms, it is of course profitable to propagate from the better specimens only, and if possible only from the very best. Obviously the best are the extremes of the whole range of diverging forms, and moreover the extremes on one side of the group. Almost always the best for practical purposes is that in which some quality is strengthened. Cases occur however, in which it is desirable to diminish an injurious peculiarity as far as possible, and in these instances the opposite extreme is the most profitable one.

These considerations lead us to a discussion

of the results of the choice of extremes, which it may be easily seen is a matter of the greatest practical importance. This choice is generally designated as selection, but as with most of the terms in the domain of variability, the word selection has come to have more than one meaning. Facts have accumulated enormously since the time of Darwin, a more thorough knowledge has brought about distinctions, and divisions at a rapidly increasing rate, with which terminology has not kept pace. Selection includes all kinds of choice. Darwin distinguished between natural and artificial selection, but proper subdivisions of these conceptions are needed.

In the fourth lecture we dealt with this same question, and saw that selection must, in the first place, make a choice between the elementary species of the same systematic form. This selection of species or species-selection was the work of Le Couteur and Patrick Shirreff, and is now in general use in practice where it has received the name of variety-testing. This clear and unequivocal term however, can hardly be included under the head of natural selection. The poetic terminology of selection by nature has already brought about many difficulties that should be avoided in the future. On the other hand, the designation of the process as a natural selection of species complies as closely as possible with existing terminology, and does not seem liable to any misunderstanding.

It is a selection *between species*. Opposed to it is the selection *within the species*. Manifestly the first should precede the second, and if this sequence is not conscientiously followed it will result in confusion. This is evident when it is considered that fluctuations can only appear with their pure and normal type in pure strains, and that each admixture of other units is liable to be shown by the form of the curves. Moreover, selection chooses single individuals, and a single plant, if it is not a hybrid, can scarcely pertain to two different species. The first choice therefore is apt to make the strain pure.

In contrasting selection between species with that within the species, of course elementary species are meant, including varieties. The terms would be of no consequence if only rightly understood. For the sake of clearness we might designate the last named process with the term of *intra-specific selection*, and it is obvious that this term is applicable both to natural and to artificial selection.

Having previously dealt with species-selection at sufficient length, we may now confine ourselves to the consideration of the intra-specific selection-process. In practice it is of secondary importance, and in nature it takes a very subordinate position. For this reason it will be best to confine further discussions to the experience of the breeders.

Two different ways are open to make fluctuating variability profitable. Both consist in the multiplication of the chosen extremes, and this increase may be attained in a vegetative manner, or by the use of seeds. Asexual and sexual propagation are different in many respects, and so they are also in the domain of variability.

In order to obtain a clear comprehension of this difference, it is necessary to start from the distinction between individual and partial fluctuations, as given in the last lecture. This distinction may be discussed more understandingly if the causes of the variability are taken into consideration. We have dealt with them at some length, and are now aware that inner conditions only, determine averages, while some fluctuation around them is allowable, as influenced by external conditions. These outward influences act throughout life. At the very first they impress their stamp on the whole organism, and incite a lasting change in distinct directions. This is the period of the development of the germ within the seed; it begins with the fusion of the sexual cells, and each of them may be influenced to a noticeable degree before this union. This is the period of the determination of individual variability. As soon as ramifications begin, the external conditions act separately on every part, influencing some to a greater and others to a lesser degree. Here we have the beginning of partial variability. At the outset all parts may be affected in the same way and in the same measure, but the chances of such an agreement, of course, rapidly diminish. This is partly due to differences in exposure, but mainly to alterations of the sensibility of the organs themselves.

It is difficult to gain a clear conception of the contrast between individual and partial variability, and neither is it easy to appreciate their coöperation rightly. Perhaps the best way is to consider their activity as a gradual narrowing of possibilities. At the outset the plant may develop its qualities in any measure, nothing being as yet fixed. Gradually however, the development takes a definite direction, for better or for worse. Is a direction once taken, then it becomes the average, around which the remaining possibilities are grouped. The plant or the organ goes on in this way, until finally it reaches maturity with one of the thousands of degrees of development, between which at the beginning it had a free choice.

Putting this discussion in other terms, we find every individual and every organ in the adult state corresponding with a single ordinate of the curve. The curve indicates the range of possibilities, the ordinate shows the choice that has been made. Now it is clear at once that this choice has not been made suddenly but gradually. Halfway of the development, the choice is halfway determined, but the other half is still undefined. The first half is the same for all the organs of the plant, and is therefore termed individual; the second differs in the separate members, and consequently is known as partial. Which of the two halves is the greater and which the lesser, of course depends on the cases considered.

Finally we may describe a single example, the length of the capsules of the evening-primrose. This is highly variable, the longest reaching more than twice the length of the smallest. Many capsules are borne on the same spike, and they are easily seen to be of unequal size. They vary according to their position, the size diminishing in the main from the base upwards, especially on the higher parts. Likewise the fruits of weaker lateral branches are smaller. Curves are easily made by measuring a few hundred capsules from corresponding parts of different plants, or even by limiting the inquiry to a single individual. These curves give the partial variability, and are found to comply with Quetelet's law.

Besides this limited study, we may compare the numerous individuals of one locality or of a large plot of cultivated plants with one another. In doing so, we are struck with the fact that some plants have large and others small fruits. We now limit ourselves to the main spike of each plant, and perhaps to its lower parts, so as to avoid as far as possible the impression made by the partial fluctuations. The differences remain, and are sufficient to furnish an easy comparison with the general law. In order to do this, we take from each plant a definite number of capsules and measure their average length. In some experiments I took the twenty lowermost capsules of the main spikes. In this way one average was obtained for each plant, and combining these into a curve, it was found that these fluctuations also came under Quetelet's law. Thus the individual averages, and the fluctuations around each of them, follow the same rule. The first are a measure for the whole plant, the second only for its parts.

As a general résumé we can assert that, as a rule, a quality is determined in some degree during the earlier stages of the organism, and that this determination is valid throughout its life. Afterwards only the minor points remain to be regulated. This makes it at once clear that the range of individual and partial variability together must be wider than that of either of them, taken alone. Partial fluctuations cannot, of course, be excluded. Thus our comparison is limited to individual and partial variability on one side, and partial fluctuations alone on the other side.

Intra-specific selection is thus seen to fall under two heads: a selection between the individuals, and a choice within each of them. The first affords a wider and the latter a narrower field.

Individual variability, considered as the result of outward influences operative during extreme youth, can be excluded in a very simple manner. Obviously it suffices to exclude extreme youth, in other words, to exclude the use of seeds. Multiplication in a vegetative way, by grafting and budding, by runners or roots, or by simple division of rootstocks and bulbs is the way in which to limit variability to the partial half. This is all we may hope to attain, but experience shows that it is a very efficient means of limitation. Partial fluctuations are generally far smaller than individual and partial fluctuations together.

Individual variability in the vegetable kingdom might be called seed-variation, as opposed to partial or bud-fluctuation. And perhaps these terms are more apt to convey a clear conception of the distinction than any other. The germ within the unripe seed is easily understood to be far more sensitive to external conditions than a bud.

Multiplication of extremes by seed is thus always counteracted by individual variability, which at once reopens all, or nearly all, the initial possibilities. Multiplication by buds is exempt from this danger and thus leads to a high degree of uniformity. And this uniformity is in many cases exactly what the breeder endeavors to obtain.

We will treat of this reopening of previous possibilities under the head of regression in the next lecture. It is not at all absolute, at least not in one generation. Part of the improvement remains, and favors the next generation. This part may be estimated approximately as being about one-third or one-half of the improvement attained. Hence the conclusion that vegetative multiplication gives rise to varieties which are as a rule twice or thrice as good as selected varieties of plants propagated by seeds. Hence, likewise the inference that breeders generally prefer vegetative multiplication of improved forms, and apply it in all possible cases.

Of course the application is limited, and forage crops and the greater number of vegetables will always necessarily be propagated by seed.

Nature ordinarily prefers the sexual way. Asexual multiplications, although very common with perennial plants, appear not to offer important material for selection. Hence it follows that in comparing the work of nature with that of man, the results of selection followed by vegetative propagation should always be carefully excluded. Our large bulb-flowers and delicious fruits have nothing in common with natural products, and do not yield a standard by which to judge nature's work.

It is very difficult for a botanist to give a survey of what practice has attained by the asexual multiplication of extremes. Nearly all of the large and more palatable fruits are due to such efforts. Some flowers and garden-plants afford further instances. By far the greatest majority of improved asexual varieties, however, are not the result of pure intra-specific selection. They are due largely to the choice of the best existing elementary species, and to some extent to crosses between them, or between distinct systematic species. In practice selection and hybridization go hand in hand and it is often difficult to ascertain what part of the result is due to the one, and what to the other factor.

The scientist, on the contrary, has nothing to do with the industrial product. His task is the analysis of the methods, in order to reach a clear appreciation of the influence of all the competing factors. This study of the working causes leads to a better understanding of the practical processes, and may become the basis of improvement in methods.

Starting from these considerations, we will now give some illustrative examples, and for the first, choose one in which hybridization is almost completely excluded.

Sugar-canes have long been considered to be plants without seed. Their numerous varieties are propagated only in a vegetative way. The stems are cut into pieces, each bearing one or two or more nodes with their buds. An entire variety, though it may be cultivated in large districts and even in various countries, behaves with respect to variability as a single individual. Its individual fluctuability has been limited to the earliest period of its life, when it arose from an unknown seed. The personal characters that have been stamped on this one seed, partly by its descent, and partly in the development of its germ during the period of ripening, have become the indelible characters of the variety, and only the partial fluctuability, due to the effect of later influences, can now be studied statistically.

This study has for its main object the production of sugar in the stems, and the curves, which indicate the percentage of this important substance in different stems of the same variety, comply with Quetelet's law. Each variety has its own average, and around this the data of the majority of the stems are densely crowded, while deviations on both sides are rare and become the rarer the wider they are. The "Cheribon" cane is the richest variety cultivated in Java, and has an average of 19% sugar, while it fluctuates between 11% and 28%. "Chunnic" averages 14%, "Black Manilla" 13% and "White Manilla" 10%; their highest and lowest extremes diverge in the same manner, being for the last named variety 1% and 15%.

This partial variability is of high practical interest, because on it a selection may be founded. According to the conceptions described in a previous lecture, fluctuating variability is the result of those outward factors that determine the strength of development of the plant or the organ. The inconstancy of the degree of sensibility, combined with the ever-varying weather-conditions preclude any close proportionality, but apart from this difficulty there is, in the main, a distinct relation between organic strength and the development of single qualities. This correlation has not escaped observation in the case of the sugar-cane, and it is known that the best grown stocks are generally the richest in sugar. Now it is evident that the best grown and richest stems will have the greater chance of transmitting these qualities to the lateral-buds. This at once gives a basis for vegetative selection, upon which it is not necessary to choose a small number of very excellent stems, but simply to avoid the planting of all those that are below the average. By this means the yield of the cultures has often noticeably been enhanced.

As far as experience goes, this sort of selection, however profitable, does not conduce to the production of improved races. Only temporary ameliorations are obtained, and the selection must be made in the same manner every year. Moreover the improvement is very limited and does not give any promise of further increase. In order to reach this, one has to recur to the individual fluctuability, and therefore to seed.

Nearly half a century ago, Parris discovered, on the island of Barbados, that seeds might occasionally be gathered from the canes. These, however, yielded only grass-like plants of no real value. The same observation was made shortly afterwards in Java and in other sugar-producing countries. In the year 1885, Soltwedel, the director of one of the experiment stations for the culture of sugar-cane in Java, conceived the idea of making use of seedlings for the production of improved races. This idea is a very practical one, precisely because of the possibility of vegetative propagation. If individuals would show the same range as that of partial fluctuability, then the choice of the extremes would at once bring the average up to the richness of the best stocks. Once attained, this average would be fixed, without further efforts.

Unfortunately there is one great drawback. This is the infertility of the best variety, that of the "Cheribon" cane. It flowers abundantly in some years, but it has never been known to produce ripe seeds. For this reason Soltwedel had to start from the second best sort, and chose the "Hawaii" cane. This variety usually yields about 14% sugar, and Soltwedel found among his seedlings one that showed 15%. This fact was quite unexpected at that time, and excited widespread interest in the new method, and since then it has been applied to numerous varieties, and many thousands of seedlings have been raised and tested as to their sugar-production.

From a scientific point of view the results are quite striking. From the practical standpoint, however, the question is, whether the "Hawaii" and other fertile varieties are adequate to yield seedlings, which will surpass the infertile "Cheribon" cane. Now "Hawaii" averages 14% and "Cheribon" 19%, and it is easily understood that a "Hawaii" seedling with more than 19% can be expected only from very large sowings. Hundreds of thousands of seedlings must be cultivated, and their juice tested, before this improvement can be reached. Even then, it may have no significance for practical purposes. Next to the amount of sugar comes the resistance to the disease called "Sereh," and the new race requires to be ameliorated in this important direction, too. Other qualities must also be considered, and any casual deterioration in other characters would make all progress illusory. For these reasons much time is required to attain distinct improvements.

These great difficulties in the way of selecting extremes for vegetative propagation are of course met with everywhere. They impede the work of the breeder to such a degree, that but few men are able to surmount them. Breeding new varieties necessitates the bending of every effort to this purpose, and a clear conception of the manifold aspects of this intricate problem. These fall under two heads, the exigencies of practice, and the physiologic laws of variability. Of course, only the latter heading comes within the limits of our discussion which includes two main points. First comes the general law of fluctuation that, though slight deviations from the average may be found by thousands, or rather in nearly every individual, larger and therefore important deviations are very rare. Thousands of seedlings must be examined carefully in order to find one or two from which it might be profitable to start a new race. This point is the same for practical and for scientific investigation. In the second place however, a digression is met with. The practical man must take into consideration all the varying qualities of his improved strains. Some of them must be increased and others be decreased, and their common dependency on external conditions often makes it very difficult to discover the desired combinations. It is obvious, however, that the neglect of one quality may make all improvement of other characters wholly useless. No augmentation of sugar-percentage, of size and flavor of fruits can counterbalance an increase in sensitiveness to disease, and so it is with other qualities also.

Improved races for scientific investigation can be kept free from infection, and protected against numerous other injuries. In the experimental garden they may find conditions which cannot be realized elsewhere. They may show a luxuriant growth, and prove to be excellent material for research, but have features which, having been overlooked at the period of selection, would at once condemn them if left to ordinary conditions, or to the competition of other species.

Considering all these obstacles, it is only natural that breeders should use every means to reach their goal. Only in very rare instances do they follow methods analogous to scientific processes, which tend to simplify the questions as much as possible. As a rule, the practical way is the combination of as many causes of variability as possible. Now the three great sources of variability are, as has been pointed out on several occasions, the original multiformity of the species, fluctuating variability, and hybridization. Hence, in practical experiments, all three are combined. Together they yield results of the highest value, and Burbank's improved fruits and flowers give testimony to the practical significance of this combination.

From a scientific point of view however, it is

ordinarily difficult, if not impossible, to discern the part which each of the three great branches of variability has taken in the origination of the product. A full analysis is rarely possible, and the treatment of one of the three factors must necessarily remain incomplete.

Notwithstanding these considerations, I will now give some examples in order to show that fluctuating variability plays a prominent part in these improvements. Of course it is the third in importance in the series. First comes the choice of the material from the assemblage of species, elementary species and varieties. Hybridization comes next in importance. But even the hybrids of the best parents may be improved, because they are no less subject to Quetelet's law than any other strain. Any large number of hybrids of the same ancestry will prove this, and often the excellency of a hybrid variety depends chiefly, or at least definitely, on the selection of the best individuals. Being propagated only in a vegetative way, they retain their original good qualities through all further culture and multiplication.

As an illustrative example I will take the genus *Canna*. Originally cultivated for its large and bright foliage only, it has since become a flowering plant of value. Our garden strains have originated by the crossing of a number of introduced wild species, among which the *Canna indica* is the oldest, now giving its name to the whole group. It has tall stems and spikes with rather inconspicuous flowers with narrow petals. It has been crossed with *C. nepalensis* and *C. warczewiczii,* and the available historic evidence points to the year 1846 as that of the first cross. This was made by Année between the *indica* and the *nepalensis;* it took ten years to multiply them to the required degree for introduction into commerce. These first hybrids had bright foliage and were tall plants, but their flowers were by no means remarkable.

Once begun, hybridization was widely practiced. About the year 1889 Crozy exhibited at Paris the first beautifully flowering form, which he named for his wife, "Madame Crozy." Since that time he and many others have improved the flowers in the shape and size, as well as in color and its patterns. In the main, these ameliorations have been due to the discovery and introduction of new wild species possessing the required characters. This is illustrated by the following incident. In the year 1892 I visited Mr. Crozy at Lyons. He showed me his nursery and numerous acquisitions, those of former years as well as those that were quite new, and which were in the process of rapid multiplication, previous to being given to the trade. I wondered, and asked, why no pure white variety was present. His answer was: "Because no white species had been found up to the present time, and there is no other means of producing white varieties than by crossing the existing forms with a new white type."

Comparing the varieties produced in successive periods, it is very easy to appreciate their gradual improvement. On most points this is not readily put into words, but the size of the petals can be measured, and the figures may convey at least some idea of the real state of things. Leaving aside the types with small flowers and cultivated exclusively for their foliage, the oldest flowers of *Canna* had petals of 45 mm. length and 13 mm. breadth. The ordinary types at the time of my visit had reached 61 by 21 mm., and the "Madame Crozy" showed 66 by 30 mm. It had however, already been surpassed by a few commercial varieties, which had the same length but a breadth of 35 mm. And the latest production, which required some years of propagation before being put on the market, measured 83 by 43 mm. Thus in the lapse of some thirty years the length had been doubled and the breadth tripled, giving flowers with broad corollas and with petals joined all around, resembling the best types of lilies and amaryllis.

Striking as this result unquestionably is, it remains doubtful as to what part of it is due to the discovery and introduction of new large flowered species, and what to the selection of the extremes of fluctuating variability. As far as I have been able to ascertain however, and according to the evidence given to me by Mr. Crozy, selection has had the largest part in regard to the size, while the color-patterns are introduced qualities.

The scientific analysis of other intricate examples is still more difficult. To the practical breeder they often seem very simple, but the student of heredity, who wishes to discern the different factors, is often quite puzzled by this apparent simplicity. So it is in the case of the double lilacs, a large number of varieties of which have recently been originated and introduced into commerce by Lemoine of Nancy. In the main they owe their origin to the crossing and recrossing of a single plant of the old double variety with the numerous existing single-flowered sorts.

This double variety seems to be as old as the culture of the lilacs. It was already known to Munting, who described it in the year 1671. Two centuries afterwards, in 1870, a new description was given by Morren, and though more than one varietal name is recorded in his paper, it appears from the facts given that even at that time only one variety existed. It was commonly called *Syringa vulgaris azurea plena,* and seems to have been very rare and without real ornamental value.

Lemoine, however, conceived the desirability of a combination of the doubling with the bright colors and large flower-racemes of other lilacs, and performed a series of crosses. The "*azurea plena*" has no stamens, and therefore must be used in all crosses as the pistil-parent; its ovary is narrowly inclosed in the tube of the flower, and difficult to fertilize. On the other hand, new crosses could be made every year, and the total number of hybrids with different pollen-parents was rapidly increased. After five years the hybrids began to flower and could be used for new crosses, yielding a series of compound hybrids, which however, were not kept separate from the products of the first crosses.

Gradually the number of the flowering specimens increased, and the character of doubling was observed to be variable to a high degree. Sometimes only one supernumerary petal was produced, sometimes a whole new typical corolla was extruded from within the first. In the same way the color and the number of the flowers on each raceme were seen to vary. Thousands of hybrids were produced, and only those which exhibited real advantages were selected for trade. These were multiplied by grafting, and each variety at present consists only of the buds of one original individual and their products. No constancy from seed is assumed, many varieties are even quite sterile.

Of course, no description was given of the rejected forms. It is only stated that many of them bore either single or poorly filled flowers, or were objectionable in some other way. The range of variability, from which the choices were made, is obscure and only the fact of the selection is prominent. What part is due to the combination of the parental features and what to the individual fluctuation of the hybrid itself cannot be ascertained.

So it is in numerous other instances. The dahlias have been derived from three or more original species, and been subjected to cultivation and hybridization in an ever-increasing scale for a century. The best varieties are only propagated in the vegetative way, by the roots and buds, or by grafting and cutting. Each of them is, with regard to its hereditary qualities, only one individual, and the individual characters were selected at the same time with the varietal and hybrid characters. Most of them are very inconstant from seed and as a rule, only mixtures are offered for sale in seed-lists. Which of their ornamental features are due to fluctuating deviation from an average is of course unknown. *Amaryllis* and *Gladiolus* are surrounded with the same scientific uncertainties. Eight or ten, or even more, species have been combined into one large and multiform strain, each bringing its peculiar qualities into the mixed mass. Every hybrid variety is one individual, being propagated by bulbs only. Colors and color-patterns, shape of petals and other marks, have been derived from the wild ancestors, but the large size of many of the best varieties is probably due to the selection of the extremes of fluctuating variability. So it is with the begonias of our gardens, which are also composite hybrids, but are usually sown on a very large scale. Flowers of 15 cm. diameter are very showy, but there can be no doubt about the manner in which they are produced, as the wild species fall far short of this size.

Among vegetables the potatoes afford another instance. Originally quite a number of good species were in culture, most of them having small tubers. Our present varieties are due to hybridization and selection, each of them being propagated only in the vegetative way.

Selection is founded upon different qualities, according to the use to be made of the new sort. Potatoes for the factory have even been selected for their amount of starch, and in this case at least, fluctuating variability has played a very important part in the improvement of the race.

Vegetative propagation has the great advantage of exempting the varieties from regression to mediocrity, which always follows multiplication by seeds. It affords the possibility of keeping the extremes constant, and this is not its only advantage. Another, likewise highly interesting, side of the question is the uniformity of the whole strain. This is especially important in the case of fruits, though ordinarily it is regarded as a matter of course, but there are some exceptions which give proof of the real importance of the usual condition. For example, the walnut-tree. Thousands of acres of walnut-orchards consist of seedling trees grown from nuts of unknown parentage. The result is a great diversity in the types of trees and in the size and shape of the nuts, and this diversity is an obvious disadvantage to the industry. The cause lies in the enormous difficulties attached to grafting or budding of these trees, which make this method very expensive and to a high degree uncertain and unsatisfactory.

After this hasty survey of the more reliable facts of the practice of an asexual multiplication of the extremes of fluctuating variability, we may now return to the previously mentioned theoretical considerations. These are concerned with an estimation of the chances of the occurrence of deviations, large enough to exhibit commercial value. This chance may be calculated on the basis of Quetelet's law, whenever the agreement of the fluctuation of the quality under consideration has been empirically determined. In the discussion of the methods of comparing two curves, we have pointed to the quartiles as the decisive points, and to the necessity of drawing the curves so that these points are made to overlie one another, on each side of the average. If now we calculate the binomium of Newton for different values of the exponent, the sum of the coefficients is doubled for each higher unit of the exponent, and at the same time the extreme limit of the curve is extended one step farther. Hence it is possible to calculate a relation between the value of the extreme and the number of cases required. It would take us too long to give this calculation in detail, but it is easily seen that for each succeeding step the number of individuals must be doubled, though the length of the steps, or the amount of increase of the quality remains the same. The result is that many thousands of seedlings are required to go beyond the ordinary range of variations, and that every further improvement requires the doubling of the whole culture. If ten thousand do not give a profitable deviation, the next step requires twenty thousand, the following forty thousand, and so on. And all this work would be necessary for the improvement of a single quality, while practice requires the examination and amelioration of nearly all the variable characters of the strain.

Hence the rule that great results can only be obtained by the use of large numbers, but it is of no avail to state this conclusion from a scientific point of view. Scientific experimenters will rarely be able to sacrifice fifty thousand plants to a single selection. The problem is to introduce the principle into practice and to prove its direct usefulness and reliability. It is to Luther Burbank that we owe this great achievement. His principles are in full harmony with the teachings of science. His methods are hybridization and selection in the broadest sense and on the largest scale. One very illustrative example of his methods must suffice to convey an idea of the work necessary to produce a new race of superlative excellency. Forty thousand blackberry and raspberry hybrids were produced and grown until the fruit matured. Then from the whole lot a single variety was chosen as the best. It is now known under the name of " Paradox." All others were uprooted with their crop of ripening berries, heaped up into a pile twelve feet wide, fourteen feet high and twenty-two feet long, and burned. Nothing remained of that expensive and lengthy experiment, except the one parent-plant of the new variety. Similar selections and similar amount of work have produced the famous plums, the brambles and the blackberries, the Shasta daisy, the peach-almond, the improved blueberries, the hybrid lilies, and the many other valuable fruits and garden-flowers that have made the fame of Burbank and the glory of horticultural California.

Lecture XXVII

INCONSTANCY OF IMPROVED RACES

The greater advantages of the asexual multiplication of extremes are of course restricted to perennial and woody plants. Annual and biennial species cannot as a rule, be propagated in this way, and even with some perennials horticulturists prefer the sale of seeds to that of roots and bulbs. In all these cases it is clear that the exclusion of the individual variability, which was shown to be an important point in the last lecture, must be sacrificed.

Seed-propagation is subject to individual as well as to fluctuating variability. The first could perhaps be designated by another term, embryonic variability, since it indicates the fluctuations occurring during the period of development of the germ. This period begins with the fusion of the male and female elements and is largely dependent upon the vigor of these cells at the moment, and on the varying qualities they may have acquired. It comprises in the main the time of the ripening of the seed, and

might perhaps best be considered to end with
the beginning of the resting stage of the ripe
seed. Hence it is clear that the variability of
seed-propagated annual races has a wider range
than that of perennials, shrubs and trees. At
present it is difficult to discern exactly the part
each of these two main factors plays in the
process. Many indications are found however,
that make it probable that embryonic variability
is wider, and perhaps of far greater importance than the subsequent partial fluctuations.
The high degree of similarity between the single
specimens of a vegetative variety, and the large
amount of variability in seed-races strongly
supports this view. The propagation and multiplication of the extremes of fluctuating variability by means of seeds requires a close
consideration of the relation between seedling
and parent. The easiest way to get a clear conception of this relation is to make use of the
ideas concerning the dependency of variability
upon nourishment. Assuming these to be correct in the main, and leaving aside all minor
questions, we may conclude that the chosen
extreme individual is one of the best nourished
and intrinsically most vigorous of the whole
culture. On account of these very qualities it
is capable of nourishing all of its organs better
and also its seeds. In other words, the seeds

of the extreme individuals have exceptional chances of becoming better nourished than the average of the seeds of the race. Applying the same rule to them, it is easily understood that they will vary, by reason of this better nourishment, in a direction corresponding to that of their parent.

This discussion gives a very simple explanation of the acknowledged fact that the seeds of the extremes are in the main the best for the propagation of the race. It does not include however, all the causes for this preferment. Some are of older date and due to previous influences.

A second point in our discussion is the appreciation of the fact that a single individual may be chosen to gather the seed from, and that these seeds, and the young plants they yield, are as a rule, numerous. Hence it follows that we are to compare their average and their extremes with the qualities of the parents. Both are of practical as well as of theoretical interest. The average of the progeny is to be considered as the chief result of the selection in the previous generation, while the extremes, at least those which depart in the same direction, are obviously the means of further improvement of the race.

Thus our discussion should be divided into

Inconstancy of Improved Races 773

two heads. One of these comprises the relation of the average of the progeny to the exceptional qualities of the chosen parent, and the other the relation of exceptional offspring to the exceptional parents.

Let us consider the averages first. Are they to be expected to be equal to the unique quality of the parent, or perhaps to be the same as the average of the whole unselected race? Neither of these cases occur. Experience is clear and definite on this important point. Vilmorin, when making the first selections to improve the amount of sugar in beets, was struck with the fact that the average of the progeny lies between that of the original strain and the quality of the chosen parent. He expressed his observation by stating that the progeny are grouped around and diverge in all directions from some point, placed on the line which unites their parent with the type from which it sprang. All breeders agree on this point, and in scientific experiments it has often been confirmed. We shall take up some illustrative examples presently, but in order to make them clear, it is necessary to give a closer consideration to the results of Vilmorin.

From his experience it follows that the average of the progeny is higher than that of the race at large, but lower than the chosen parent.

In other words, there is a progression and a regression. A progression in relation to the whole race, and a regression in comparison with the parent. The significance of this becomes clear at once, if we recall the constancy of the variety which could be obtained from the selected extreme in the case of vegetative multiplication. The progression is what the breeder wants, the regression what he detests. Regression is the permanency of part of the mediocrity which the selection was invoked to overcome. Manifestly it is of the highest interest that the progression should be as large, and the regression as small as possible. In order to attain this goal the first question is to know the exact measure of progression and regression as they are exhibiting themselves in the given cases, and the second is to inquire into the influences, on which this proportion may be incumbent.

At present our notions concerning the first point are still very limited and those concerning the second extremely vague. Statistical inquiries have led to some definite ideas about the importance of regression, and these furnish a basis for experimental researches concerning the causes of the phenomenon. Very advantageous material for the study of progression and regression in the realm of fluctuating variability is afforded by the ears of corn or maize. The kernels are arranged in longitudinal rows, and these rows are observed to occur in varying, but always even, numbers. This latter circumstance is due to the fact that each two neighboring rows contain the lateral branches of a single row of spikelets, the axes of which however, are included in the fleshy body of the ear. The variation of the number of the rows is easily seen to comply with Quetelet's law, and often 30 or 40 ears suffice to give a trustworthy curve. Fritz Müller made some experiments upon the inheritance of the number of the rows, in Brazil. He chose a race which averaged 12 rows, selected ears with 14, 16 and 18 rows, etc., and sowed their kernels separately. In each of these cultures he counted the rows of the seeds on the ears of all the plants when ripe, and calculated their average. This average, of course, does not necessarily correspond to a whole number, and fractions should not be neglected.

According to Vilmorin's rule he always found some progression of the average and some regression. Both were the larger, the more the parent-ear differed from the general average, but the proportion between both remained the same, and seems independent of the amount of the deviation. Putting the deviation at 5, the progression calculated from his figures is

2 and the regression 3. In other words the average of the progeny has gained over the average of the original variety slightly more than one-third, and slightly less than one-half of the parental deviation. I have repeated this experiment of Fritz Müller's and obtained nearly the same regression of three-fifths, though working with another variety, and under widely different climatic conditions.

The figures of Fritz Müller were, as given below, in one experiment. In the last column I put the improvement calculated for a proportion of two-fifths above the initial average of 12.

Rows on parent ears	Average of rows of progeny	12 + ⅖ of Difference
14	12.6	12.8
16	14.1	13.6
18	15.2	14.4
20	15.8	15.2
22	16.1	16.0

Galton, in his work on natural inheritance, describes an experiment with the seeds of the sweet pea or *Lathyrus odoratus*. He determined the average size in a lot of purchased seeds, and selected groups of seeds of different, but for each group constant, sizes. These were sown, and the average of the seeds was determined anew in the subsequent harvest they yielded. These figures agreed with the rule of Vilmorin and were calculated in the manner given for the test of the corn. The progression and regression were found to be proportionate to the amount of the deviation. The progression of the average was one-third, and the regression in consequence two-thirds of the total deviation. The amelioration is thus seen to be nearly, though not exactly, the same as in the previous case.

From the evidence of the other corresponding experiments, and from various statistical inquiries it seems that the value of the progression is nearly the same in most cases, irrespective of the species used and the quality considered. It may be said to be from one-third to one-half of the parental deviation, and in this form the statement is obviously of wide and easy applicability.

Our figures also demonstrate the great preeminence of vegetative varieties above the improved strains multiplied by seeds. They have a definite relation. Asexually multiplied strains may be said to be generally two times or even three times superior to the common offspring. This is a difference of great practical importance, and should never be lost sight of in theoretical considerations of the productive capacity of selection. Multiplication by seed however, has one great advantage over the asexual method; it may be repeated. The selection is not limited to a single choice, but may be applied in two or more succeeding generations. Obviously such a repetition affords a better chance of increasing the progression of the average and of ameliorating the race to a greater degree than would be possible by a single choice. This principle of repeated selection is at present the prominent feature of race-improvement. Next to variety-testing and hybridizing it is the great source of the steady progression of agricultural crops. From a practical standpoint the method is clear and as perfect as might be expected, but this is not the side of the problem with which we are concerned here. The theoretical analysis and explanation of the results obtained, however, is subject to much doubt, and to a great divergence of conceptions. So it is also with the application of the practical processes to those occurring in nature. Some assume that here repeated selection is only of subordinate importance, while others declare that the whole process of evolution is due to this agency. This very important point however, will be reserved for the next lecture, and only the facts available at present will be considered here.

As a first example we may take the ray-florets of the composites. On a former occasion we have dealt with their fluctuation in number and found that it is highly variable and complies in the main with Quetelet's law. *Madia elegans*, a garden-species, has on the average 21 rays on each head, fluctuating between 16 and 25 or more. I saved the seeds of a plant with only 17 rays on the terminal head, and got from them a culture which averaged 19 rays, which is the mean between 21 and 17. In this second generation I observed the extremes to be 22 and 12, and selected a plant with 13 rays as the parent for a continuation of the experiment. The plants, which I got from its seeds, averaged 18 and showed 22 and 13 as extremes. The total progression of the average was thus, in two generations, from 21 to 18, and the total regression from 13 to 18, and the proportion is thus seen to diminish by the repetition rather than to increase.

This experiment, however, is of course too imperfect upon which to found general conclusions. It only proves the important fact that the improved average of the second generation is not the starting-point for the further improvement. But the second generation allows a choice of an extreme, which diverges noticeably more from the mean than any individual of the first culture, and thereby gives a larger amount of absolute progression, even if the proportion between progression and regression remains the same. The repetition is only an easy method of getting more widely deviating extremes; whether it has, besides this, another effect, remains doubtful. In order to be able to decide this question, it is necessary to repeat the selection during a series of generations. In this way the individual faults may be removed as far as possible. I chose an experiment of Fritz Müller, relating to the number of rows of grains on the ears exactly as in the case above referred to, and which I have repeated in my experimental garden at Amsterdam.

I started from a variety known to fructify fairly regularly in our climate, and exhibiting in the mean 12 – 14 rows, but varying between 8 and 20 as exceptional cases. I chose an ear with 16 rows and sowed its seeds in 1887. A number of plants were obtained, from each of which, one ear was chosen in order to count its rows. An average of 15 rows was found with variations complying with Quetelet's law. One ear reached 22 rows, but had not been fertilized, some others had 20 rows, and the best of these was chosen for the continuation of the experiment. I repeated the sowing during 6 subsequent generations in the same way, choosing each time the most beautiful ear from among those with the greatest number of rows. Unfortunately with the increase of the number the size of the grains decreases, the total amount of nourishment available for all of them remaining about the same. Thus the kernels and consequently the new plants became smaller and weaker, and the chance of fertilization was diminished in the ears with the highest number of rows. Consequently the choice was limited, and after having twice chosen a spike with 20 and once one with 24 rows, I finally preferred those with the intermediate number of 22.

This repeated choice has brought the average of my race up from 13 to 20, and thus to the extreme limit of the original variety. Seven years were required to attain this result, or on an average the progression was one row in a year. This augmentation was accompanied by an accompanying movement of the whole group in the same direction. The extreme on the side of the small numbers came up from 8 to 12 rows, and cobs with 8 or 10 rows did not appear in my race later than the third generation. On the other side the extreme reached 28, a figure never reached by the original variety as cultivated with us, and ears with 24 and 26 rows have been seen during the four last generations in increasing numbers.

This slow and gradual amelioration was partly due to the mode of pollination of the corn.

The pollen falls from the male spikes on the ears of the same plant, but also is easily blown on surrounding spikes. In order to get the required amount of seed it is necessary in our climate to encroach as little as possible upon free pollination, aiding the self-pollination, but taking no precautions against intercrossing. It is assumed that the choice of the best ears indicates the plants which have had the best pollen-parents as well as the best pistil-parents, and that selection here, as in other cases, corrects the faults of free intercrossing. But it is granted that this correction is only a slow one, and accounts in a great degree for the slowness of the progression. Under better climatic conditions and with a more entire isolation of the individuals, it seems very probable that the same result could have been reached in fewer generations.

However this may be, the fact is that by repeated selection the strain can be ameliorated to a greater extent than by a single choice. This result completely agrees with the general experience of breeders and the example given is only an instance of a universal rule. It has the advantage of being capable of being recorded in a numerical way, and of allowing a detailed and definite description of all the succeeding generations. The entire harvest of all of them has been counted and the figures combined into curves, which at once show the whole course of the pedigree-experiment. These curves have in the main taken the same shape, and have only gradually been moved in the chosen direction.

Three points are now to be considered in connection with this experiment. The first is the size of the cultures required for the resulting amelioration. In other words, would it have been possible to attain an average of 20 rows in a single experiment? This is a matter of calculation, and the calculation must be based upon the experience related above, that the progression in the case of maize is equal to two-fifths of the parental deviation. A cob with 20 rows means a deviation of 7 from the average of 13, the incipient value of my race. To reach such an average at once, an ear would be required with $7 \times {}^5/_2 = 17\frac{1}{2}$ rows above the average, or an ear with 30–32 rows. These never occur, but the rule given in a previous lecture gives a method of calculating the probability of their occurrence, or in other words, the number of ears required to give a chance of finding such an ear. It would take too long to give this calculation here, but I find that approximately 12,000 ears would be required to give one with 28 rows, which was the highest number attained in my experiment, while 100,000 ears would afford a chance of one with 32 rows.* Had I been able to secure and inspect this number of ears, perhaps I would have needed only a year to get an average of 20 rows. This however, not being the case, I have worked for seven years, but on the other hand have cultivated all in all only about one thousand individuals for the entire experiment.

Obviously this reduction of the size of the experiment is of importance. One hundred thousand ears of corn could of course, be secured directly from trade or from some industrial culture, but corn is cultivated only to a small extent in Holland, and in most cases the requisite number of individuals would be larger than that afforded by any single plantation.

Repeated selection is thereby seen to be the means of reducing the size of the required cultures to possible measures, not only in the experimental-garden, but also for industrial purposes. A selection from among 60000 – 100000 individuals may be within reach of Burbank, but of few others. As a rule they prefer a longer time with a smaller lot of plants. This

* On about 200 ears the variability ranges from 8–22 rows, and this leads approximately to one row more by each doubling of the numbers of instances. One ear with 22 rows in 200 would thus lead to the expectation of one ear with 32 rows in 100,000 ears.

is exactly what is gained by repeated selections. To my mind this reduction of the size of the cultures is probably the sole effect of the repetition. But experience is lacking on this point, and exact comparisons should be made whenever possible, between the descendants of a unique but extreme choice, and a repeated but smaller selection. The effect of the repetition on the nourishment of the chosen representatives should be studied, for it is clear that a plant with 22 rows, the parents and grandparents of which had the same number, indicates a better condition of internal qualities than one with the same number of rows, produced accidentally from the common race. In this way it may perhaps be possible to explain, why in my experiment an ear with 22 rows gave an average offspring with 20, while the calculation, founded on the regression alone would require a parental ear with 32 rows.

However, as already stated, this discussion is only intended to convey some general idea as to the reduction of the cultures by means of repeated selections, as the material at hand is wholly inadequate for any closer calculation. This important point of the reduction may be illustrated in still another manner.

The sowing of very large numbers is only required because it is impossible to tell from the inspection of the seeds which of them will yield the desired individual. But what is impossible in the inspection of the seeds may be feasible, at least in important measure, in the inspection of the plants which bear the seeds. Whenever such an inspection demonstrates differences, in manifest connection with the quality under consideration, any one will readily grant that it would be useless to sow the seeds of the worst plants, and that even the whole average might be thrown over, if it were only possible to point out a number of the best. But it is clear that by this inspection of the parent-plants the principle of repeated selection is introduced for two succeeding generations, and that its application to a larger series of generations is only a question of secondary importance.

Summing up our discussion of this first point we may assert that repeated selection is only selection on a small and practical scale, while a single choice would require numbers of individuals higher than are ordinarily available.

A second discussion in connection with our pedigree-culture of corn is the question whether the amelioration obtained was of a durable nature, or only temporary. In other words, whether the progeny of the race would remain constant, if cultivated after cessation of the selection. In order to ascertain this, I continued the culture during several generations, choosing ears with less than the average number of rows. The excellence of the race at once disappeared, and the ordinary average of the variety from which I had started seven years before, returned within two or three seasons. This shows that the attained improvement is neither fixed nor assured and is dependent on continued selection. This result only confirms the universal experience of breeders, which teaches the general dependency of improved races on continued selection. Here a striking contrast with elementary species or true varieties is obvious. The strains which nature affords are true to their type; their average condition remains the same during all the succeeding generations, and even if it should be slightly altered by changes in the external conditions, it returns to the type, as soon as these changes come to an end. It is a real average, being the sum of the contribution of all the members of the strain. Improved races have only an apparent average, which is in fact biased by the exclusion of whole groups of individuals. If left to themselves, their appearance changes, and the real average soon returns. This is the common experience of breeders.

A third point is to be discussed in connection with the detailed pedigree-cultures. It is the question as to what might be expected from a continuation of improvement selection. Would it be possible to obtain any imaginable deviation from the original type, and to reach independency from further selection? This point has not until now attracted any practical interest, and from a practical point of view and within the limits of ordinary cultures, it seems impossible to obtain a positive answer. But in the theoretical discussion of the problems of descent it has become of the highest importance, and therefore requires a separate treatment, which will be reserved for the next lecture.

Here we come upon another equally difficult problem. It relates to the proportion of embryonic or individual fluctuation, to partial variation as involved in the process of selection. Probably all qualities which may be subjected to selection vary according to both principles, the embryonic decision giving only a more definite average, around which the parts of the individual are still allowed to oscillate. It is so with the corn, and whenever two or more ears are ripening or even only flowering on the same plant, differences of a partial nature may be seen in the number of their rows. These fluctuations are only small however, ordinarily not exceeding two and rarely four

of selection here finds its limit and that centuries and perhaps geologic periods of continued effort in the same direction are not capable of adding anything more to the initial effect.

Some illustrative examples may suffice to prove the validity of this assertion. Every botanist who has studied the agricultural practice of plant-breeding, or the causes of the geographic distribution of plants, will easily recall to his mind numerous similar cases. Perhaps the most striking instance is afforded by cultivated biennial plants. The most important of them are forage-beets and sugar-beets. They are, of course, cultivated only as biennials, but some annual specimens may be seen each year and in nearly every field. They arise from the same seed as the normal individuals, and their number is obviously dependent on external conditions, and especially on the time of sowing. Ordinary cultures often show as much as 1% of these useless plants, but the exigencies of time and available labor often compel the cultivator to have a large part of his fields sown before spring. In central Europe, where the climate is unfavorable at this season, the beets respond by the production of far larger proportions of annual specimens, their number coming often up to 20% or more, thus constituting noticeable losses in the prod-

not of the whole field. Rimpau, who has made a thorough study of this evil and has shown its dependency on various external conditions, has also tried to find methods of selection with the aim of overcoming it, or at least of reducing it to uninjurious proportions. But in these efforts he has reached no practical result. The annuals are simply inexterminable.

Coming to the alternative side of the problem it is clear that annuals have always been excluded in the selection. Their seeds cannot be mixed with the good harvest, not even accidentally, since they have ripened in a previous year. In order to bear seeds in the second year beets must be taken from the field, and kept free from frost through the winter. The following spring they are planted out, and it is obvious that even the most careless farmer is not liable to mix them with annual specimens. Hence we may conclude that a strict and unexcelled process of selection has been applied to the destruction of this tendency, not only for sugar-beets, since Vilmorin's time, when selection had become a well understood process, but also for forage-beets since the beginning of beet-culture. Although unconscious, the selection of biennials must have been uninterrupted and strict throughout many centuries.

It has had no effect at all. Annuals are seen

to return every year. They are ineradicable. Every individual is in the possession of this latent quality and liable to convert it into activity as soon as the circumstances provoke its appearance, as proved by the increase of annuals in the early sowings. Hence the conclusion that selection in the long run is not adequate to deliver plants from injurious qualities. Other proofs could be given by other biennials, and among them the stray annual plants of common carrots are perhaps the most notorious. In my own cultures of evening-primroses I have preferred the annuals and excluded the biennials, but without being able to produce a pure annual race. As soon as circumstances are favorable, the biennials return in large numbers. Cereals give analogous proofs. Summer and winter varieties have been cultivated separately for centuries, but in trials it is often easy to convert the one into the other. No real and definite isolation has resulted from the effect of the long continued unconscious selection.

Striped flowers, striped fruits, and especially striped radishes afford further examples. It would be quite superfluous to dwell upon them. Selection always tends to exclude the monochromatic specimens, but does not prevent their return in every generation. Numerous rare monstrosities are in the same category, especially when they are of so rare occurrence as not to give any noticeable contribution to the seed-production, or even if they render their bearers incapable of reproduction. In such cases the selection of normal plants is very severe or even absolute, but the anomalies are by no means exterminated. Any favorable circumstances, or experimental selection in their behalf shows them to be still capable of full development. Numerous cases of such subordinate hereditary characters constitute the greater part of the science of vegetable teratology.

If it should be objected that all these cases cover too short a time to be decisive, or at least fail in giving evidence relative to former times, alpine plants afford a proof which one can hardly expect to be surpassed. During the whole present geologic epoch they have been subjected to the never failing selection of their climate and other external conditions. They exhibit a full and striking adaptation to these conditions, but also possess the latent capacity for assuming lowland characters as soon as they are transported into such environment. Obviously this capacity never becomes active on the mountains, and is always counteracted by selection. This agency is evidently without any effect, for as we have seen when dealing with the experiments of Nägeli, Bonnier and others, each single individual may change its habits and its aspect in response to transplantation. The climate has an exceedingly great influence on each individual, but the continuance of this influence is without permanent result.

So much concerning ever-sporting varieties and double adaptations. We now come to the effects of a continuous selection of simple characters.

Here the sugar-beets stand preëminent. Since Vilmorin's time they have been selected according to the amount of sugar in their roots, and the result has been the most striking that has ever been attained, if considered from the standpoint of practice. But if critically examined, with no other aim than a scientific appreciation of the improvement in comparison with other processes of selection, the support of the evidence for the theory of accumulative influence proves to be very small.

The amount of sugar is expressed by percentage-figures. These however, are dependent on various causes, besides the real quantity of sugar produced. One of these causes is the quantity of watery fluid in the tissues, and this in its turn is dependent on the culture in dryer or moister soil, and on the amount of moisture in the air, and the same variety of sugar-beets yields higher percentage-figures in a dry region than in a wet one. This is seen when comparing, for instance, the results of the analyses from the sandy provinces of Holland with those from the clay-meadows, and it is very well known that Californian beets average as high as 26% or more, while the best European beets remain at about 20%. As far as I have been able to ascertain, these figures however, are not indicative of any difference of race, but simply direct responses to the conditions of climate and of soil.

Apart from these considerations the improvement reached in half a century or in about twenty to thirty generations is not suggestive of anything absolute. Everything is fluctuating now, even as it was at the outset, and equally dependent on continual care. Vilmorin has given some figures for the beets of the first generations from which he started his race. He quotes 14% as a recommendable amount, and 7 and 21 as the extreme instances of his analyses. However incorrect these figures may be, they coincide to a striking degree with the present condition of the best European races. Of course minor values are excluded each year by the selection, and in consequence the average value has increased. For the year 1874 we find a standard of 10–14% considered as normal, bad years giving 10%, good years from 12% to 14% in the average. Extreme instances exceeded 17%. From that time the practice of the polarization of the juice for the estimate of the sugar has rapidly spread throughout Europe, and a definite increase of the average value soon resulted. This however, often does not exceed 14%, and beets selected in the field for the purpose of polarization come up to an average of 15 to 16%, varying downward to less than 10% and upward to 20 and 21%. In the main the figures are the same as those of Vilmorin, the range of variability has not been reduced, and higher extremes are not reached. An average increase of 1% is of great practical importance, and nothing can excel the industry and care displayed in the improvement of the beet-races. Notwithstanding this a lasting influence has not been exercised; the methods of selection have been improved, and the number of polarized beets has been brought up to some hundreds of thousands in single factories, but the improvement is still as dependent upon continuous selection as it was half a century ago.

The process is practically very successful, but the support afforded by it to the selection-theory vanishes on critical examination.

Lecture XXVIII

ARTIFICIAL AND NATURAL SELECTION

The comparison of artificial and natural selection has furnished material support for the theory of descent, and in turn been the object of constant criticism since the time of Darwin. The criticisms, in greater part, have arisen chiefly from an imperfect knowledge of both processes. By the aid of distinctions recently made possible, the contrast between elementary species and improved races has become much more vivid, and promises to yield better results on which to base comparisons of artificial and natural selection.

Elementary species, as we have seen in earlier lectures, occur in wild and in cultivated plants. In older genera and systematic species they are often present in small numbers only, but many of the more recent wild types and also many of the cultivated forms are very rich in this respect. In agriculture the choice of the most adequate elementary forms for any special purpose is acknowledged as the first step in the way of selection, and is designated by the name of variety-testing, applying the term variety to all the subdivisions of systematic species indiscriminately. In natural processes it bears the title of survival of species. The fact that recent types show large numbers, and in some instances even hundreds of minor constant forms, while the older genera are considerably reduced in this respect, is commonly explained by the assumption of extinction of species on a correspondingly large scale. This extinction is considered to affect the unfit in a higher measure than the fit. Consequently the former vanish, often without leaving any trace of their existence, and only those that prove to be sufficiently adapted to the surrounding external conditions, resist and survive.

This selection exhibits far-reaching analogies between the artificial and the natural processes, and is in both cases of the very highest importance. In nature the dying out of unfit mutations is the result of the great struggle for life. In a previous lecture we have compared its agency with that of a sieve. All elements which are too small or too weak fall through, and only those are preserved which resist the sifting process. Reduced in number they thrive and multiply and are thus enabled to strike out new mutative changes. These are again submitted to the sifting tests, and the frequent repetition of this process is considered to give a good explanation of the manifold, highly complicated, and admirable structures which strike the beginner as the only real adaptations in nature.

Exactly in the same way artificial selection isolates and preserves some elementary species, while it destroys others. Of course the time is not sufficient to secure new mutations, or at least these are only rare at present, and their occurrence is doubtful in historic periods. Apart from this unavoidable difference the analogy between natural and artificial selection appears to me to be very striking.

This form of selection may be termed selection between species. Opposed to it stands the selection within the elementary species or variety. It has of late, alone come to be known as selection, though in reality it does not deserve this distinction. I have already detailed the historical evidence which gives preference to selection between species. The process can best be designated by the name of intra-specific selection, if it is understood that the term intra-specific is meant to apply to the conception of small or elementary species.

I do not wish to propose new terms, but

I think that the principal differences might better become understood by the introduction of the word *election* into the discussion of questions of heredity. Election meant formerly the preferential choice of single individuals, while the derivation of the word selection points to a segregation of assemblies into their larger parts. Or to state it in a shorter way, individual selection is exactly what is usually termed election. Choosing one man from among thousands is to elect him, but a select party is a group of chosen persons. There would be no great difficulty in the introduction of the word election, as breeders are already in the habit of calling their choice individuals " élite," at least in the case of beets and of cereals.

This intra-specific selection affords a second point for the comparison between natural and artificial processes. This case is readily granted to be more difficult than the first, but there can be no doubt that the similarity is due to strictly comparable causes. In practice this process is scarcely second in importance to the selection between species, and in numerous cases it rests upon it, and crowns it, bringing the isolated forms up to their highest possible degree of usefulness. In nature it does quite the same, adapting strains of individuals to the local conditions of their environment. Improved races do not generally last very long in practice; sooner or later they are surpassed by new selections. Exactly so we may imagine the agency of natural intra-specific selection. It produces the local races, the marks of which disappear as soon as the special external conditions cease to act. It is responsible only for the smallest lateral branches of the pedigree, but has nothing in common with the evolution on the main stems. It is of very subordinate importance.

These assertions of course, are directly opposed to the current run of scientific belief, but they are supported by facts. A considerable part of the evidence has already been dealt with and for our closing discussion only an exact comparison remains to be made between the two detailed types of intra-specific selection. In coming to this I will first dwell upon some intermediate types and conclude with a critical discussion of the features of artificial selection, which to my mind prove the invalidity of the conclusions drawn from it in behalf of an explanation of the processes of nature.

Natural selection occurs not only in the wild state, but is also active in cultivated fields. Here it regulates the struggle of the selected varieties and improved races with the older types, and even with the wild species. In a previous lecture I have detailed the rapid increase of the wild-oats in certain years, and described the experiments of Risler and Rimpau in the running out of select varieties. The agency is always the same. The preferred forms, which give a larger harvest, are generally more sensitive to injurious influences, more dependent on rich manure and on adequate treatment. The native varieties have therefore the advantage, when climatic or cultural conditions are unfavorable for the fields at large. They suffer in a minor degree, and are thereby enabled to propagate themselves afterwards more rapidly and to defeat the finer types. This struggle for life is a constant one, and can easily be followed, whenever the composition of a strain is noted in successive years. It is well appreciated by breeders and farmers, because it is always liable to counteract their endeavors and to claim their utmost efforts to keep their races pure. There can be no doubt that exactly the same struggle exempt from man's intrusion is fought out in the wild state.

Local races of wild plants have not been the object for field-observations recently. Some facts however, are known concerning them. On the East Friesian Islands in the North Sea the flowers are strikingly larger and brighter colored than those of the same species on the neighboring continent. This local difference is ascribed by Behrens to a more severe selection by the pollinating insects in consequence of their lesser frequency on these very windy isles. Seeds of the pines from the Himalayas yield cold-resisting young plants if gathered from trees in a high altitude, while the seeds of the same species from lower regions yield more sensitive seedlings. Similar instances are afforded by *Rhododendron* and other mountain species. According to Cieslar corresponding differences are shown by seeds of firs and larches from alpine and lowland provinces.

Such changes are directly dependent on external influences. This is especially manifest in experiments extending the cultures in higher or in more northern regions. The shorter summer is a natural agent of selection; it excludes all individuals which cannot ripen their seeds during so short a period. Only the short-lived ones survive. Schübeler made very striking experiments with corn and other different cereals, and has succeeded in making their culture possible in regions of Norway where it formerly failed. In the district of Christiania, corn had within some few years reduced its lifetime from 123 to 90 days, yielding smaller stems and fewer kernels, but still sufficient to make its culture profitable under the existing conditions.

This change was not permanent, but was observed to diminish rapidly and to disappear entirely, whenever the Norwegian strain was cultivated in the southern part of Germany. It was a typical improved race, dependent on continual selection by the short summers which had produced it. Similar results have been reached by Von Wettstein in the comparison of kinds of flax from different countries. The analogy between such cultivated local races and the local races of nature is quite striking. The practice of seed-exchange rests for a large part on the experience that the characters, acquired under the definite climatic and cultural conditions of some select regions, hold good for one or two, and sometimes even more generations, before they decrease to practical uselessness. The Probstei, the Hanna and other districts owe their wealth to this temporary superiority of their wheat and other cereals.

Leaving these intermediate forms of selection, we now come to our principal point. It has already been discussed at some length in the previous lecture, but needs further consideration. It is the question whether intra-specific selection may be regarded as a cause of lasting and ever-increasing improvement. This is assumed by biologists who consider fluctuating variability as the main source of progression in the organic world. But the experience of the breeders does not support this view, since the results of practice prove that selection according to a constant standard soon reaches a limit which it is not capable of transgressing. In order to attain further improvements the method of selection itself must be improved. A better and sharper method assures the choice of more valuable representatives of the race, even if these must be sought for in far larger numbers of individuals, as is indicated by the law of Quetelet.

Continuous or even prolonged improvement of a cultivated race is not the result of frequently repeated selection, but of the improvement of the standard of appreciation. Nature, as far as we know, changes her standard from time to time only in consequence of the migrations of the species, or of local changes of climate. Afterwards the new standard remains unchanged for centuries.

Selection, according to a constant standard, reaches its results in few generations. The experience of Van Mons and other breeders of apples shows that the limit of size and lusciousness may be soon attained. Vilmorin's experiments with wild carrots and those of Carrière with radishes lead to the same conclusion as regards roots. Improvements of flowers in size and color are usually easy and rapid in the beginning, but an impassable limit is soon reached. Numerous other instances could be given.

Contrasted with these simple cases is the method of selecting sugar-beets. More than once I have alluded to this splendid example of the influence of man upon domestic races, and tried to point out how little support it affords to the current scientific opinion concerning the power of natural selection. For this reason it is interesting to see how a gradual development of the methods of selection has been, from the very outset, one of the chief aims of the breeders. None of them doubts that an improvement of the method alone is adequate to obtain results. This result, in the main, is the securing of a few per-cent more of sugar, a change hardly comparable with that progress in evolution, which our theories are destined to explain.

Vilmorin's original method was a very simple one. Polarization was still undiscovered in his time. He determined the specific weight of his beets, either by weighing them as a whole, or by using a piece cut from the base of the roots and deprived of its bark, in order to test only the sugar-tissues. The pieces were floated in solutions of salt, which were diluted until the pieces began to sink. Their specific weight at that moment was determined and considered to be a measure of the corresponding value of the beet. This principle was afterwards improved in two ways. The first was a selection after the salt-solution-method, but performed on a large scale. After some few determinations, a solution was made of such strength as to allow the greater number of the beets to float, and only the best to sink down. In large vessels thousands of beets could be tested in this way, to select a few of the very heaviest. The other improvement was the determination of the specific weight of the sap, pressed out from the tissue. It was more tedious and more expensive, but more direct, as the influence of the air-cavities of the tissue was excluded. It prepared the way for polarization.

This was introduced about the year 1874 in Germany, and soon became generally accepted. It allowed the amount of sugar to be measured directly, and with but slight trouble. Thousands of beets could be tested yearly by this method, and the best selected for the production of seed. In some factories a standard percentage is determined by previous inquiries, and the mass of the beets is tested only by it. In others the methods of taking samples and clearing the sap have been improved so far as to allow the exact determination of three hundred thousand polarization-values of beets within a few weeks. Such figures give the richest material for statistical studies, and at once indicate the best roots, while they enable the breeder to change his standard in accordance with the results at any time. Furthermore they allow the mass of the beets to be divided into groups of different quality, and to produce, besides the seeds for the continuation of the race, a first-class and second-class product and so on. In the factory of Messrs. Kuhn & Co., at Naarden, Holland, the grinding machine has been markedly improved, so as to tear all cell-walls asunder, open all cells, and secure the whole of the sap within less than a minute, and without heating.

It would take too long to go into further details, or to describe the simultaneous changes that have been applied to the culture of the élite strains. The detailed features suffice to show that the chief care of the breeder in this case is a continuous amelioration of the method of selecting. It is manifest that the progression of the race is in the main due to great technical improvements, and not solely to the repetition of the selection.

Similar facts may be seen on all the great lines of industrial selection. An increasing appreciation of all the qualities of the selected plants is the common feature. Morphological characters, and the capacity of yielding the desired products, are the first points that strike the breeder. The relation to climate and the dependence on manure soon follow, but the physiological and chemical sides of the problem are usually slow of recognition in the methods of selection. When visiting Mr. de Vilmorin at Paris some years ago, I inspected his laboratory for the selection of potatoes. In the method in use, the tubers were rubbed to pulp and the starch was extracted and measured. A starch-percentage figure was determined for each plant, and the selection of the tubers for planting was founded upon this result. In the same way wheat has been selected by Dippe at Quedlinburg, first by a determination of its nitrogenous contents in general, and secondly by the amount of the substances which determine its value for baking purposes.

The celebrated rye of Schlanstedt was produced by the late Mr. Rimpau in a similar manner and was put on the market between 1880 and 1890 and was received with great favor throughout central Europe, especially in Germany and in France. It is a tall variety, with vigorous stems and very long heads, the kernels of which are nearly double the size of those of the ordinary rye, and are seen protruding, when ripe, from between the scales of the spikelets. It is unfit for poor soils, but is one of the very best varieties for soils of medium fertility in a temperate climate. It is equal in the production of grain to the best French sorts, but far surpassing them in its amount of straw. It was perfected at the farm of Schlanstedt very slowly, according to the current conceptions of the period. The experiment was started in the year 1866, at which time Rimpau collected the most beautiful heads from among his fields, and sowed their kernels in his experiment-garden. From this first culture the whole race was derived. Every year the best ears of the strain were chosen for repeated culture, under experimental care, while the remainder was multiplied in a field to furnish the seeds for large and continually increasing areas of his farms.

Two or three years were required to produce the quantity of seed of each kind required for all the fields of Schlanstedt. The experiment-garden, which through the kindness of Mr. Rimpau I had the good fortune of visiting more than once between 1875 and 1878, was situated in the middle of his farm, at some distance from the dwellings. Of course it was treated with more care, and especially kept in better conditions of fertility than was possible for the fields at large. A continued study of the qualities and exigencies of the *élite* plants accompanied this selection, and gave the means of gradually increasing the standard. Resistance against disease was observed and other qualities were ameliorated in the same manner. Mr. Rimpau repeatedly told me that he was most anxious not to overlook any single character, because he feared that if any of them might become selected in the wrong way, perchance unconsciously, the whole strain might suffer to such a degree as to make all the other ameliorations quite useless. With this purpose the number of plants per acre was kept nearly the same as those in the fields, and the size of the culture was large enough every year to include the best kernels of quite a number of heads. These were never separated, and exact individual pedigrees were not included in the plan. This mixture seemed to have the advantage of keeping up an average value of the larger number of the characters, which either from their nature or from their apparent unimportance had necessarily to be neglected.

After ten years of continuous labor, the rye of Rimpau caught the attention of his neighbors, being manifestly better than that of ordinary sowings. Originally he had made his cultures for the improvement of his own fields only. Gradually however, he began to sell his product as seed to others, though he found the difference still very slight. After ten years more, about 1886, he was able to sell all his rye as seed, thereby making of course large profits. It is now acknowledged as one of the best sorts, though in his last letter Mr. Rimpau announced to me that the profits began to decline as other selected varieties of rye became known. The limit of productiveness was reached, and to surmount this, selection had to be begun again from some new and better starting point.

This new starting point invokes quite another principle of selection, a principle which threatens to make the contrast between artificial and natural selection still greater. In fact it is nothing new, being in use formerly in the selection of domestic animals, and having been applied by Vilmorin to his sugar-beets more than half a century ago. Why it should ever have been overlooked and neglected in the selection of sugar-beets now is not clear.

The principle in itself is very simple. It agrees that the visible characters of an animal or a plant are only an imperfect measure for its hereditary qualities, instead of being the real criterion to be relied upon, as is the current belief. It further reasons that a direct appreciation of the capacity of inheritance can only be derived from the observation of the inheritance itself. Hence it concludes that the average value of the offspring is the only real standard by which to judge the representatives of a race and to found selection upon.

These statements are so directly opposed to views prevalent among plant-breeders, that it seems necessary to deal with them from the theoretical and experimental, as well as from the practical side.

The theoretical arguments rest on the division of the fluctuating variability into the two large classes of individual or embryonic, and of partial deviations. We have dealt with this division at some length in the previous lecture. It will be apparent at once, if we choose a definite example. Let us ask what is the real significance of the percentage-figure of a single plant in sugar-beets. This value depends in the first place, on the strain or family from which the beet has been derived, but this primary point may be neglected here, because it is the same for all the beets of any lot, and determines the average, around which all are fluctuating.

The deviation of the percentage-figure of a single beet depends on two main groups of external causes. First come those that have influenced the young germs of the plant during its most sensitive period, when still an embryo within the ripening seed. They give a new limitation to the average condition, which once and forever becomes fixed for this special individual. In the second place the young seedling is affected during the development of its crown of leaves, and of its roots, by numerous factors, which cannot change this average, but may induce deviations from it, increasing or decreasing the amount of sugar, which will eventually be laid down in the root. The best young beet may be injured in many ways during periods of its lifetime, and produce less sugar than could reasonably be expected from it. It may be surpassed by beets of inferior constitution, but growing under more favorable circumstances.

Considered from this point of view the result of the polarization-test is not a single value, but consists of at least two different factors. It may be equal to the algebraic sum of these, or to their difference, according to whether the external conditions on the field were locally and individually favorable or unfavorable. A large amount of sugar may be due to high individual value, with slight subsequent deviation from it, or to a less prominent character combined with an extreme subordinate deviation.

Hence it is manifest that even the results of such a highly improved technical method do not deserve the confidence usually put in them. They are open to doubt, and the highest figures do not really indicate the best representatives of the race. In order to convey this conception to you in a still stronger manner, let us consider the partial variability as it usually shows itself. The various leaves of a plant may noticeably vary in size, the flowers in color, the fruits in flavor. They fluctuate around an average, which is assumed to represent the approximate value of the whole plant. But if we were allowed to measure only one leaf, or to estimate only one flower or fruit, and be compelled to conclude from it the worth of the whole plant, what mistakes we could make! We might indeed hit upon an average case, but we might as easily get an extreme, either in the way of increase or of decrease. In both cases our judgment would be badly founded. Now who can assure us that the single root of a given beet is an average representative of the partial variability? The fact that there is only one main root does not prove anything. An annual plant has only one stem, but a perennial species has many. The average height of the last is a reliable character, but the casual height of the former is very uncertain.

So it is with the beets. A beet may be divided by its buds and give quite a number of roots, belonging to the same individual. These secondary roots have been tested for the amount of sugar, and found to exhibit a manifest degree of variability. If the first root corresponded to their average, it might be considered as reliable, but if not anyone will grant that an average is more reliable than a single determination. Deviations have as a fact been observed, proving the validity of our assertion.

These considerations at once explain the disappointment so often experienced by breeders. Some facts may be quoted from the Belgian professor of agriculture at Gembloux, the late Mr. Laurent. He selected two beets, from a strain, with the exceptional amount of 23% sugar, but kept their offspring separate and analyzed some 60 of each. In both groups the average was only 11–12%, the extremes not surpassing 14–15%. Evidently the choice was a bad one, notwithstanding the high polarization value of the parent. Analogous cases are often observed, and my countrymen, Messrs. Kuhn & Co., go so far as to doubt all excessive variants, and to prefer beets with high, but less extraordinary percentages. Such are to be had in larger numbers and their average has a good chance of exemption from a considerable portion of the doubts adhering to single excessive cases.

It is curious to note here what Louis de Vilmorin taught concerning this point in the year 1850. I quote his own words: "I have observed that in experiments on heredity it is necessary to individualize as much as possible. So I have taken to the habit of saving and sowing separately the seeds of every individual beet, and I have always found that among the chosen parent-plants some had an offspring with a better average yield than others. At the end I have come to consider this character only, as a standard for amelioration."

The words are clear and their author is the originator of the whole method of plant-breeding selection. Yet the principle has been abandoned, and nearly forgotten under the impression that polarization alone was the supreme guide to be relied upon. However, if I understand the signs rightly, the time is soon coming when Vilmorin's experience will become once more the foundation for progress in breeding.

Leaving the theoretical and historical aspects of the problem, we will now recall the experimental evidence, given in a former lecture, dealing with the inheritance of monstrosities. I have shown that in many instances monstrosities constitute double races, consisting of monstrous and of normal individuals. At first sight one might be induced to surmise that the monstrous ones are the true representatives of the race, and that their seeds should be exclusively sown, in order to keep the strain up to its normal standard. One might even suppose that the normal individuals, or the so-called atavists, had really reverted to the original type of the species and that their progeny would remain true to this.

My experiments, however, have shown that quite the contrary is the case. No doubt, the seeds of the monstrous specimens are trustworthy, but the seeds of the atavists are not less so. Fasciated hawkweeds and twisted teasels gave the same average constitution of the offspring from highly monstrous, and from apparently wholly normal individuals. In other words the fullest development of the visible characteristic was not in the slightest degree an indication of better hereditary tendencies. In unfavorable years a whole generation of a fasciated race may exhibit exclusively normal plants, without transmitting a trace of this deficiency to the following generation. As soon as the suitable conditions return, the monstrosity reassumes its full development.

The accordance of these facts with the experience of breeders of domestic animals, and of Louis de Vilmorin, and with the result of the theoretical considerations concerning the factors of fluctuation has led me to suggest the method of selecting, which I have made use of in my experiments with tricotyls and syncotyls.

Seedling variations afford a means of counting many hundreds of individuals in a single germinating pan. If seed from one parent-plant is sown only in each pan, a percentage-figure for the amount of deviating seedlings may be obtained. These figures we have called the hereditary percentages. I have been able to select the parent-plants after their death on the sole ground of these values. And the result has been that from varieties which, on an average, exhibited 50 – 55% deviating seedlings, after one or two years of selection this proportion in the offspring was brought up to about 90% in most of the cases. *Phacelia* and mercury with tricotylous seedlings, and the Russian sunflower with connate seed-leaves, may be cited as instances.

Besides these tests, others were performed, based only on the visible characters of the seedlings. The result was that this characteristic was almost useless as a criterion. The atavists gave, in the main, nearly the same hereditary percentages as the tricotyls and syncotyls, and their extremes were in each case far better constituted than the average of the chosen type. Hence, for selection purposes, the atavists must be considered to be in no way inferior to the typical specimens.

If it had been possible to apply this principle to twisted and fasciated plants, and perhaps even to other monstrosities, I think that it will readily be granted that the chance of bringing even these races up to a percentage of 90% would have been large enough. But the large size of the cultures required for the counting of numerous groups of offspring in the adult state has deterred me from making such trials. Recently however, I have discovered a species, *Viscaria oculata* which allows of counting *twisted specimens* in the pans, and I may soon be able to obtain proofs of this assertion. The validity of the hereditary percentage as a standard of selection has, within the last few years, been recognized and defended by two eminent breeders, W. M. Hays in this country and Von Lochow in Germany. Both of them have started from the experience of breeders of domestic animals. Von Lochow applied the principle to rye. He first showed how fallacious the visible characters often are. For instance the size of the kernels is often dependent on their number in the head, and if this number is reduced by the injurious varietal mark of lacunae (Lückigkeit), the whole harvest will rapidly deteriorate by the selection of the largest kernels from varieties which are not quite free from this hereditary deficiency.

In order to estimate the value of his rye-plants, he gathers the seed of each one separately and sows them in rows. Each row corresponds to a parent-plant and receives 200 or 150 seeds, according to the available quantity. In this way from 700 to 800 parent-plants are tested yearly. Each row is harvested separately. The number of plants gives the average measure of resistance to frost, this being the only important cause of loss. Then the yield in grain and straw is determined and calculated, and other qualities are taken into consideration. Finally one or more groups stand prominent above all others and are chosen for the continuation of the race. All other groups are wholly excluded from the "élite," but among them the best groups and the very best individuals from lesser groups are considered adequate for further cultivation, in order to produce the commercial product of the race. As a matter of fact the rye of Von Lochow is now one of the best varieties, and even surpasses the celebrated variety of Schlanstedt. It was only after obtaining proof of the validity of his method that Von Lochow decided to give it to the public.

W. M. Hays has made experiments with wheat at the Minnesota Agricultural Experiment Station. He chose a hundred grains as a proper number for the appreciation of each parent-plant, and hence has adopted the name of "centgener power" for the hereditary percentage.

The average of the hundred offspring is the standard to judge the parent by. Experience shows at once that this average is not at all proportional to the visible qualities of the parent. Hence the conclusion that the yield of the parent-plant is a very uncertain indication of its value as a parent for the succeeding generation. Only the parents with the largest power in the centgener of offspring are chosen, while all others are wholly discarded. Afterwards the seeds of the chosen groups are propagated in the field until the required quantities of seed are obtained.

This centgener power, or breeding-ability, is tested and compared for the various parent-plants as to yield, grade, and percentage of nitrogenous content in the grain, and as to the ability of the plant to stand erect, resist rust, and other important qualities. It is evident that by this test of a hundred specimens a far better and much more reliable determination can be made than on the ground of the minutest examination of one single plant. From this point of view the method of Hays commands attention. But the chief advantage lies in the fact that it is a direct proof of that which it is desired to prove, while the visible marks give only very indirect information.

Thus the results of the men of practice are in full accordance with those of theory and scientific experiment, and there can be little doubt that they open the way for a rapid and important improvement. Once attained, progress however, will be dependent on the selection-principle, and the hereditary percentage, or centgener power or breeding-ability, must be determined in each generation anew. Without this the race would soon regress to its former condition.

To return to our starting point, the comparison of artificial and natural selection. Here we are at once struck by the fact that it is hardly imaginable, how nature can make use of this principle. In some measure the members of the best centgener will manifestly be at an advantage, because they contain more fit specimens than the other groups. But the struggle for existence goes on between individuals, and not between groups of brethren against groups of cousins. In every group the best adapted individuals will survive, and soon the breeding-differences between the parents must vanish altogether. Manifestly they can, as a rule, have no lasting result on the issue of the struggle for existence.

If now we remember that in Darwin's time this principle, breeding-ability, enjoyed a far more general appreciation than at present, and that Darwin must have given it full consideration, it becomes at once clear that this old, but recently revived principle, is not adequate to support the current comparison between artificial and natural selection.

In conclusion, summing up all our arguments, we may state that there is a broad analogy between breeding-selection in the widest sense of the word, including variety-testing, race-improvement and the trial of the breeding-ability on one side, and natural selection on the other. This analogy however, points to the importance of the selection between elementary species, and the very subordinate role of intraspecific selection in nature. It strongly supports our view of the origin of species by mutation instead of continuous selection. Or, to put it in the terms chosen lately by Mr. Arthur Harris in a friendly criticism of my views: " Natural selection may explain the survival of the fittest, but it cannot explain the arrival of the fittest.''

INDEX

A

Abies concolor fastigiata, 618
Acacia, 176, 196, 217, 458, 697
  bastard, 343, 617, 618, 664, 665, 666
Acer compestre nanum, 613
Achillea millefolium, 131, 132, 441
Adaptation, 702
  double, 430, 451, 452, 454, 455, 457, 458, 643
Aegilops ovata, 265
  speltaeformis, 265
Agave vivipara, 684
Ageratum coeruleum, 613
Agrostemma Coronaria bicolor, 125
  Githago, 282
  nicaeensis, 163
Agrotis, 204
Alder, cut-leaved, 147, 596
Alfalfa, 264
Algae, 699
Allen, Grant, 237
Alliaria, 638
Alnus glutinosa laciniata, 615
Alpine plants, 437, 695, 794
Althaea, 490
Amaranth, 282, 453
Amaranthus caudatus, 282
Amaryllis, 272, 275, 762
  brasiliensis, 275
  leopoldi, 275
  pardina, 275
  psittacina, 275
  vittata, 275
Amen-Hotep, 697
Ampelopsis, 239
Amygdalus persica laevis, 126

Anagallis arvensis, 162
Androsace, 634
Anemone, 266, 331
  coronaria, 241, 491 var. "Bride," 510
  magellanica, 266
  sylvestris, 266
Anemone, garden, 241
Année, 760
Anomalies, taxonomic, 658–685
Anthemis, 236
  nobilis, 130
Anthurium scherzerianum, 639
Antirrhinum majus, 315
  luteum rubro-striatum, 315
Apetalous flowers, 622
Apples, 134, 240, 328, 454, 806
  elementary species, 75
  method of cultivating, 76
  origin of cultivated varieties, 73
  use by the Romans, 74
  "Wealthy," 78, 79
  wild, 73, 74, 75, 76
Aquilegia chrysantha, 161
Arabis ciliata glabrata
  hirsuta glaberrima, 126
Aralia crassifolia, 663
Arbres fruitiers ou Pomonomie belge, 76
Aralia papyrifera, 663
Arctic flora, 695
Arnica, 494
  montana, 236
Aroids, 222, 631, 639
Artemisias, 131
Artificial selection, 18, 71, 77, 93, 95, 743, 744, 798–826

827

828 *Index*

first employed, 72, 92
nature of, 19
Arum maculatum immaculatum, 125
Ascidia, 310, 366, 367, 427, 428, 669, 670, 671, 672, 673, 674, 675
Ash, 135, 341
　one-bladed, 666, 667
　weeping, 196, 596
Ashe, 343
Aster, 132, 152, 242
　seashore, 200, 282*
Aster Tripolium, 132, 200, 236, 282, 410
Astragalus alpinus, 696
Atavism, 154, 170, 172, 175, 176, 178, 182, 185, 187, 188, 198, 220, 222, 226, 235, 344, 354, 399, 405, 411, 660, 661
　bud, 183, 226
　definition of, 170, 631
　false, 185, 187
　negative, 344
　positive, 344
　seed, 176
　systematic, 174, 222, 630–657
Atavists, 156, 201
　heredity of, 413
Atropa Belladonna lutea, 592
Aubretia, 241
Avena fatua, 100, 207
Azalea, 178, 323
Azolla caroliniana, 239

B

Babington, Manual of British Botany, 36
Bailey, 78, 306, 684
Balsams, 334
Bananas, 90, 134
Banyan, 244
Barberry, 133, 180
　European, 270
　purple, 596
Barbarea vulgaris, 427
Barley, 98, 105, 133, 203, 678, 679

"Nepaul," 203, 676, 677, 679, 681, 683
Bastard-acacia, 133, 136, 140
Bateson, 250
Bauhin, Caspar, 72, 610
Baumann, 618
Beans, 90, 152, 327, 727, 735
Bedstraw, 648
Beech, 133, 135, 243
　cut-leaved, 179, 196, 616
　laciniated, 196
　oak-leaved, 595
　purple, 196, 593, 595
Beeches, 427
　fern-leaved, 147
Beets, 68, 72, 92, 93, 792, 796, 801, 815, 817, 818
　Californian, 796
　European, 796
　forage, 71, 72, 791
　salad, 71
Beet-sugar, 67, 68, 69, 70, 71, 109, 165, 717, 791, 807, 813, 814
Begonia, 218, 366, 509, 765
　ever-flowering, 148
　tuberous, 272
　clarkii, 273
　davisii, 273
　rosiflora, 273
　sedeni, 273
　semperflorens, 133, 148, 620
Begonia
　bulbous, 372
　veitchi, 273
Behrens, 804
Belladonna, 145
Bellis perennis, 236
　perennis plena, 195
Bentham, 237
Bentham & Hooker
　Handbook of British Flora, 36
Berberis, 133, 180, 455
　ilicifolia, 270
　vulgaris, 270
Bertin, 596
Berula angustifolia, 457
Bessey, 660
Beta maritima, 69

patula, 69, 70
vulgaris, 69, 70
Betula, 133
Between-race, 358
Bewirkung, Theorie der directen (Nägeli), 448
Biastrepsis, 402
Bidens, 131
 atropurpurea, 131
 cernua, 131, 158
 leucantha, 131
 tripartita, 131
Bilberries, 577
Bindweed, 419, 424
Binomium, of Newton, 767
Birch, 133, 243
 cut-leaved, 596, 616
 fastigiate, 618
 fern-leaved, 179
Biscutella, 283
 laevigata glabra, 125
Bitter-sweet, 125
Blackberry, 268, 768
 "Paradox," 769
Blue-bells, variation in, 54, 491, 577
Blueberries, 769
Blue-bottle, 499, 507, 509, 510
Blueflag, atavism of, 173
Boehmeria, 675
 bilboa, 685
Bonnier, 439, 441, 442, 444, 451, 795
Boreau, 663
Brambles, 126, 127, 147, 239, 244, 245, 268, 740, 769, 663
Brassica, 244
Braun, 738
Braun and Schimper, 494
Bread-fruits, 90
Briot, 618
Britton and Brown's Flora, 162
Brooks, 711
Broom, 140
 prickly, 217
Broom-rape, 220
Broussonetia papyifera dissecta, 616

Brunella, 146, 268
 vulgaris, 577
 vulgaris alba, 201
Bryophyllum calycinum, 218
Buckwheat, 453
Bud-variation, 750
Buds, adventitious, 218
Burbank, Luther, 57, 79, 116, 134, 268, 758, 768, 769, 784
Buttercup, 331, 357, 410, 725, 740
 Asiatic, 241

C

Cabbages, 428, 684
 atavism in, 638
 origin of varieties, 621
Cactuses, 444
Cactus-dahlia, 625
Calamintha Acinos, 437, 453
Calamus root, 222
Calendula officinalis, 503
Calliopsis tinctoria, 195
Calluna, 146
 vulgaris, 437, 577
Caltha, 490
 palustris, 331
Camelina, 684
Camellia, 178, 323
 japonica, 368
Camellias, 331
Camomile, 130, 132, 156, 366, 494, 503, 509, 513
Campanula persicifolia, 161, 234
 rotundifolia, 437
Campion, 283, 302, 304
 evening, 281
 red, 238
Canna, 751, 759, 761
 indica, 760
 "Madame Crozy," 760, 761
 nepalensis, 760
 warczewiczii, 760
Capsella Bursa-pastoris apetala, 585
 heegeri, 22, 582, 583, 684
Carex, 53

Carnation, 178, 241, 491
  wheat-ear, 227
Carpinus Betulus heterophylla, 180
Carrière, 491, 596, 612, 806
Carrots, 806
Catch-fly, 419
Carboniferous period, 699
Casuarina quadrivalvis, 649
Cauliflowers, origin of, 621
Caumzet, 614
Causation, theory of direct, (Nägeli), 448
Cedar, pyramidal, 618
Celandine, 147, 245, 280, 365
  oak-leaved, 603, 610, 611
Celosia, 621
Celosia cristata, 327, 411
Centaurea, 242
Centgener power, 20, 823
Centranthus macrosiphon, 424
Cephalotaxus, 170, 220
  pedunculata fastigiata, 169
Cereals, 105, 106, 107, 119, 801, 804
  origin of cultivation, 104
Character-units, 633
Charlock, 424
Cheiranthus, 490
  Cheiri, 370
  Cheiri gynantherus, 371
Chelidonium laciniatum, 22, 609
  majus, 147, 365, 600, 610, 611
  majus foliis queznis, 610
Cherries, 79
Cherry, bird's, 617
Chestnuts, 427
Chromosomes, 306
Chrysanthemum, 178, 274
  corn, 739
Chrysanthemum carinatum, 494
  coronarium, 161, 202, 510
  grandiflorum, 739
  imbricatum, 494
  indicum, 490
  inodorum, 503

  inodorum plenissimum, 366
  new double, 501
  segetum, 202, 493, 504, 729
  segetum, var. *grandiflorum*, 43, 495, 498, 504, 504
Chrysopogon montanus, 450
Cieslar, 804
Cineraria cruenta, 514
Cinquefoil, 53
Clarkia, 420
  elegans, 198
  pulchella, 282
  pulchella carnea, 163
Clematis Vitalba, 663
  Viticella nana, 613
Clover, 80, 102, 674
  crimson (Italian), 353, 358, 359, 360
  five-leaved, 340, 362, 374, 431, 509, 789
  four-leaved, 340, 346, 353
  red, 235, 281
  white, 133, 366
Clusius, 610
Cochlearia anglica, 52
  danica, 52
  officinalis, 52
Coconut, 67, 82, 83, 87, 88, 89
  dispersal of, 85, 89
  geographic origin of, 88, 89
Coconut palm, 84, 88
Cockerell, T. D. A., 139, 140, 591
Cocklebur, 139
Cockscomb, 165, 327, 356, 411, 621
Cocos nucifera stupposa, 83, 84
  cupuliformis, 83
  rutila, 83
Codiaeum appendicularum, 673
Colchium, 490
Coleus, 133
Columbine, 725
  yellow, 161
Columbus, 89, 118
Columella, 106

Composites, 130, 131, 336, 723, 778
Conifers, 168, 226, 239, 455
  weeping, 617
Connation, of petals, 660, 661
"Conquests," 243
Contra-selection, 425
Cook, 84, 86, 88, 89
Corn, 81, 90, 118, 119, 135, 283, 287, 288, 775, 786, 788, 804
  American, 205
Corn-cockle, 163
Corn-chrysanthemum, 739
Corn-flowers, 491, 493
Corn, "Forty-day," 118
  "Harlequin," 327
  sterile variety of, 623
  sugar, 135. 158
  "Tuscarora." 205
Corn-marigold, 493, 494
Cornel berry, yellow, 196
Cornaceae, 675
Cornu, 338
Cornus Mas, 196
Correlation, 143
Corylus, 133
  Avellana, 181
  tubulosa, 181
Cotton, 725
Cotyledon, 674
  variation in, 416
Crambe maritima, 621
Cranesbill, 599
  European, 628
  meadow, 323
Crataegus, 196
  oxyacantha, 133
Crowfoot, 331
  corn, 283
Crepis biennis, 410, 411
Cress, Indian, 193
Crosses
  bisexual, 255, 276, 294, 298
  reciprocal, 279
  unisexual, 255, 261
  varietal (see Hybrids).
Croton, 673, 674
Crozy, 760, 762
Crucifers, 222, 635

Cryptomeria, 169, 226
  japonica, 239
Cucumbers, 118
Cucumis, 52
Cucurbita, 52
Cultivated plants, 65, 66
  elementary species of, 63
  improvement of, 92
  mixed nature of, 96, 118
  origin of, 91
Currants, 79
  Californian, 270
  flowering, 166
  "Gordon's," 270
  Missouri, 270
  white, 158
  white-flowered, 167
Cuttings, 721
Cyclamen, 323, 355, 627, 684
  Butterfly, 627
  vernum, 619
Cypripedium caudatum, 487
Cytisus adami, 271
  candicans Attleyanus, 367
  Laburnum, 271
  prostratus, 139
  prostratus ciliata, 125
  purpureus, 271
  spinescens, 139

D

Dahlia, 131, 241, 272, 625
  cactus, 625
  "Jules Chrétien," 628
  purple-leaved, 626
  "surprise," 230
  tubular, 627
  274, 490, 764
  first double ones, 490
  green, 227, 229, 230
Daisies, 131, 132, 494
  double, 195
  hen-and-chicken, 514
  ox-eye, 202
  Shasta, 769
  yellow, 202
Dandelion, 411
  parthenogenesis, 61
  variations in, 60

Daphne Mezereum, 146
Darwin, 1, 2, 3, 4, 5, 6, 7,
  18, 76, 85, 93, 109, 110,
  180, 196, 205, 206, 242,
  306, 324, 338, 448, 571,
  604, 612, 689, 702, 710,
  715, 743, 798, 825
Darwin, George, 711
Darwinian theory, 461
  basis of, 5
Date, 134
Datura Stramonium, 139, 142
  Stramonium inermis, 300
  Tatula, 139, 142, 300
Dead-nettle, 237
De Bary, 38, 47, 49
De Candolle, 76, 84, 85, 89,
  228, 370, 403, 621
  Alphonse, 74, 129, 226
  A. P., 129
  Casimir, 659, 676
De Graaff, 275
Delphinium Ajacis, 192
Deniau, 617
Descent, theory of, 690, 694,
  702, 707, 716, 798
De Serres, Olivier, 72
Desmodium gyrans, 655, 656,
  663, 664, 65
Dewberry, California, 269
Dianthus barbatus, 322, 648
  twisted variety, 408
Diatoms, 699
Dictoyledons
  ancestors of monocotyledons, 15
Digitalis parviflora, 161, 640
  purpurea, 483
  pelorism of, 483
Dimorphism, 445, 447, 454,
  457, 458
Dippe, 810
Dipsacus fullonum, 402
  sylvestris, 402, 403
Dominant character, 280
Double flowers
  poppies 490
  production of, 489
  types of, 330
Double races (see also ever-

sporting varieties), 419,
  427, 428
Dubois, Eugène, 712
Duchesne, 185, 188, 596
Duckweed, 222
Draba, 692, 693
  verna, 47, 50, 51, 53, 125,
  126, 518, 533, 546, 547,
  561
Dracocephalum moldavicum,
  419
Dragon-head, 419
Drosera anglica, 268
  filiformis, 268
  intermedia, 268
  obovata, 267
  rotundifolia, 268

E

Earth, age of, 710
Edelweiss, 438
Eichler, 660
Election, 801
Electric light, growth in, 442
Elementary species, 11, 13, 32,
  67, 74, 76, 77, 78, 79, 91,
  95, 116, 119, 124, 126,
  128, 129, 207, 238, 252,
  256, 307, 430, 435, 695,
  696, 698, 702, 715, 787,
  798, 800, 825
  apples, 75
  coconut, 82
  corn, 81
  cultivated plants, 63
  definition of, 12, 35, 127
  flax, 80
  how produced, 16, 248
  hybrids of, 253, 255
  mutation of, 141
  origin of, 459, 603
  origin of, how studied, 463
  selection of, 92
  varieties vs., 14, 15, 141,
  152, 224, 243, 247, 251,
  495
Elm, 136, 219, 239, 427
Epilobium, 268
  hirsutum, 683

hirsutum cruciatum, 588
montanum, 269
tetragonum, 269
Equisetum Telmateja, 642, 649
Erica Tetralix, 577, 661
Ericaceae, 146, 660
Erigeron asteroides, 450
canadensis, 132, 236, 453, 600, 695
Erodium, 146
Erodium cicutarium album, 161
Erucastrum, 630, 638, 639
pollichii, 222, 637
Eryngium campestre, 674
maritimum, 674
Erysimum cheiranthoides, 638
Erythraea pulchella, 453
Erythrina, 621
Crista-galli, 620
Eschcholtzias, 59
Esimpler, 337
Eucalyptus citriodora, 669
Globulus, 217
Euphorbia Ipecacuanha, 55
Evening-primrose, 62, 204, 256, 424, 686, 687, 688, 690, 691, 694, 695, 699, 702, 703, 705, 707, 708, 713, 747, 793
Evolution, 93, 685, 686, 689, 704, 707, 709, 710, 713, 718
degressive, 222, 223, 249
progression in, 630
progressive, 221, 222, 223, 248
regression in, 630
regressive, 221, 222, 223, 249
retrograde, 221, 631
Extremes, asexual multiplication of, 742, 769

F

Fabre, 265
Fagus, 133

Fagus sylvatica pectinata, 179
Fan, genealogical, 700
Fasciated stems, 409, 413
Ferns, 63
cristate, 427
plumose, 427
Ficaria, 53
Ficus radicans, 436
religiosus, 244
repens, 436
stipulata, 436
ulmifolia, 436
Figs, 436
Filago, 53
Fir, 134, 804
Fittest, survival of, 826
Flax, 80, 805
springing, 80
threshing, 80
white-flowered, 158, 160
Fleabane, Canada, 132, 236, 600
Flowers, gamopetalous, 660
Fluctuability
embryonic, see individual
Fluctuation, 708, 715, 716, 718, 719, 724, 737, 741
curves of, 729, 734
defined, 191
individual, 718, 723, 732, 741, 745, 749, 788
mutation vs. 7, 16, 719
partial, 718, 723, 732, 741, 745, 748, 749, 771
inadequate for evolution, 18
in elementary species, 19
nature of, 18
specific and varietal characters vs. 17
Forget-me-not, 368
Fothergill, John, 521
Foxglove, 163
peloric, 164, 356, 367
yellow, 161, 640
Fraxinus excelsior monophylla, 667
exheterophylla, 667
simplicifolia, 667

French flora (Grenier and Godron), 433
Fries
 on *Hieracium*, 60
Frostweed, 440
 species of, 53
Fuchsia, 272, 355
Fuchsias, 491

G

Gaertner, 279
Galeopsis Ladanum canescens, 139
Galium, 648
 Aparine, 409, 648
 elatum, 52
 erectum, 52
 Mollugo, 52
 verum, 648
Gallesio, 138
Galton, 736, 776
Gamopetaly, 663
Garden-pansy, origin of, 38
Garlic, 638
Gauchery, 453
Geikie, 711
Genera
 artificial character of, 36
 polymorphous, 693
Gentiana punctata concolor, 125
Gentians, 577
Georgics (Vergil), 106
Geranium pratense, 323, 628
 album, 628
 pyreniacum, 599
German flora (Koch), 433
Geum, 282
Gherkins, 118
Gideon, Peter M., 78
Glacial period, 696
Gladiolus, 241, 272, 274, 368, 765
 cardinalis, 275
 gandavensis, 275
 psittacinus, 275
 purpureo-auratus, 275
Glaucium, 241
Gleditschia sinensis, 614

triacanthos pendula, 617
Gloxinia, 282, 485
 erect, 626
Gloxinia erecta, 485
 peloric variety, 485
Gnaphalium Leontopodium, 438
Godetia amoena, 161
Godetias, 59, 232
Godron, 265, 433
Goeppert, 370
Gooseberry, 79, 140, 626
 red, 133, 165, 241
Grapes, 90, 158, 328
Grape-hyacinth, plumosa, 134
Grasses, 102, 631, 681
Grenier, 433
Groundsel, 132
Growth, nutrition and, 714, 720, 722
Guelder-rose, 134, 239
Gum-tree, Australian, 217
Gypsophila paniculata
 twisted variety, 409

H

Haeckel, 707
Half-races, 358, 372, 409, 419, 424, 427, 428
Hall, 444
Hallet, F. F., 109
Harebell, 232
 peach-leaved, 234
Harris, Arthur, 825
Harshberger, John W., 591
 on *Euphorbia* in New Jersey, 55
Hawksbeard, 410, 411, 412
Hawkweed, 411 439, 443, 819
Hawkweeds.
 seeding without fertilization, 61
Hawthorn, white, 133
Hays, W. M.
 on individual selection, 20, 94, 95, 117, 821, 823, 824
Hazelnut, 133, 181, 243
Hazels, cut-leaved, 596, 616
Heath family, 146, 222, 660

Heaths, origin of, 662
Heather, 577
Hedera Helix arborea, 437
Hedgehog burweed, 140
Hedysarum, 664
Heeger, 582
Heer, Oswald, 74, 105
Heinricher, 172, 173, 174
Helianthemum, 53, 125, 126, 561
 apenninum, 53
 pilosum, 53
 polifolium, 53
 pulverulentum, 53
 vulgare, 440
Helichrysum, 420
Helwingia, 678, 678, 683
 rusciflora, 675
Hemp, 419
Henbane, 283
Hepatica, 322, 490
Heredity, 731, 734, 818
 bearers of, 632
 in teasels, 643
Hesperis, 241, 322
 matronalis, 323, 411
Heylandia latebrosa, 450
Hibiscus Moscheutos, 591
Hieracium, 59, 439
 alpinum, 696
Hildebrand, 160, 240, 241
Hoffman, 160, 663
Hofmeister, 160, 370, 480
Holbein, 164, 596
Holly, 140, 196
Holtermann, 449, 451
Hollyhock, 427
Honeysuckle, 674
 ground, 443
Hordeum distichum, 677
 hexastichum, 677, 678
 tetrastichum, 677
 trifurcatum, 676, 678
 vulgare trifurcatum, 203
Hornbeam, European, 180
Horse-chestnut, 219
 thornless, 234
Horsetail, Canadian, 695
 European, 649

Horsetail, family, 641
Horse-weed, 132
 Canadian, 453
Hortensia, 134, 181
Horticulture, mutations in, 604
Houseleek, 370, 371
Hunneman, John, 521
Hyacinths, 178, 323
 white, 160
Hybrids, 58, 201, 202, 206, 250, 575
 between elementary species, 253
 constant, 263, 264, 265, 266, 267, 268, 269
 law of varietal, 716
 Mendelian, 324
 nature of, 20
 species, 256, 260
 splitting of, 210
 varietal, 208, 209, 247 277, 278, 279, 281, 285, 293, 294
Hybridization, 706, 751, 752, 758, 759, 764
Hydrocotyle, 668
Hyoscyamus niger, 283
 pallidus, 283
Hypericum perforatum, 725
Hyssopus officinalis, 161

I

Iberis umbellata rosea, 195
Improved races, inconstancy of
Indian cress, 668
 pelorism of, 485
Indian pipe, 661
Ipecac spurge, 55
Iris, 456
 falcifolia, 173
 kaempferi, 174
 lortetii, 521
 pallida, 173
 pallida abavia, 681
Isolation, 108
Ivy, 436

J

Jacob's ladder, 200, 202
Jacques, 614
Jacquin, 52, 633
Jäggi, 594, 595
Jaeger, 228, 663
Jalappa, 165
Janczewski, 266
Japanese plum, 58
Jasminum Sambac, 663
Joly, 712
Jordan, Alexis, 45, 47, 49, 50, 129
  experiments with species, 37, 40
Juncus effusus spiralis, 684
Juniper, 684

K

Kapteyn, 716
Kelvin, Lord, 710, 711
Kerner von Marilaun, 266, 267
Keteleer, 618
Knight, 390, 719, 720
Koch, 433, 667
Koelreuter, 279
Korshinsky, 609, 612, 614, 617, 667
Krelage, 510, 619
Kuhn & Co., Messrs., 801, 809, 817

L

Labiates, 237
  pelories of, 577
Labiatiflorae, pelorism of, 468
Labrador tea, 661
Laburnum, 270, 284, 343
  oak-leaved 147, 179
  pelorism of, 485
Lactuca, 52
  Scariola, 456
Lagasca, Mariano, 96, 97, 114
Lamarck, 1, 447, 461, 522, 523
Lamarckism
  objections to, 449
Lamium album, 237
  maculatum, 237
  pelorism of, 486
  purpureum, 237
Larch, 804
Larkspur, 124, 192, 311, 452
  hybrid, 213
  white, 160
Latency, 657
  individual, 219
  specific, 246
  systematic, 219, 220, 235
  varietal, 246
Latent characters, 216
Lathyrus odoratus, 776
Laurea pinnatifida, 450
Laurel, lady's, 146
Laurent, 802
Leaves, cleft, 685
  variegated, 426, 431
LeBrun, Mme., 614
Le Couteur, 96, 97, 107, 108, 114, 115, 116, 743
Ledum, 222, 661
Lemna, 222
Lemoine, 762, 763
Lettuce, 684
  crisped, 158
  prickly, 456
Life, struggle for, 103, 119, 120
Lilacs, 59, 769
  double, 762
Lilium candidum flore pleno, 331
  pardalium, 116
Lime-tree, 355, 366, 428, 669
  fern-leaved, 147
Linaria, 467, 471, 480
  dalmatica, 482
  genistifolia, 267
  italica, 267
  vulgaris, 267, 471
  vulgaris peloria, 464
Lindley, 63, 129, 506
Linnaeus, 32, 33, 129, 132, 256, 663
  on the idea of species, 11, 13

on origin of species, 2, 34
on primroses, 52
Linum angustifolium, 80
  crepitans, 81
  usitatissimum, 80, 161
Link, 466
Liver-leaf, 322
Lobelia syphilitica, 161
Lonicera etrusca, 640
  tartarica nana, 614
Lorenz, Chr., 482
Lothelier, 454
Lotus corniculatus, 443
  cornioulatus hirsutus, 139
Loudon, 615, 616, 667
Lucerne, 264
Ludwig, 738
Lupines, 90
Lychnis, 283
  chalcedonica, 161
  diurna, 238, 578
  preslii, 578
  vespertina, 238, 281, 585
Lycium, 455
Lycopersicum, 655
  grandifolium, 654
  latifolium (see *L. grandifolium*).
  solanopsis, 654, 656
  validum (see *L. solanopsis*)
Lyell, 1, 710
Lysimachia vulgaris, 684

M

MacDougal, D. T., 62, 575, 590
Macfarlane, 56, 255, 268
Madia elegans, 779
Magnolia, 355, 366, 428, 674, 675
  obovata, 355, 669
Magnus, 228
Mahonia aquifolia, 270
Maize, 134, 775
  " Cuzco," 152
  European, 206
  " Gracillima," 152
  " Horse-dent," 152
  " Quarantino," 118

Mallow, 663, 684
Malva crispa, 684
Maples, laciniate, 615
Marchant, 592
Marigold, 131, 158
  corn, 729
  field, 503, 505, 508
  garden, 503
  Japanese, 490, 494, 495
Marsh-marigold, 331
Martinet, 80
Massart, 434
Masters, 228, 370, 372
Matricaria Chamomilla, 130
  Chamomilla discoidea, 156
Matricaria discoidea, D. C., 157
May-thorn, red, 196
Medicago media, 264
  falcata, 264
Melanium, 39
Melons, 118
Mendel, 6, 210, 294, 296, 306, 308
Mendel's law, 276, 293, 294, 298, 299, 300, 301, 307, 611, 613, 616, 716
Mendelism, 307
Mentha, 52
Mercurialis annua, 420
  annua laciniata, 592
Mercury, 420, 422, 425, 820
Methods of investigation, 21
Metzger, 205, 206
Milde, 38
Milfoil, 441
Millardet, 266
Miller, 611
Millet, 105
Mimulus, 151
  quinquevulnerus, 725
Mimusops, 697
Miocene period, 698
Miquel, 83
Mirabilis, 241
  Jalappa, 322
Mirbel, 615
Monardella macrantha, 444
Monstrosities, 400, 401, 445, 446, 447

Monkey-flower, 725
Monocotyledons
    ancestry of, 15
    regression in, 630
Monotropa, 222, 661
Morphologic units, 145, 153
Monstrosities, 818
Morgan
    on mutation-theory, 9
Morren, 244, 763
Mountain-ash, 342
Müller, Fritz, 775, 776, 780
Multiplication, vegetative (see Asexual propagation).
Munting, Abraham, 164, 165, 490, 762
Munting's drawings, 512
Murr, 158, 236
Muscari comosum, 134
Muséum d'Histoire Naturelle, Paris, 522
Mutability vs. fluctuating variability, 568
Mutation, 659, 674, 677, 685, 686, 694, 713, 716, 825
    absence of intermediate steps in, 474, 480
    conditions for observing, 601
    decided within the seed, 28
    definition of, 7
    easily observed, 30
    experimental, 688
    few observations of, 8
    fluctuation vs., 7, 16, 719
    influence of on variability, 335
    iterative nature of, 476, 703
    laws of, 556, 558, 560, 562, 564, 566, 568, 570
    limited in time, 29
    observation of, 16
    in *Oenothera*, 521, 525, 690
    oldest known, 609
    oldest recorded, 22
    periodic, 690, 692, 694
    perodicity of, 519
    progressive, 307
    repetition of, 476
    in *Saponaria calabrica*, 612
    simultaneous, 614
    in tomato, 655
Mutations, 141, 275, 280, 445, 449, 573, 608, 620, 626, 678, 685, 686, 701, 704, 712, 713, 716, 800
    artificial, 402
    chance for useful, 598
    defined, 191
    frequency of, 597
    in garden-flowers, 488
    in horticulture, 604, 706
    latent, 703
    mode of appearance, 517
    numerical proportion of, 475
    original production of, 703
    peloric, 707
    periodic, 686, 705
    progressive, 704
    retrograde, 704
    stray, 704, 705, 706
    synonyms of, 191
Mutation-period, 714
Myosotis azorica, 368
Myrtus communis, 684

N

Nägeli, 60, 439, 443, 448, 795
Nägelian principle, 448, 450, 451
Natural selection, 18, 119, 120, 445, 456, 682, 694, 703, 743, 744, 798-826
    basis, 604
    nature of, 6, 19
Naudin, 118
Nectarines, 137, 138, 226, 627
Němec, 578
Neo-Lamarckians
    principle of, 8
Neo-Lamarckism 447
Nepenthes, 671, 672, 673, 674
Newton, 1, 732, 767
Nicandra, 152
Nigella, 134
Nightshade, 298
    black, 282

Nourishment
  meaning of, 733
  variability and 771
Nuphar, 268
Nutrition and growth, 720, 722
Nymphaea, 698

O

Oats, 98, 100, 101, 105, 112, 113, 115, 119, 133, 453
  " Early Angus," 115
  " Early Fellow," 115
  " Fine Fellow," 115
  " Hopetown," 112
  " Longfellow," 115
  " Make-him-rich," 113
  wild, 207, 803
Oak, 136, 239
Oenothera, 260, 262, 279, 700, 706, 708, 709
  European species, source of, 575
  mutation in, 521, 525, 585, 690, 708
  new species of, 516–546
  albida, 537, 553, 555, 563, 565, 573
  biennis, 62, 205, 256, 257, 258, 259, 262, 263, 264, 521, 524, 527, 574, 575, 586, 587, 683, 690, 708
  biennis cruciata, 22, 587
  brevistylis, 263, 280, 526, 529, 530, 547, 563, 564, 565, 573, 574, 702, 706
  cruciata, 575, 585, 586, 589, 590, 683
  elliptica, 540, 545, 555, 563
  gigas, 533, 534, 535, 536, 537, 553, 554, 563, 565, 566, 567, 573, 574, 703
  glauca, 424
  hirtella, 263
  laevifolia, 526, 528, 529, 547, 563, 564, 573, 574, 701, 706
  lamarckiana, 17, 262, 263, 522, 523, 527, 528, 529, 533, 574, 575, 586, 690, 699
    pollination of, 524.
  lata, 540, 541, 542, 549, 550, 551, 552, 555, 559, 563, 566, 573, 574, 703
  leptocarpa, 540
  muricata, 256, 257, 258, 259, 262, 263, 264, 513, 575, 690
    pollination of, 524.
  nanella, 526, 531, 549, 50, 551, 552, 555, 563, 564, 565, 566, 703
  oblonga, 537, 538, 552, 555, 563, 565, 566, 573
  rubrinervis, 533, 534, 536, 537, 550, 551, 552, 555, 563, 565, 568, 573, 574
  scintillans, 540, 543, 553, 555, 563, 566, 573, 574
    mutability of, 544
  semilata, 540
  suaveolens, 521
Oleander, 684
Onagra, 262, 708, 709
Onions, wild, 684
Ononis repens, 577
Orange, 90, 133, 134
Orchids, 631
Origin of species (Darwin) 109
Orobanche, 220
Othonna crassifolia, 443
Otin, 618
Oviedo, 89

P

Paeonia corallina leiocarpa, 126
Paillat, 618
Pangenes, 306
Pangenesis, 306, 689
Panicum, 105
Pansies, 640
Pansy, 118, 121
Papaver alpinum, 139
  bracteatum, 661
  bracteatum monopetalum, 661

commutatum, 357
dubium glabrum, 126
hybridum, 663
somniferum Danebrog, 163
somniferum monstruosum, 371
somniferum polycephalum, 371
Parris, 754
Parsley
crisped, 158, 181
Parsnip, water, 457
Pea-family, 344
Peach, 138, 226, 240
Peach-almond, 769
Pears, 79, 90, 134, 147, 152, 203, 283
Pearson, Karl, 716
Peas, sugar, 135, 158
Pedicularis, 410
palustris, 410
Pedigree-culture, 109
experimental, 547
Pelargonium, 272, 355
Peloria, definition of, 164
Peloric toad-flax
first record of, 466
origin of, 459, 464, 473
sterility of, 467
Pelorism
Antirrhinum majus (see snapdragon).
Digitalis purpurea, 483
Gloxinia, 484, 485
labiates, 486
Laburnum, 485
Lamium, 486.
Linaria, see Toad-flax
Linaria dalmatica, 482
Linaria vulgaris, 464
orchids, 479, 486, 487
Salvia, 486
Scrophularia nodosa, 486
snapdragon, 481
toad-flax, 459-487
Tropaeolum majus, 485
Uropedium Lindenii, 487
wild sage, 486
Peltaria alliacea, 663

Pennywort, marsh, 668
Penzig, 638
Periodicity, law of, 365, 368, 721, 722
Periods, mutative, 706, 708
Periwinkles, 322
Persicaria, water, 433, 434, 435, 643
Petalomany, 330
Petunia, 491, 626
Phacelia, 420, 422, 820
Phaseolus lunatus, 592
multiflorus, 202
nanus, 202
Phleum alpinum, 696
Phlox, 232
drummondi, 161
Phyllonoma ruscifolia, 676
Physiologic units, 144, 153, 249
Picris hieracioides, 411
Pimpernel, scarlet, 162
Pinacothec, Munich, 164
Pine, 368, 804
Pine-apples, 90, 134
Pinks, 178
Pinus sylvestris, 368
Pistillody in poppies, 369, 370, 372
Pitcher-plants, 671
Plankton, 711
Plantago, 53
lanceolata, 520, 671, 684
Plantain, 684
Plater, 610
Plum, 79, 134, 769
beach, 58
Japanese, 58
purple-leaved, 619
Plusia, 204
Poa alpina vivipara, 684
Podocarpus koraiana, 169
Polemonium coeruleum, 282
coeruleum album, 200
dissectum, 161, 202
Polygala, 242
Polygonum amphibium, 433
var. *natans* Moench, 433, 434

var. *terrestris* Moench, 433, 434
Convolvulus, 419, 424
viviparum, 684
Polymorphy, 188
Pomegranate, 90
Pond-lily, yellow, 268
Poplar, fastigiate, 623, 624
  Italian, 623
Populus italica, 623
  nigra, 624
Poppy, 146, 151, 152, 163, 165, 241, 356, 640, 723
  " Danebrog," 283, 291
  garden, 661
  " Mephisto," 283, 291
  opium, 89, 189, 195, 198, 282, 291, 369, 371, 373, 379, 383, 391, 405, 406, 420, 452, 720, 789
  pistillody in, 369
  pistillofd, 508
  polycephalous, 405
Potatoes, 765, 810
Potentilla Tormentilla, 53
Pre-Linnean attitude, 2
Primrose, 268, 372, 410
  evening (see evening-primrose)
Primula acaulis, 52, 633
  elatior, 52, 633, 635
  grandiflora, 268
  imperialis, 697
  japonica, 410
  officinalis, 52, 268, 633, 635
  variabilis, 268
  veris, 52, 633, 634
Prodromus (De Candolle) 370
Progression, 430, 705, 774, 775, 777, 779, 805
  in evolution, 630
Propagation
  asexual, 745, 751, 766, 767, 770, 774, 777
  sexual, 745, 777
  vegetative (see asexual).
Proskowetz, Em. von, 70
Prototype
  definition of, 170

Prunus, 52
  cerasifera, 619
  Mahaleb, 617
  nana, 613
  maritima
  Padus, 617
  Pissardi, 619
  variation in, 56
Pyrethrum roseum, 511
Pyrola, 222, 661

Q

Quartile, 736, 737, 767
Quercus pedunculata fastigata, 596
Quetelet's law, 463, 716, 717, 725, 730, 734, 738, 748, 753, 759, 767, 775, 779, 780, 806

R

Races, inconstancy of improved, 770–797
Raciborsky, 682
Radishes, 325, 806
Ragwort, tansy, 157
Raisins, 134
Rameses, 697
Ranunculus, 331
  acris, 331
  arvensis, 283
  arvensis inermis, 125
  asiaticus, 241
  bulbosus, 357, 410, 740
Ra-n-Woser, King, 104
Raphanus Raphanistrum, 202, 424, 520
  caudatus, 202
Rasor, John, 588, 589
Raspberry, 268, 768
  " Phenomenal," 268
  " Primus," 269
  Siberian, 269
Ratzeburg, 467
Raunkiaer
  on variation in *Taraxacum*, 60
Recessive character, 280

Regression, 95, 630, 705, 732, 774, 775, 777, 779, 789
Retrogression, 430
Reversion, 155, 167, 170
  atavistic, 199
  bud, 167, 168, 183, 284
  definition of, 166
  seed, 175
  significance of, 215
Reversionists, 156
Rhingia, 173
Rhododendron, 804
Rhododendron ferrugineum, 267
  hirsutum, 267
  intermedium, 267
  ponticum, 661
Ribes, 170, 226, 625
  aureum, 270
  sanguineum, 166, 270
  scarlet, 166
  Uva-crispa, 140
Rice, crown, 133
Ricinus, 139
Rimpau, 69, 70, 94, 98, 99, 207, 792, 803, 810, 811, 812, 813
Risler, 99, 207, 803
Rivett, 98, 99
Riviere, 134
Robinia Pseud-Acacia, 133, 343, 664
  Pseud-Acacia monophylla, 196
Robinson, B. L., 590
Rose, 126, 127, 152, 178, 233
Rose, corn, 282
  moss, 627
Rose, 610, 611
Rosen, 38, 47
Rothamstead, 102
Rubia tinctorum, 410
Rubus flexuosus, 663
  fruticosus, 268
  idaeus, 268
  odoratus, 663
Rudberg, 466
Rumex scutatus, 139
Ruscus, 676

Rye, 105, 410, 453, 810, 813, 821, 822

S

Sagina apetala, 52
  patula, 52
Sagittaria japonica, 671
Salix alba, 267
  Ehrhartiana, 267
  pentandra, 267
Salpiglossis sinuata, 622
Salter, Bell, 269
Salvia, 242
  pelorism of, 486
  sylvestris, 161
Sambucus niger laciniata 616
  racemosa laciniata, 616
Saponaria calabrica, 612
  officinalis, 409, 663
Sarracenia, 672
Saxifraga crassifolia, 366
  umbrosa, 684
Saxifrage, 366
Scabiosa, 514
Schimper, 663, 738
Schimper (Braun and), 494
Schindler, 70
Schlanstedt, 822
Schübeler, 805
Scirpus lacustris, 684
Scrophularia nodosa, pelorism of, 486
Sea-burdock, 139
Secale Cereale, 410
Seden, 273
Sedum, 165
Seed-variation, 750
Sekera, 578
Selection, 108, 111, 114, 390, 399, 743, 751, 789, 790, 792, 793, 794, 797, 799, 800, 801, 804, 806, 807, 808, 813, 825
  artificial (see Artificial selection).
  between species, 744, 800, 801
  continuous, 778, 784, 786,

787, 788, 795, 797, 805, 806, 825
double meaning of, 109, 110

individual, 801
intra-specific, 741, 744, 749, 751, 800, 801, 802, 805, 825
natural (see Natural selection).
repeated (see continuous).
species, 743, 744
within the species, 744, 800
Self-heal, 268
white, 201
Sempervivum tectorum, 370
Senecio jacobaea, 157
vulgaris, 132
"Sereh," 756
Series, The, of Braun and Schimper, 494
Seringe, 523
Setaria, 105
Shepherd's purse, 582, 638, 639
Heeger's, 638, 684
Shirreff, Patrick, 107, 108, 109, 110, 111, 113, 114, 115, 116, 743
Silene annulata, 663
Armeria, 161, 232, 282
rosea, 163
conioa, 419
connoidea, 419
Silverchain, 133
Sinning, 668
Sisymbrium, 637
hirsutum, 637
officinalis, 637
supinum, 637
Sium latifolium, 457
Smith, 667
Snakeroot, 674
Snapdragon, 150, 152, 281, 315, 316, 321, 324, 326, 420, 452
"Black prince" variety, 782
"Brilliant," 151
"Delila," 151, 195, 782

"Firefly," 195
"Fleshy," 151
peloric, race of, 781
self-fertility of, 781
striped, 740
yellow, 194
Soapwort, 409
Solanum, 655, 685
Dulcamara tomentosum, 125
nigrum chlorocarpum, 298
Solms-Laubach, 104, 107, 582, 583, 584
Soltwedel, 755
Sophora japonica pendula, 617
japonica, 136
Sorbus Aucuparia, 342
Species
artificial character of, 36
constancy of, 693, 697
crosses of with varieties, 247, 277, 278, 281
dimorphous, 447
elementary (see Elementary species).
experimental study of, 37
meaning of term, 10, 122
origin of, 307, 461, 550, 560, 825
origin of, easily observed, 26
polymorphous, 700
selection between, 744
selection within, 744
smaller (see Elementary species).
spontaneous cross, 209
survival of, 799
systematic, see Systematic species
two sorts, 12
Variety vs., 122, 154, 220
hybrid (see Hybrids).
Specific marks, origin of, 275
Spath, 619
Spergula media, 53
salina, 53
Spinage, 139, 158, 419
New Zealand, 162
Sport, 111, 310, 311, 316

844 Index

Sports, 191, 715, 689
  bud, 427
Sprenger, 610, 611
Stability, 155
Stahl, 611
Stellaria Holostea apetala,
  585
Stocks, 146, 322, 328, 329, 332,
  334, 336, 338, 432
Stock
  "Brompton," 329
  chamois-colored, 198
  "Queen," 324
  white, 160
Stork's-bill, white hemlock,
  161
Strasburger, 196, 448
Strawberry, 158, 266, 343
  "Gaillon," 135
  "Giant of Zuidwijk," 614
  one-leaved, 164, 596, 666
  white, 158, 165
Striped flowers, 309, 374, 431,
  606, 607
  races, types of, 328
Struggle for life, 674, 571,
  682, 702, 799, 803, 824,
  825
St. Johnswort, 725
St. Sebastian, 164
Sub-species (see also Elementary species), 224,
  225
Sugar-beets (see Beets, sugar).
Sugar-cane, 731, 752
  "Black Manilla," 753
  "Cheribon," 753, 755, 756
  "Chunnic," 753
  "Hawaii," 755, 756
  seeds of, 754
  "White Manilla," 753
Sundew, 268
Sunflower, 410, 425, 820
Sweet-flag, 222
Sweet-pea, 160, 776
Sweet William, 163, 282, 322,
  648
  twisted variety
Syncotyls, 417, 424

Syringa vulgaris azurea plena, 763
Systematic species, 12, 64,
  101, 128
  nature of, 54, 63
Systematic units, 61, 91

T

Tagetes africana, 510
  signata, 612
"Talavera de Bellevue," 97
Tanacetum vulgare, 131, 132,
  236
Tansy, 131, 132, 236
Taraxacum, 125, 126
  officinale, 59, 411
Tares, 105
Taxus, 136
  baccata, 169
  baccata fastigiata, 170, 618
  minor, 169
Teasels, 402, 642, 645, 674,
  675
  twisted, 405, 412, 446, 447,
  643, 646, 647, 648, 819
Tetragonia expansa, 162
Theatre d'Agriculture, 72
Thibault, 618
Thomson, Sir William (see
  Kelvin, Lord).
Thorn-apples, 139, 142, 143,
  145, 238, 283, 300, 453
  thornless, 234
Thorn-broom, 457
Thrincia hirta, 411
Thuret, 38, 47, 49
Thyme, white creeping, 201
Thymus Serphyllum album,
  201
  vulgaris, 577
Tilia parvifolia, 355, 669
Toad-flax, 267, 282, 707
  cross pollination of, 471
  experiment with, described,
  468
  invisible dimorphous state
  of, 470, 471, 478
  latent tendency to mutation
  in, 479

Index

peloric, see Peloric toad-flax.
sterility of mutants, 477
unusual pelorism, 486
Tomato, 653
"Acme," 656, 657
"Mikado," 654
mutation of, 655
upright, 654
"Washington," 657
Tournefort
author of genera, 33
Tracy, W. W. 592
Trees, genealogic, 707, 708
Tricotyls, 416, 418, 419, 420
Trifolium incarnatum, 353
Triticum dicoccum, 105
Tropaeolum, 193, 668
majus, pelorism of, 485
"True Exercises with Plants" (Munting), 490
Tulips, 149, 178, 274, 323
black, 620
Turnip, 244, 621
Twisted stems, 402, 403, 405, 413
Twisted varieties
atavists of, 406

U

Ulex europaeus, 140, 217
Ulmus pedunculata, 615
pedunculata urticaefolia, 615
Umbellifers, 457
Umbilicus, 669
Unger, 105
Unit-characters, 249, 261, 306, 307, 313, 658, 689, 715, 716
Urban, 265
Uropedium lindenii, 487
Utility, 685, 724
Utricularia, 672

V

Vaccinium Myrtillus, 577
Valerian, 402, 409 648

twisted, 403
Valeriana officinalis, 402
Vallisneria, 684
Van den Berg, 625
Van de Water, 614
Van Mons, 76, 77, 78, 806
Variability (see also Fluctuation), 188, 190, 191
analogous, 244
apple, 75
asexual, 320
correlative, 142, 143, 148, 167
cultivated plants, 66
embryonic, 770, 771, 814
ever-recurring, 190
fluctuating (see also individual), 62, 142, 190, 233, 375, 416, 454, 698, 759, 762, 765, 766, 767, 770, 771, 789, 805, 814
fluctuating vs. mutability 568
homologous, 244
individual (see also fluctuating), 190, 716, 718, 746, 749, 770, 814
influence of mutation on, 335
kinds of, 715
nutrition and, 390, 391, 719, 771
parallel, 243
partial, 440, 444, 718, 746, 748, 753, 814, 816
repeated, 242
restricted, 598
sectional, 317
sexual, 320
sources of, 758
Variation
bud, 176, 178, 180, 284, 317, 318, 321, 338, 427, 750
definition of, 188
partial, 788, 789
seed, 750
spontaneous, 191
use of term, 189
Variegation, 426, 427

Varietal marks, origin of, 275
Varieties, 84, 95, 126, 127, 128, 129, 132, 142
  broom-like, 618, 624
  constancy of, 532
  constant, 135
  crosses of species with, 247, 277, 278, 281
  elementary species vs. 459
  ever-sporting, 178, 309, 310, 311, 312, 313, 321, 324, 328, 329, 332, 333, 334, 350, 358, 365, 368, 372, 399, 413, 420, 430, 431, 432, 434, 445, 606, 607, 628, 740, 789, 790, 795
  fasciated (see Fasciated stems).
  groups of, 606
  horticultural, 607, 609
  hybrid, 122, 190, 608
  hybrids of, 210, 254, 255
  inconstant, 135, 154, 155, 161
  mutation of, 141
  negative (retrogressive), 131, 132, 134, 224, 226, 238, 245, 277
  positive, 131, 132, 134, 224, 238, 245
  pure, 122, 190
  retrograde, 14, 15, 16, 95, 121, 208, 430, 435, 606, 607
  retrogressive (see negative).
  seed, 123
  single, 191
  spontaneous crosses, 209
  sporting (see inconstant).
  stability of, 207
  sterile, 622
  types of, 142
  variable, 606
  vegetative, 123
  weeping, 617
Variety, 130
  definition of, 11, 12
  elementary species vs. 141, 152, 154, 224, 243, 247, 251
  origin of, 141, 152, 224
  use of term, 189, 435
Variety-testing, 95, 97, 116, 119, 743, 799, 825
Varro, 106
Veitch & Sons, 273
Venus' looking-glass, 367
Verlot, 186, 612
Vernon, 133
Vernonia cinerea, 450
Veronica longifolia, 282, 284
  scutellata, 139
  spicata nitens, 126
Viburnum Opulus, 134, 239
Vicinism, 185, 188, 203, 205, 206, 213, 214, 776
  definition of, 188, 192, 606
Vicinist, 199, 201
Vicoa auriculata, 450
Victoria regia, 668
Villars
  on *Draba verna*, 49
Vilmorin, 570, 607, 612, 622, 661, 662, 773, 775, 776, 792, 795, 796, 797, 806, 807, 810, 813, 818, 820
Vilmorin, Louis de, 72, 92, 93, 97, 108, 109, 110, 114, 185, 818
Vilmorin, Messrs., 322
Vinca, 242, 490
  minor, 322
Vine, parsley-leaved, 179
Viola, 126, 546, 547, 693
  agrestis, 45
  alpestris, 40
  altaica, 39
  anopetala, 44
  arvensis, 39, 40, 41, 44
    curtisepala, 45
    striolata, 45
  aurobadia, 44
  calcarata, 39
  cornuta, 39, 281
  lutea, 38
  lutescens, 44
  nemausensis, 45

Index

ornatissima, 44
palescens, 45
patens, 45
roseola, 44
segetatis, 45
stenochila, 41
tricolor, 38, 40, 41, 44, 46
  ammotropha, 41
  coniophila, 41
  genuina, 42
  versicolor, 42
Violets, 63, 232, 233, 490
Violet, dame's, 322, 323, 411
  long-spurred, 281
Virgil, 105, 106, 108
Viscaria oculata, 4, 648, 821
  twisted variety, 408
Vitis, 52
Volckamer, 228
Von Lochow, 821, 822, 823
Von Rümker, 94
Von Wettstein, 448, 805
Vrolik, 164, 483

W

"*Waare Oeffeninge der Planten*" (Munting), 490
Wallace, 5, 7, 8, 30, 205
Wall-flower, 370, 371
Walnut, 243, 766
  cut-leaved, 616
  one-bladed, 666
Water-lilies, 668
Weber, 228
Weeping-willow, 180
  crisped, 181
Weigelias, 740
Wellingtonia, 618
Wheat, 96, 98, 105, 113, 119, 283, 810, 823
  bearded, 98
  "Blue-stem," 117
  "Galland," 100, 207
  "Hopetown," 112, 113
  "Hunter's," 111, 113
  "Minnesota No. 169," 117
  "Mungoswell's," 110, 111
  "Pedigree," 109
  "Pringle's," 114
  "Rivett's bearded," 207
  "Sheriff's bearded red," 114
  "Sheriff's bearded white," 114
  "White Hunter's," 113
Wheat-ear carnation, 227
White, C. A., 656, 657
White varieties, 577
Whitlow-grasses, 63, 118, 119
Whorls, ternate, 684
Wild sage (see *Salvia*).
Willdenow, 468, 666, 667
Williamson, 491
Willows, 135, 267
Willow
  weeping (see Weeping-willow).
Willow-herb, 268, 269, 683
Wintercress, 427
Wintergreen, 661
Wittmack, 682
Wittrock, 38, 40, 41, 42, 43, 44, 45, 46
Wooton, E. O., 140
Wormseed, 638

X

Xanthium canadense, 140
  commune, 140, 152, 591
  commune Wootoni, 22
  wootoni, 140, 152, 591

Y

Yarrow, 131, 132
Yew, 136, 169
  pyramidal, 618

Z

Zea Mays cryptosperma, 641
  tunicata, 641
Zinnia, 490
Zioberg, 466
Zocher & Co., 230